THE DIRTY ANIMAL

There is much to be done. And we are losing ground. The air and water grow heavier with the debris of our spectacular civilization. The domain of nature shrinks before the demands of commerce.

President Lyndon B. Johnson in "Protecting Our National Heritage," an address to Congress on January 30, 1967

THE DIRTY ANIMAL

by Henry Still

HAWTHORN BOOKS, INC., *Publishers*
New York

First Edition: 1967

3131

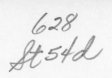

Contents

*From all destroyers of natural beauty
in this parish and everywhere; from all
polluters of earth, air and water; from all
makers of visible abominations; from
jerry-builders, disfiguring advertisers,
road hogs and spreaders of litter; from
the villainies of the rapacious and the
incompetence of the stupid; from the carelessness of individuals and the somnolence
of local authorities; from all foul smells,
noises and sights—good Lord, deliver us!*

Invocation for church litany drawn
up in 1931 by the Council for
Preservation of Rural England

Introduction

THE ONLY THING WRONG WITH THE WORLD IS THE FACT THAT
people live on it.

This statement may seem both self-evident and contradic-
tory to people who have labored long and valorously to solve
the world's problems, as well as those who take the earth's
beauty and bounty for granted, those who eat its food and
leave their droppings behind as carelessly as any beast, bird,
or bug. The statement may arouse vague outrage among those
millions who believe the earth was divinely created exclusively
for man's inheritance. It may likewise disturb those scholars
and historians who believe the human being is an accident of
intelligence in the universe, but nonetheless a growing, matur-
ing accident which one day may learn to live with itself and
its native environment. But, from any point of view, man is
the dirtiest animal that has ever inhabited this planet. This is
so because of the intelligence which enables him to change
chemicals and trees, water and stone, gold and iron, to shapes
and substances serving his desires and changing his natural
environment. Hunger for affluence, shortsightedness and greed
—all emerging to some extent from the same intelligence—
have simultaneously blinded all but a few to the vast residue
of filth we leave behind as we pass. "It is my contention,"

stated Dr. Franklin D. Murphy, chancellor of the University of California at Los Angeles, "that none of God's creatures has succeeded in fouling his nest so completely as man. His performance in this regard, as compared to the birds and lower animals, can only raise grave questions as to his self-asserted 'superiority.'"

If we are superior to any creature, it is certainly the locust. We have learned with great skill to destroy forests, to rip iron from the earth, to plow up virgin grasslands so they may blow away on the wind, to cover miles of the world's surface with freeways and dead automobiles. We have learned well how to devour and destroy the wealth and beauty around us in order to build the fragile, transitory structures which dominate our lives. We are only beginning to learn the how, and the cost, of cleaning up the mess we leave on nature's factory floor.

For centuries we have been quite on a par with the locust. We feed upon the field until it is bare, then move to the next, complacent in our greed that a new green field always will be waiting. Locusts never return to clean up their manure and replant the green wheat; by this profligacy the locust could multiply and eat itself to extinction. In like fashion, intelligent man now is entering an age in which he must choose between the continued indiscriminate befouling of the earth, or new methods of digesting his droppings and replacing his divots. The green lands of new discovery are no more on earth. It is time to turn back and clean up the nest.

Almost overnight in the time scale of history, our rivers and lakes have become so loaded with sewage and industrial waste that clean, fresh water is virtually nonexistent. Factory smoke and automobile exhaust fumes have so polluted the air of many cities and entire regions that doctors wonder when it will become completely unbreathable. Insecticides, flushed by rain and irrigation from millions of acres of farmland, are killing fish and have already threatened human health. Radioactive wastes are kept under careful control, yet disposal of this material causes increasing concern as the infant nuclear power industry reaches toward its mature potential. Millions of tons of garbage and rubbish must be buried or burned each day and the bulk of ordure from meat and vegetable packing plants grows greater with each new child born. The carcasses of discarded automobiles pile ever higher and wider in ugly hills of rusting metal because it is more profitable to take iron from the earth than to reuse what we have already consumed.

All of this filth—from feces to ferrous oxide—is the work of man the intelligent, dirty animal.

No one is at fault, yet everyone is.

If massive, coherent, intelligent—and vastly expensive—steps are not taken to clean up our air, our water and our land, we'll choke to death or drown in our filth.

We've been told this many times before. To conservationists, university professors and government officials the lessons and warning have been clear for many years. For half a century it has been evident that the Industrial Revolution would breed mountains of indigestible waste by lacerating the verdant land, by pouring its mechanical effluent into the rivers, and by calling people together in clots called cities where their collective stink becomes more than they can bear.

One fundamental law of nature postulates that nothing in the universe can be irrevocably lost or wasted. If wood is burned in a fire, its molecules are conserved in heat energy, smoke and ashes. A discarded tin can eventually reverts to reusable chemical combinations. Animals and their simple waste products are converted to soil by bugs, sunlight, bacteria and water. The earth with its resident creatures is a vast and wonderful sewage disposal system. The dirty animal is simply overloading that system with kinds and quantities of waste matter it was not designed to handle.

Until a few decades ago, America was essentially a rural land with an endless sweep of open space, deep rivers of limitless fresh water, air swept clean by westerly winds. A farm wife washed dishes and clothes with lye soap made of hog fat and wood ashes. When the dishes or garments were clean, she threw the dirty water out the door to sink into the soil of the back yard. It mattered little that the grass might be weakened in that area because it would be rejuvenated by chicken droppings as domestic fowl searched the yard for table scraps. Contents of the nightly slop jar were carried somewhat farther from the door, and the privy was located perhaps one hundred feet away from the well. There were few cases of actual water contamination because bacteria, sun and fresh air were sufficient to decompose the human sewage. Animal manures were hauled out of the barn to fertilize the fields. Perhaps once a month the contents of the junk barrel, kept behind the farm shed, would be hauled to a ditch or gully in a back field. There were few tin cans, because the farm wife did most of her own food preserving and used the same glass mason jars over and over again. There were few plastic and cellophane cartons because the American supermarket fetish of overwrapping every item of food had not yet become universal. Wood smoke rising lazily from a farmhouse chimney on a still, cold winter morning was the sign of cheer and warmth. Only in the gray, sooty valleys of Pennsylvania, Virginia and Kentucky coal miners coughed a warning that the atmosphere was not a limitless reservoir of cleansing power.

Small Town, America, brought necessary but gradual changes in the situation. It was distasteful for a neighbor to live only a few feet from a privy and soon town officials found that many wells were being contaminated by disease-bearing water. Indoor plumbing led to covered underground cisterns or cesspools and towns began drawing their water from nearby streams or deep wells where it could be tested and purified before distribution to the residents. Trash and junk were hauled by individuals to the town dump where combustible matter was burned, glass and metal left to degenerate and settle into the soil. Smoke from coal-burning trains and small factories was unsightly but troublesome only to people who lived on "that" side of the tracks.

Big Town, America, grew from Small Town, America. Ingenious engineers invented the central sewer system which drained into the river where a wealth of moving water, bacteria, residual oxygen and sunlight soon dissipated its contamination. The stench and smudge of smoke from the city dump was accepted as a way of life which only depressed real estate values on that side of the city and urged residential and commercial growth in the opposite direction. It was not considered important because the land around growing cities appeared to be inexhaustible. The only question taken into serious consideration by landowners was how to achieve zoning laws providing the most profitable sale of their property. Loathsome chemicals oozing into a river from a paper mill were the hallmark of prosperity, jobs for more and more men whose wives would hurry to the city's stores to buy more and more of the material comforts of life. Coal smoke belching from power plants and factories was only the breath of a growing industrial giant. Big Town, America, must grow ever bigger and busier—and dirtier. Young men came from the farm in growing thousands to earn their way to wealth and luxury. It was only later that they began to notice the city was an ugly place to live in. Then, as soon as they could, they began pressing outward again into cleaner, suburban countryside.

Now the suburbs, too, are beginning to stink. Soon there no longer will be a direction to run from the rivers we have converted to sewers, the land we have littered with junk, the air we have polluted with smoke and poisonous gases from the horseless carriage. The world has performed a heroic job serving as our waste disposal system, but as with any system, when its capacity is reached something new must be done. The realities of air, water and land pollution have been nibbling at our consciousness for a long time. Now they have their teeth set painfully and unshakably in the seat of our pants.

The realities appear to have come upon us abruptly, in the years since World War II, but the abruptness is only apparent. What has happened to our air, water and land is as simple as the operation of a septic tank and cesspool serving an average suburban home. When such a septic system is new and buried underground, it is a highly efficient machine for disposing of human waste matter. Water, which makes up more than 90 percent of the material flushed from a home, seeps into the ground while bacteria and yeasts dispose of the solids. As a family grows, so does the burden of the disposal system. First a garbage grinder is added to the plumbing to ease the woman's work. Then comes an automatic washing machine for clothes and a dishwasher operated with highly efficient detergents, again to ease the toil of America's woman. The pulverized garbage, however, is an overload and the detergents are foreign to nature's underground scavengers. Thus one day the American wife is horrified to find sewage backed up in the water pipes, its stench signaling a breakdown of the disposal system and an immediate threat to health and aesthetics. The frantic housewife has three alternatives: stop pouring waste into the system (impossible); have the cesspool pumped out (a temporary solution at best); or connect the home plumbing to an entirely new sewage system (the only logical, long-term action).

Comparing the simple cesspool with America's landscape, its rivers and its overlying blanket of moving air, is both apt and direct. As with the underground septic tank, most of us have not noticed the rivers becoming more and more loaded with physical and chemical putrefaction, the air becoming progressively saturated with molecules of hydrocarbon and nitrous oxides, the land made increasingly hideous with auto junk piles and highways littered with beer cans and broken bottles. Now, suddenly, the overload point is here. It assails our nostrils, affects our breathing and offends our eyes. Beyond the scope of our senses the level of radioactivity grows imperceptibly higher. More tons of insecticide, weed killers and contamination salts pour through our farm drainage ditches to the sea.

The speed with which we have overloaded nature's digestive system is illustrated by the prodigious growth of our population, the way it moves and lives, and the industrial plant which serves it. In 1900, for example, the waste matter from cities and towns that flowed into American streams was equal to the raw sewage from 24 million people. Organic wastes from industry equaled raw sewage from 15 million people. Only sixty years later, cities and towns were dumping into our streams the equivalent of raw sewage from 75 million people, more than three times that in 1900. At the same time, in 1960, industrial waste equaled the physical raw sewage output of 160 million people, an increase of more than tenfold. It is estimated that by 1970 municipal wastes dumped in streams will grow to equal raw sewage of 85 million people, but industrial wastes will jump to the equivalent of 210 million.

A tourist driving through the beautiful woods of Virginia or the sparkling thin air of the Colorado Rockies breathes deeply, aware of pleasant clean air in his lungs. He is not conscious of polluting that air with each gallon of gasoline burned in his automobile. During the brief days of his vacation, however, he will avoid as much as possible the great urban centers of New York, Chicago, Pittsburgh, Baltimore and St. Louis, where he can see and smell the aerial contamination. That motorist clucks with concern when he drives over the last range of coastal mountains into the once-splendrous Los Angeles basin of southern California. There below he sees the stratified layers of smog, ranging from dirty yellow over the highways to dirty gray a little higher where it has been partially altered by sunlight.

The tourist would find it difficult to believe, but it is true, that *12,420 tons of aerial pollutants are thrown into the Los Angeles atmosphere each day by automobiles alone.* Another 1310 tons per day comes from industry, power plants and home furnaces. The resultant smog ranges from substances which irritate eyes and nasal membranes to carbon monoxide of such density over the freeways that a motorist may become drowsy or temporarily unconscious, a great hazard to traffic safety. Los Angeles is known as the smog center of the nation not because it is the only city with such a problem, but because in that area the problem, its causes and its alleviation, have been under study for more than two decades. Nearly every major city in the nation, probably in the world, suffers

7

from atmospheric pollution to some degree. All major cities must face the day when something is done about it, and already municipal action is not enough. Entire regions now are involved. For example, a waste management study conducted recently for the state of California shows that more than a third of the entire state is polluted by smog generated in the major population centers of Los Angeles, San Diego, San Francisco, and Sacramento. Damage from this source of pollution alone runs to the billions of dollars.

Trash such as waste paper, glass bottles, tin cans and other scrap metal is taken for granted by most urbanites, who clean out the garage and move junk to the street curbing assured that it will be hauled away to a dump somewhere. What the average city dweller does not think about is that most such waste deteriorates slowly by natural decomposition. The non-combustibles must be buried. If the combustibles, such as the millions of tons of paper which sustain modern civilization each day, are burned, the smoke again adds to atmospheric contamination. In California alone, municipal trash amounts to about 12 million tons per year and this is expected to more than triple to 40 million tons per year by 1990. California contains about one-tenth of the nation's population, thus by 1990, less than twenty-five years from now, we as a nation must find a place to put 400 million tons of rubbish every year.

The amounts of radioactive substances, insecticides and other farm chemicals flowing into our waterways and the atmosphere still remain at barely measurable and undangerous levels. These, however, must be taken into account because the quantities will increase in the years ahead, adding to pollution which already exists.

It seems ridiculous that a nationwide crisis in waste disposal could occur in a land which stands above all others in the control of communicable disease and the supply of pure drinking water. The reasons why the world's wealthiest nation should be in such a state are many and complex. For one thnig, American industry is only beginning to realize it must sacrifice some of its margin of profit to eliminate its own waste. On the municipal level, the city council of Davenport, Iowa, may insure a pure water supply for its citizens from the Mississippi River but think nothing of Baton Rouge, Louisiana, where people must clean out Davenport's raw sewage before they use the water again.

In free enterprise America it is logical that a company must think of profits for its shareholders. Municipal governments must provide services at the lowest possible cost. Now, however, such selfishness can no longer be tolerated. Regional authorities must be formed pooling their resources to clean up entire river basins, atmospheric basins and junk yards. Cities, states, industry and the federal government must join forces to find new methods and bear the mammoth cost of the face-washing America must have.

Federal laws, passed only within the past three years, will go far toward alerting the nation to the severity of the task ahead. Even those laws, however, extend only to increasing the utilization of waste disposal methods already known. For example, at least one-third of American cities have no sewage treatment facilities at all, dumping their effluent raw into the country's streams. Many industries have resisted spending the money necessary to clean up their own pollution, both in the air and water. The new laws may force many more such groups to comply with simple standards of decent cleanliness, using methods which have been known for half a century.

This, however, is not enough. In Los Angeles, for example, twenty years of effort with industrial and other fixed sources of air pollution has succeeded in stopping *5000 tons per day* of smoke and gases from spewing into the atmosphere. During the same twenty years, however, the total air pollution has increased to more than 14,000 tons per day due to the explosive increase in the number of automobiles which travel more millions of miles each year. In a word, the growth in population, industry, intensive farming and numbers of motor vehicles is so great as to cancel out the effectiveness of current methods of pollution control even as they are being applied and enforced on a general scale.

Completely new methods of managing the nation's waste products must be brought to bear on a massive scale. Such methods already are emerging from the technology of the world's greatest industrial nation.

The only alternative to paying for and using them is a beautiful land choking to death in its own filth.

The Metropolitan Metabolism

*Sometimes it seems to me that man is come where
he is not wanted, where there is no place for
him; for if not, why should he run about here and
there making a great noise about himself,
talking about the stars, disturbing the
blades of grass?*

Joseph Conrad, Lord Jim

A CITY—LIKE A MAN—IS BORN, LIVES, AND CONTRIBUTES TO THE
world's appetite for products and ideas. Like a man, the city
also eats, breathes, defecates and dies.

During its life cycle, a city grows and changes. It may mature with the loveliness of years, as Paris and Vienna; it may
burst with the virile sound and smell of work, as Chicago; it
may wear a sheen of power and sophistication, as New York;
it may be illiterate and diseased, as Calcutta.

A metropolis, by original definition, means mother or parent city of a state or region. Today the definition remains essentially valid. The metropolis draws its millions of individual human cells from the surrounding region, and out of the seething industrial, commercial and thoughtful motion of those individual cells, pours forth the wealth, products and culture which feeds and matures the surrounding region.

Cities of the world are as diverse as the human beings who inhabit them. Many were born by their access to the sea, others at the junction of ancient caravan routes. Some flourish as religious shrines, others exist only because a rail line happened to pass that way or because of benign climate. Many cities have been born and died after a short period of time because their function ceased to be. This is typified by the ghost towns of the American West where mining of precious metals created cities which dwindled with the narrowing of the quartz veins. It is often difficult to determine why ancient cities died. Likewise it is not easy to understand why the settlement of Denver became a thriving metropolis while Cripple Creek, only seventy miles away, went to sleep above the deposits of gold and silver which once made it large and famous. Sociologists and archaelogists may be able to trace the factors which contribute to the life or death of any individual city, but the great ones throb with an indefinable life of their own—New Orleans and Sydney, Moscow and Copenhagen, Tokyo and Hong Kong, Buenos Aires and Bombay.

A great metropolis is often judged by the energy and output of its industrial hands; the speed and dexterity of its feet (the transportation systems which feed people and materials in and out); the alimentary canal of its commercial establishments; the education and culture which emerge from its brain (the school system and centers of art, music and literature). When the major parts of the organism are functioning in proper coordination, according to the collective needs of the individual human cells, a city glows with health. Conversely, a city may suffer the cancer of poverty and slums in its center, or dwindle to death when a major function, such as transportation, becomes inadequate and chokes upon its own senility.

It is only in recent years that another threatening cause of municipal death has become apparent. Unless drastic and expensive new steps are taken, the sprawling metropolitan centers of the future will smother in their own waste matter, just as a man will die if the wastes are not removed from his body.

The world's first cities took shape about 3500 years before Christ was born. Five thousand years later, no society on earth could be considered urbanized, but since 1850, when coal and the steam engine brought forth the Industrial Revolution, every industrial nation has become city-oriented. By the year 2000, more than two-thirds of the world's projected 6.5 billion population will live in metropolitan centers.

The people of America and the world are moving ever more rapidly to the city for the jobs, services and produce they want and need. Because of this movement, the "town" is becoming increasingly unpleasant as a place to live because land, water and aerial wastes are accumulating faster than they can be removed. Wherever the dirty animal congregates in greatest numbers, his waste materials mount up in enormous quantities. It stands to reason, therefore, that if successful waste management methods can be devised for the major population centers, these methods eventually will serve all mankind around the globe, just as mosquito control and penicillin now save lives in poor nations as well as in the rich.

Cities—Athens, Rome, Constantinople—always have cradled the great civilizations, but how did it happen that man alone sought other men so persistently that permanent communities first were formed? History does not record the original man with an extra measure of grain who met a man with an axe to trade. Their meeting point marked the first community although it may have existed for only a few moments or a few days. From there developed trading posts, a division of labor, villages and towns; and the towns began to stink with human and animal manure, the smoke of campfires and the gaseous excreta from forges where bronze was born.

More than five millennia have passed since the first cities took shape in the Fertile Crescent of the Tigris and Euphrates rivers in Mesopotamia. The names Eridu, Erech, Lagash and Kish whisper faintly down from the past, a sound of ancient ghosts and dust-crumbled bones, of clay huts and temples separated by narrow streets where even then children played, skipping warily around heaps of night soil and camel dung. In comparison with the modern metropolis, these first cities were but embryos. Mighty Ur was estimated by its excavator Sir Leonard Woolley to have contained no more than 34,000 people at its height shortly after the year 2000 B.C., but this was a huge city when the civilized world was young and thinly populated.

When the Phoenicians spread westward along the shores of the Mediterranean some two thousand years before Christ, they established towns along the coasts of Africa and Spain as terminal points of commerce. Other cities grew along the Great Silk Road from China to Turkestan—Suchow, Khotan, Nanking and Canton. These all were located at oasis points where camel trains could pause and be refreshed. Nonagricultural laborers congregated to share in work and services which flourished as a by-product of the commercial riches represented by spices, silks and jewels. Over the civilized world, such cities grew and flowered, harboring the rulers and priest cults which fed—and fed upon—multitudes of little people who were born, lived a few years at hard labor, and died. Due to the accumulations of animal and human excreta, some cities were virtually wiped out by disease, then grew again as more people came in from the country. It is probable that some cities ceased to be solely because pollution was so severe and disease so persistent that the inhabitants through the years simply drifted away to avoid the "evil spirits." Other cities grew upward, with new buildings constructed on the dung heap of the old.

A modern example of such a city is Shibam in Kuwait south of Saudi Arabia. Dating from 692 A.D., Shibam contains five hundred buildings seven and eight stories high connected by doors and passageways now high above the ground. Many Arab housewives visit back and forth without ever descending to street level. The gate to this ancient metropolis is barely wide enough to admit an automobile; it was built for men, donkeys and camels. Most unpaved passageways are no more than eight feet wide. Sewage dribbles directly into the streets from pipes projecting from the buildings, and a pedestrian must be always agile and alert to avoid being drenched. Shibam's drinking water for centuries was hauled by donkey train. Only in recent years has it been pumped in by a water company. In such a community as this, it seems a miracle that human life can persist where there is literally not enough water to wash the city's face.

As we pass by the famous cities of history, the names themselves evoke images of greater population centers than actually existed. Pompeii, for example (which suffered history's most severe air pollution problem when it was buried under eighteen feet of ash from Mt. Vesuvius) probably numbered no more than twenty thousand residents at its death in 79 A.D. Rome itself, that lusty, glittering, fabulously cruel and wealthy head of the Empire, probably never grew above 300,000 population.

When the Empire crumbled, many borderland cities vanished or shrank back to small towns and villages. Rome decayed and many historians leave the impression that cities virtually disappeared from Europe. Actually, many continued to function, principally in Italy and southern France, where they were the centers of the political and religious elite who held much of the world's power and prestige through the Dark Ages. Another fact obscured by the historians' obsession with priests, kings and wars is that the total population of the world during those Dark Ages was only a small fraction of the 3.3 billion alive today, never large enough, except for a few rare municipal concentrations, to make waste management a problem. Human and animal carcasses and manure were dispersed and consumed by water and wind, bacteria and maggots. Nature was still able to dissipate, absorb and convert these fairly simple waste products back to usable form according to the universal law of conservation. If a home stank with sewage and spoiled food, no one was gravely concerned. It was the way of life. Indeed, men did not know that disease-bearing microbes existed in filth, carried by rats and insects which fed upon the banquet of decay. Disease and death still were believed to come from evil spirits and indefinable vapors.

For centuries men of the Western world and much of the East accepted fatalistically the fact that the plague would sweep periodically across the land, ceasing only when the black miasmic spirit apparently had become sated with swollen, festering corpses. Through those centuries the population of many cities pulsated in cycles of health and death like a wounded heart not certain that it would continue beating. Only the superb adaptability of man, once he had learned to congregate in large numbers, prevented his extinction by the dirt of his own manufacture. In the affluent industrialized world today, with its home freezers and plastic wrapper on every prune, most people no longer think of the acute difficulty of maintaining food in edible condition in a primitive society. At the same time, it is not far in flying time to a village in the Philippines or Southeast Asia where fly-blackened carcasses of fresh-slaughtered meat still hang in the market place above open ditch sewers.

Few cities grew to large size during the Middle Ages. For the most part they were limited by the perimeter of a wall built around the citadel where dwelt the feudal lord, his personal retinue of astrologers and priests and enough horses and men to protect his castle against neighborly onslaughts. The people lived outside under the shadow and protection of the wall, offering up food and taxes in return for this dubious security. History unfortunately does not record the peasant wife who grew weary of sewage and half-chewed dog bones trickling down the slope from the castle walls. She it was, undoubtedly, who goaded her husband into channeling this effluent into a ditch so that rain would carry it away to a river. Such ditches later were covered and became sewers.

The feast for the rats, provided by people throughout medieval times, more than anything else was responsible for limiting the growth of cities and the population in general. In the eleventh century, the plague broke out in Germany at least six times and raged so violently that it appeared mankind might be obliterated. In fact this belief prevented officials from taking effective action. Stoic apathy during personal suffering was considered an act of piety. In their desperate and irrational fear of the unknown, many people suspected the Jews of poisoning wells. The Hungarian peasantry likewise suspected the nobility when the cholera swept away so many of the poorer classes in that nation.

Germany suffered intermittently from this pestilence for twenty-five years during the twelfth century and in the thirteenth it was brought back to western Europe by the Crusaders. It was in the fourteenth century, when the hideous disease swept all of Europe, that the name Black Death came into common usage. It broke out first in England in 1348 and spread over the entire nation, its ravages most severe in the towns and cities. From that year through 1369, it was estimated the Black Death destroyed nearly one-half of England's entire population. Social consequences were immense. Laborers became so scarce that wages spurted to double their former rate. Acts passed to regulate this only resulted in ill feeling which culminated in Wat Tyler's insurrection. Many states were broken up into farms and put out on lease due to the scarcity of hired labor for cultivation. Also the Black Death resulted in acquisition by the people of much land owned by the Church, a landmark in English social history. All of this occurred because of rotting garbage in city streets and polluted water supplies. Later, when people began to sense that spirits and demons were not responsible, they believed the dread disease came with changes in the air, by poisonous vapors which descended from the atmosphere, or clouds of insects which were inhaled or eaten. The latter notion, finally a hint of the villainous microbes proliferating in filth, was still no more than an idea three centuries later in 1664 when the

17

plague again swept England. Hidden away in the dry charm of the diary kept by Samuel Pepys are notes of the apathy and despair which cloaked the menaced millions as they waited to hear for whom the bells tolled over the great city of London.

"This day, much against my will, I did in Drury Lane see two or three houses marked with the red cross upon the doors, and 'Lord have mercy on us' writ there," Pepys wrote on June 7, 1664, "which was a sad sight to me, being the first of the kind that, to my remembrance, I ever saw. It put me into an ill conception of myself and my smell, so that I was forced to buy some roll-tobacco to smell to and chaw, which took away the apprehension."

On July 30: "It was a sad noise to hear our bell to toll and ring so often today, either for deaths or burials; I think five or six times."

And on August 12: "The people die so that now it seems they are fain to carry the dead to be burried by daylight, the nights not sufficing to do it in. And my Lord Mayor commands people to be within at nine at night all, as they say, that the sick may have liberty to go abroad for ayre."

Bodies accumulated in the streets of London faster than they could be carted away and finally it was necessary to resort to fire. Neither the demons or spirits or vapors were responsible, only the combination of unwholesome and insufficient food, overcrowding, bad ventilation, and accumulation of decaying animal and vegetable refuse.

Accustomed as we are to the explosive pace of science and technology in our century, it seems incomprehensible that nearly two hundred years after Pepys lived not much had yet been done about keeping cities clean although water pollution laws had existed in England since the fourteenth century. London's water in the middle of the 1800s still came mainly from wells and rivers which drained cesspools, graveyards and tidal areas. Mortality tables for the year 1841 indicated that the average life span in London was 36 years. In all of England and Wales the life expectancy was 41 but in Liverpool and Manchester as low as 26.

After 1850, some improvements were made in nutrition,

housing and sanitation, but as late as the decade 1901–1910, the death rate in urban England remained 33 percent higher than in the country. "Living in the town involved not only a higher risk of epidemic and crown disease," remarked Bernard Benjamin of the British General Register Office, "but also a higher risk of degenerative disease—the harder wear and tear of factory employment and urban discomfort." Now the Industrial Revolution had moved in to add its miasma of coal smoke and flood of noisome chemicals to the natural waste matter generated by people and animals in their social and commercial intercourse.

The horse, God rest its hard-working soul, was responsible for a great portion of the dirt and mess in the industrial world's major cities. The *Scientific American* of April 1866 carried the following brief account from New York City:

> At a recent meeting of the Polytechnic Association of the American Institute, Professor Charles Joy of Columbia College remarked that engineering problems involved in providing means of transit between different parts of New York City were not in the line of his studies or of his knowledge, but that the social side of the question, which had been broached, was of interest to every citizen.
>
> He wondered that the people of New York City did not rise in their majesty and put an end to the abuses of our horse-railroad system. He had traveled during the past year 6000 miles in Europe. Five hundred of this was by means other than steam, and 5500 by steam. He had ridden in first, second, third and fourth class cars; he had traveled underground and above ground, on water and land, and he had never experienced discomfort approaching that to which he had been subjected that evening in coming down from 49th street to the Cooper Institute.
>
> He had come directly from his laboratory, but he had never had in his lab odors so vile—his science was not able to produce so foul a compound of stenches as filled the car in which he rode. If the railroad companies treat us thus above ground what will they do when they get us into subterranean tunnels? . . .

In London, heart of the not-yet motorized Industrial Revolution, the sight, sound and smell of the horse in 1890 was described as follows:

A more assertive mark of the horse was the manure that, despite the activities of a numerous corps of red-jacketed boys who dodged among wheels and hoofs with pan and brush in service to iron bins at the pavement-edge, either flooded the streets with churnings of "pea soup" that at times collected in pools overbrimming the kerbs, and at others covered the road-surface as with axle grease or bran-laden dust to the distraction of the wayfarer.

In the first case, the swift-moving hansom or gig would fling sheets of such soup—where not intercepted by trousers or skirts—completely across the pavement, so that the frontages of the Strand throughout its length had an 18-inch plinth of mud-parge thus imposed on it. The pea-soup condition was met by wheeled "mud-carts" each attended by two ladlers clothed as for Icelandic seas in thigh boots, oilskins collared to the chin, and sou'westers sealing to the back of the neck. Splash Ho! The foot passenger now gets the mud in his eye! The axle grease condition was met by horse-mechanized brushes and travelers in the small hours found fire hoses washing away the residues. . . .

And after the mud the noise, which, again endowed by the horse, surged like a mighty heart-beat in the central districts of London's life. It was a thing beyond all imaginings. The streets of workaday London were uniformly paved in "granite" sets . . . and the hammering of a multitude of iron-shod hairy heels, the deafening side-drum tattoo of tyred wheels jarring from the apex of one set to the next, like sticks dragging along a fence; the creaking and groaning and chirping and rattling of vehicles, light and heavy, thus maltreated; the jangling of chain harness, augmented by the shrieking and bellowings called for from those of God's creatures who desired to impart information or proffer a request vocally—raised a din that is beyond conception. It was not any such paltry thing as noise. It was an immensity of sound.

While the great dray horse clip-clopped his way through history, new things were coming to crack open the invisible and arbitrary shell which had more or less limited the size of the world's cities. Although it is not a hard or provable rule, at least one municipal researcher has postulated that a city's maximum size is determined by the amount of time it takes to travel from its edge to the central market place. The time period considered reasonable is forty-five minutes. On foot this limits a man to two or three miles, less if he is carrying produce to exchange for food and other necessities for his family. With a horse-drawn vehicle, or on horseback, the range opened out to as much as five miles. Then came the wood- and coal-burning steam locomotive to haul thousands of wide-eyed country boys to town looking for work in the new factories, electric streetcars and subways, and finally the automobile which killed the dray horse and opened the road for seemingly limitless expansion of the modern metropolis. Gone are the smell and slime of equine sweat and manure; in their place is a monster which kills thousands of people every month of every year and brings a new, sickening, and potentially fatal stench to our atmosphere.

The world is sprinkled with thousands of cities, large and small, old and new, ugly and beautiful, clean and dirty.

Cedar Rapids, with nearly 100,000 people, rests in a fertile undulating heart of Iowa farmland, enshrouded most of the year with dust and mold from cereal grain. This is a healthy little city, busy with industry and accepting without question the stink roused in processing corn syrup and Quaker Oats. Chicago, on Lake Michigan, reeks with the stench of stockyards, the offal from packing plants, and red chemical smoke from surrounding steel plants.

Bogotá, Colombia, is a metropolis of two million persons. Mayor Jorge Gaitan Cortez says it has fewer slums than any other large Latin American city. However, eight thousand people live in a squatter's shantytown called Policarpa Salavarienta on land owned by the National University. There are no sewers, but the squatters, who consider they have a right to occupy land not being used, have tapped a nearby water main to help themselves and strung electric wires from a street pole to provide a modicum of light. The rural invasion of the city is increasing Bogotá's population by 7 percent a year, a growth far exceeding the city's ability to digest it.

One-fourth of Rio de Janeiro's four million inhabitants live in *favelas*, slum shantytowns clinging to the sides of the city's steep melon-shaped hills. Little ditches run past or under every house to carry away the sewage, all tributaries to larger ditches which become open trenches wide enough to require footbridges. The slum dwellers must walk down their hill and back to obtain drinking water, but somehow manage to keep fairly clean despite swarms of flies and other insects.

Only three hours' drive south from California's City of the Angels is the border city of Tijuana, Mexico, where 50 percent of the people lack running water, electricity, washing machines, sinks, and roofs that don't leak. More than 100,000 people in this community live in primitive one-room shacks with no indoor toilets, or even official outhouses. Dusty, unpaved streets are alive with the chatter of unwashed children, the barking of scrawny dogs, and crowing chickens almost too bony to eat. When it rains, scores of shacks on the canyon slopes crumble and float down with the floodwaters.

In Hyderabad, India, where drought turned the land to powder in 1966, hundreds of parched and emaciated citizens hijacked a train as it attempted to pass slowly through the town. Swarming around the puffing steam engine, the citizens demanded that the engineer give them water from the engine tanks. When he refused, the crowd opened the water cock and filled pots and pails before letting the train proceed.

Lima, Peru, was founded by Pizarro in 1535, but gone from the old balconies now are the senoritas in black lace shawls waving languidly to the street throngs below. The aristocracy has deserted the heart of the old city and moved to mansions in new districts with spacious lawns and two- or three-car garages. The famous old wooden balconies which overhang the streets are due to come down to ease the appalling traffic jams formed by Lima's 250,000 automobiles. Hundreds of people are protesting the historic desecration, but appear to be losing. Hector Velarde, a member of the protesting old guard, claims that real-estate developers, city planning technocrats, socioeconomic legal hacks, and venal city officials are raising a "curtain of dust" between Lima and its past.

"These people leave us adrift without identity in a river of automobiles, rubber-stamped papers, contracts, smelly tenements, typewriters, telephones, Coca Cola, parking lots and glass office buildings where people exchange little words of greeting in English," Velarde complains bitterly. Virtually gone is the charm of the old city where people could live in quiet beauty without the din and dirt which seems inevitably to accompany "progress" in its modern sense.

In London, typically choked by the twentieth century's automotive monster, one of man's most modern tools, the computer, is being invoked to help solve the traffic problem. By 1967 a six-square-mile section of the city, involving sixty-eight major intersections and the busiest roads leading to western England and London Airport, will go under computer control. Artistic, shopping and tourist areas of Chelsea and Kensington as well as Hyde Park Corner, the world's busiest intersection, will be included. Increased traffic flow thus achieved is expected to cost not more than one percent of a road rebuilding program which would be necessary to do the same job.

By sharp contrast, Moscow does not suffer from auto congestion and the inevitable air pollution which follows. The Communist economy, which deprives its citizens of the "good" things in life, may have protected them from the automobile, one of man's most vicious inventions. At dawn in Moscow, armies of women armed with snow shovels in the interminable winter and with small twig brooms the rest of the year, spread out over the streets to polish up the city for the day ahead. Traffic is feather light and so few cars are on the road that Muscovites have not learned the big city reflex of leaping out of the way of onrushing traffic.

From one extreme to another, there are two major forms of large metropolitan centers in the world today, both diseased and threatened with extinction in the foreseeable future. On the one hand lies the ancient crowded city, such as Calcutta or Hong Kong, dying by the cancerous explosive growth of its own population. On the other is the modern megalopolis, such as Los Angeles, spread over such huge expanses of land that it is rapidly choking to death on its own traffic, millions of automobiles which, in the absence of a decent mass transit system, struggle each day to haul millions of people to and from their place of work and shopping.

There are some 250 cities in the world with populations above half a million. Nearly half of these are in ancient countries where development lagged, or in emerging countries where development is only beginning. They differ from the modern metropolis in that they were not triggered and nurtured by the Industrial Revolution. Such a city is Calcutta, India's largest urban center, where seven million people are crowded into four hundred square miles and form the stage for a major confrontation between ancient institutions and urban pressures which presage India's industrial revolution.

Calcutta was founded by traders of the British East India Company in 1690 around the nucleus of Hooghly River villages on the Ganges Delta seventy miles inland from the Bay of Bengal. The city's harbor is one of the world's greatest, forming a major trade link between East and West. It also is becoming an increasingly diversified manufacturing center, but the pressures of the changing world are increasing faster than can be borne by the metropolis. The population density is 102,000 persons per square mile (compared with 27,000 in New York City) and Calcutta is growing at the rate of 200,000 per year. More than 75 percent of the people live in overcrowded tenement and bustee (slum) quarters. A majority of multimember families share only one room. The poor man, woman or child in the bustee shares a single water tap with thirty other people, and one latrine with twenty-three others. Thousands live on sidewalks. Hovels in which most of the city's residents live were described as "dung heaps" by Mahatma Gandhi.

Part of Calcutta's problem arises from the fact that the Hooghly River on one side and salt water swamps on the other prevent the city from spreading, so the population density continues to increase. There is a serious shortage of safe water. Most sewage facilities are open ditches. So severe are these conditions, along with swarms of flies and rats, that the World Health Organization has termed the city an international health hazard. Lying in the steamy, low-lying tropical delta of the Ganges, Calcutta is an endemic source of the plague and threatens, with every traveler who passes by air and sea, to spread the Black Death to the rest of the world.

Nature itself is working against the monstrous, struggling city. The port handles 42 percent of India's exports and 25 percent of the country's imports—but the port is dying. The Ganges is gradually shifting away and the Hooghly has become so silt-laden that dredges are unable to keep up with it. More critically, the Hooghly's level has dropped so low that fresh water is more and more difficult to acquire. The flow of the sluggish stream is insufficient to flush away the vast quantity of sewage dumped into the river. There are no schools for half a million children. Hospitals are so overcrowded that any patient judged incurably ill is turned back out into the streets. There they die in the gutters to be carted away eventually, reminiscent of the hideous days of London's old plagues. "We're really in a race with time," one official said wearily. "Given the resources of the area, the city is faced with a hopeless task. There is a great air of hopelessness, despair and cynicism."

That air, saturated with the stink of sewage and decaying flesh, could well lead to an uncontrollable epidemic and ultimate abandonment of the city. In some future age, the rectangular tracing of millions of hovels washed into the muck of the Ganges Delta might be the only archaeological clue to the race which passed this way.

Twelve thousand miles to the west, archaeologists will find their main clue to the Los Angeles culture in broken slabs of concrete where hundreds of miles of freeway covered the once-beautiful land of southern California. With its mile upon mile of pink and white candy-box homes and shimmering chrome and glass shopping centers, it would appear that Los Angeles has nothing in common with Calcutta, yet the seeds of self-destruction here also have sprouted and begun to grow.

True, Los Angeles water is sparkling pure and good, pouring westward three hundred miles from the Colorado River. True, there is no smell of sewage in Los Angeles streets because that vast effluent from nearly ten million people is poured into the Pacific Ocean, miles at sea and deep beneath the surface so that the contamination may be diluted and ultimately dispersed. But above Los Angeles, there is a cloud of smog now more than two-thirds of all the days in the year. Only the old-timers, some of them native Californians, can remember when Los Angeles was a sparkling jewel-city of white stucco homes under a bright blue sky and warm clear sun. Above and beyond the surrounding citrus groves, the mountain peaks were etched sharp against the sky and the breeze carried the scent of orange blossoms.

In the past half century and most explicitly since the end of World War II, the complex of many cities which have grown together to become known as Los Angeles has become the prototype of slurbia, the suburban slum. As the central portion of this vast loosely-connected megalopolis became more crowded and land more expensive, people, industries and shopping complexes moved farther from the center. When regions, such as the San Fernando Valley, became similarly saturated, the frog leaped again, each expansion made possible by extension of the freeway system and the metropolitan water supply.

Los Angeles and its suburbs now engulfs five counties and is expected to extend from the Mexican border north to Santa Barbara in twenty years. Since 1960, the five countries in the megalopolitan area have gained 1.75 million people, more than the combined population of San Francisco and Boston. Population in the southern California area was 10 million by mid-1967, will hit 25 million by the year 2000.

"Most companies that have factories requiring more space are leaving the central district for outlying areas where land is cheap," commented Dr. Joseph E. Haring of Occidental College. "When the metropolis comes to them, they'll move out farther. That's how we grow." During 1965 alone, 177 manufacturing firms expanded in this leapfrog fashion and 23 new ones arrived in the Los Angeles area. The problem is as bad, if not worse, in other major cities, particularly New York.

The total movement of people in southern California defies the ability of any planning group except those in small, isolated areas which are quickly engulfed by the human tidal wave. Ventura County to the west of the San Fernando Valley was a dry-land farming and citrus area eight years ago. Today the hills are being ripped down to form stair-step pads for thousands of new homes. Land which could be bought for $10 an acre in 1910 now is worth $20,000. The same vast migration is pushing north and east as well and would be pressing southward except that the Pacific Ocean is there. All neighboring counties are braced for the day when Los Angeles will press on into their areas.

"I can already see those Los Angeles people crawling and swarming like ants across the mountains through the Tejon Pass," said Kern County Administrative Officer John E. Veon. "They are reaching for Bakersfield and Taft already and soon more of them will pour down on top of us. People are tired of living in Los Angeles and not even knowing the people next door."

The best way to meet the people next door in the five-county area is on the freeway. Beginning at 6:30 A.M. each workday morning, millions of cars move out from millions of homes and a blue haze of exhaust fumes begins to build up over the freeway. By 7:30 A.M. the traffic on most of the main arteries has chugged virtually to a halt and autos move by inches and spurts averaging 10 to 20 miles an hour rather than the 60 mph the freeways were designed for. There, if you haven't seen your neighbor lately, you may find his car in the lane next to yours. You have plenty of time to chat. In the meantime, the smog builds up carbon monoxide concentrations that make many drivers drowsy and reaches near fatal levels. Here, then, is how the Los Angeles megalopolis is beginning to choke itself to death, just as Calcutta, halfway around the world, is dying on its own sewage and disease. The two problems seem to be completely dissimilar,

27

but actually are only different manifestations of one all-inclusive and staggering task: removal of the pollution men produce around themselves.

The major components in the metabolism of a typical metropolis fit into a fairly simple formula of products which must come in and those which must go out. The quantities, on the other hand, are prodigious.

The average city dweller, directly or indirectly, uses about 150 gallons (1250 pounds) of water per day, 4 pounds of food, and 19 pounds of fossil fuel. This is converted into roughly 120 gallons of sewage, assuming 80 percent recovery of water input; 4 pounds of solid refuse, and 1.9 pounds of air pollutants.

Multiply the above figures to exemplify a typical city of one million people. Into this city flows 625,000 tons of water each day. The residents consume 2000 tons of food and 9500 tons of fuel. The fuel, in turn, breaks down to 1000 tons of motor fuel, 2700 of natural gas, 2800 of oil and 3000 of coal.

Solid refuse which must be hauled out—tin cans, newspapers, cartons and other junk—amounts to 2000 tons, equal to the food which was imported. After about 20 percent of the water has been used on lawns and otherwise consumed, 500,000 tons per day returns, contaminated, to the city's sewers. It is interesting to note that in the 500,000 tons of sewage, only 120 tons actually are solid matter in suspension.

The 9500 tons of fuel consumed each day is converted into energy for running trucks and automobiles, producing electric power, operating the wheels of industry and heating or air conditioning residential homes and other buildings, but a residual 10 percent—950 tons—is spewed out to pollute the air of the city. This air pollution, in turn, consists of 150 tons of particles, such as soot; 150 tons of sulfur dioxide; 100 tons of nitrogen oxides; 100 tons of hydrocarbons, and *450 tons of carbon monoxide*. Automobiles, buses and trucks account for more than half of the air pollution in American towns and cities today, the role which was played by the horse seventy years ago.

Although these pollution figures are enormous, the city of one million remains but a small fraction of the total problem in the U.S. As of 1963, for example, about 150 million of the 189 million Americans (roughly 80 percent) lived in some 22,000 communities served by 19,200 waterworks systems. These 150 million used about 23 *billion* gallons of water per day and returned nearly 20 billion gallons of it to rivers and streams as sewage. This does not count the prodigious quantities of water used and contaminated by public utilities, industry and irrigation of agricultural land. In 1960, water required for all purposes in the U.S. totaled *320 billion gallons per day*.

From the viewpoint of waste removal alone, it would appear that the great cities of the world—New York, London, Tokyo, Berlin and others—have gone about as far as they can go, but population experts tell us the opposite is true. The absolute number, as well as the proportion, of people living in cities of the future throughout the world is expected to increase greatly as time goes on.

David Owen, a United Nations expert on metropolitan growth, warns that the world could be plunged into "unprecedented personal violence and human suffering" if the population in cites continues uncontrolled. He states that in the next few years the entire world will change from predominantly rural to predominantly urban in nature. Owen declares that the trend has been building toward an explosion for 165 years. He points out that between 1800 and 1965, the population of the world increased five times, but cities over 100,000 population multiplied by twenty times and the rate of urban growth is increasing every year.

"On a very conservative estimate," Owen says, "there are likely to be as many people living in large urban complexes by the year 2000 as were living in the entire world in 1950.

"In the past," he continues, "there has been a tendency on the part of policy-makers to regard city development as a non-productive investment which has to be made to improve worsening social conditions. We must somehow seek to break out of these confining fetters to our thinking and try to regain some of our original feelings toward the city as the cradle of civilization."

The large city, that "cradle of civilization," now houses 135 million Americans, seven out of ten people now living. By the year 2000, thirty-three years away, 80 percent of the nation's estimated 330 million population will live in metropolitan areas. From a slightly different viewpoint, by that date some 240 million people will live on 8.7 percent of the nation's land, almost twice the number now living in large cities. The population density in major urban areas is expected to average 774 people per square mile. By comparison, the population density in Japan now is 672 per square mile.

President Johnson, in announcing the new federal Department of Housing and Urban Development in December 1965, said that the American city has come to its "time of decision." Major cities, he declared, are on a "suicidal course and already scarcely fit to live in." He commented that New York City is meeting its annual $4 billion budget with deficit financing, while all cities and states in the nation now are spending $70 billion a year in a well-nigh futile effort to keep up with their problems.

R. B. Cowles, professor emeritus of zoology at the University of California at Los Angeles, believes there is little time left to save the world from being completely despoiled. The cause, he points out wisely, is not "ruthless exploiters" but man's "intemperate breeding." Anyone who uses electric power, gasoline, oil, water, or who lives in a house or drives an auto is contributing a "full share" to man's depredations of nature.

"But we can't stop eating, go naked, or dispense with cooked food or the warmth of fires and furnaces," Cowles states, "nor can we blame mothers or fathers or children or even sex. Conservationists can no longer afford to divert their energies on scapegoats, whipping boys or with tongue-clucking platitudes about exploiters, unless they are also willing to face the key issue of over population.

30

"Today we measure economic progress by the increases in the gross national product, the 'sacred GNP.' That's the same thing as measuring progress by the rate we are consuming our limited irreplaceable natural resources. Gross national product is really gross national depletion."

Professor Cowles pointed out that the Indians could have lived in America forever without thinking about conservation: "Their long occupation left not a scar on the land, nor a sign of damage, and going on the way they were would not have caused a blemish, nor the extinction of a single species of animal or plant. By number and culture they were in balance with their environment." The white man, on the other hand, has been attempting to throw the natural ecology out of balance, and with considerable success, at least since the westward migration began in the nineteenth century.

Another similar and somber warning has been voiced by Robert C. Cook, president of the Population Reference Bureau. "Already we are nationally distraught by the perplexing problems of urban congestion, water shortage, juvenile crime, chronic deficiency in educational facilities and inadequate care of the aged," he said. "Those who think growth to 195 million Americans should be celebrated with noisemakers and paper hats might well prepare their children to celebrate the 400 million mark with padlocked personal water bottles and oxygen masks."

The Population Reference Bureau estimates the 400 million mark will be reached sixty years from now, and more than 320 million of those people will be crowded into the large metropolises. Before that day, expensive medicine must be brought to bear upon the metropolitan metabolism, most particularly the disposal of its wastes.

"Increases in per capita costs of pollution abatement, municipal water supplies, outdoor recreation and urban transport are all consequences of increasing numbers," according to Dr. Roger Revelle, director of the Center for Population Studies at Harvard University. "Perhaps more serious is the decline in the quality of life; many of our fellow citizens waste one or two hours each day driving to and from work under what only can be described as miserable conditions."

Many experts, watching the megalopolitan sprawl now linking many of the world's major population centers, worry at the pace with which open land is being gobbled up and covered with homes, stores and industries. This is particularly true in southern California, where suburbia is destroying citrus, walnut and truck farming land. However, William L. C. Wheaton, director of the University of California Institute for Urban and Regional Development at Berkeley, points out that only thirty thousand square miles of this nation's more than three million square miles now are devoted to urban use.

"This is only one percent of the land area," Wheaton said, "and within this thirty thousand square miles almost half of the land is unused. A population of 300 million could readily be accommodated in our present urban areas with no more discomfort than is suffered by millions of citizens of Boston or New Haven or Cleveland or Chicago." He predicted that within thirty years, the population of America still would occupy only 2 percent of the nation's land.

"We will not accept a continuation of slurbs [urban slums]," Wheaton declared. "The American people are deluged into believing that a high-priced tract is a substitute for a planned community. But the search is in vain—the smog rolls in inexorably, the traffic builds up and the well runs dry.

"Our greatest challenge is to demonstrate that these things are not inevitable, that at virtually no increase in cost we can produce a decent environment."

Littered Land

*We could be known as the generation which put a
man on the moon while standing ankle-deep
in garbage.*

Mayor Ralph Locher, Cleveland, Ohio

"THE TIME HAS ARRIVED WHEN MANURE HEAPS, SLAUGHTER
houses, fat and bone boiling establishments, glue manufacturers, outdoor or unsewered privies and all kindred occupations and nuisances cannot be much longer tolerated within
the built-up portions of New York or Brooklyn."

With the above edict, the Metropolitan Board of Health of
New York City declared war on garbage, trash and other filth
littering America's greatest city. It was issued on March 10,
1866, a century ago. The declaration forbade the "throwing
of dead animals, garbage or ashes into the streets" and referred
to "filthy and overcrowded tenements." The decree presaged
the cry which now, a hundred years later, is being heard on
the national scale, a plea for new awareness and methods for
cleaning up our littered land.

In 1866 the New York Board of Health commented crisply that the "poor have the right of protection against avarice and inhumanity." Since then the life expectancy in that metropolis of steel and glass has gone up from forty-five to seventy years. In those days the killers were yellow fever, cholera, typhus, measles, scarlet fever, dysentery, tuberculosis and smallpox.

"The streets are extremely dirty and offensive," the Board's report said. "The gutters are obstructed with filth, composed of houseslops, refuse vegetables, decayed fruit, ashes, dead animals and even human excrement."

The writer commented that Manhattan visitors contracted disease in unclean hotels and eating places, that food markets were huddles of farm wagons and litter, and the only garbage collection was being done by private scavengers.

The Board of Health lost no time putting its words to work. Before the year 1866 was out, hundreds of cowbarn owners had been chased beyond the city limits. Two hundred and ninety-nine local piggeries were evicted from the city and 3949 refuse-heaped back yards were cleaned up. The Board introduced the first watertight garbage cans and persuaded garbage collectors to make regular rounds with sturdier vehicles. In its first eight months of operation, the New York Board of Health isued 23,000 orders and five thousand warnings to abate nuisances.

By 1869, all slaughterhouses had been shut down below 40th Street, but street-cleaning and rubbish removal was a dirtier problem because William Marcy ("Boss") Tweed had let out the work to private contractors on a ten-year basis. These contracts had to come to an end before efficiency could be instituted in the operation.

Carcass-strewn streets, in fact, remained a problem in New York City through 1914. That year, the Board of Health reported, it removed from the streets the bodies of 14,956 horses, 2105 steers, 56 mules, deer, monkeys and camels, and 56,903 dead dogs and cats.

Between 1869 and 1914, although not strictly limited by those years, the United States became the most industrialized nation on earth. At the beginning of the period, barely a fifth of all Americans lived in metropolitan areas; at the end, cities contained nearly one-half of the people. In 1906 hundreds of socialites climbed Russian Hill in San Francisco to view the great earthquake damage and watch their city burn. Other cities went up in flames and were rebuilt with new rules, new materials and new citizens. Immigrants flooded in from Europe. The railroads took trade and travel in all directions and concentrated commerce in the growing metropolitan areas. A concern for better sanitation led to such innovations as a three-story outdoor privy in St. Louis serving tenement dwellers. (An ingenious combination of multi-level piping offered some protection for people living on the ground floor.) In 1956, when nearly another half-century had passed, the city council of Trenton, New Jersey, passed an ordinance outlawing the last thirty outhouses within the city limits. Through a century, we learned not to leave the carcasses and natural wastes of man and animals lying around on the ground. To replace them came the world of paper, glass bottles, tin cans, plastics and the multimillion carcasses of dead automobiles.

The land is polluted with thousands of substances and things. These range from eroding mountainsides, where beautiful forests have been stripped away, to beer-can-littered miles of asphalt and concrete. Land pollution ranges also from salts and fertilizer deposited in the process of growing food, to residual pesticides and weed killers. While making our world ugly and increasingly unpleasant, all of these pollutants are the tracks we leave in trying to make our world a more pleasant place in which to live. Littering of the land, again, is the mark of a population which has outrun nature's waste conversion abilities.

In the words of Wallace Stegner, novelist, historian and conservationist:

> Man is not an inert member of the life community, he is a link with a motor and self-starter. Except in low-energy tribal civilizations that subsist by hunting and gathering, he has al-

ways to some degree controlled his environment and hence, to a degree, his own evolution.

It is by his own volition that Western man has become the greatest of weed species—a weed being defined as a species that crowds out others by expropriating their room and nutriment. By 1965 the weed was rank enough to have spread into every former low-energy area of the globe, and to threaten not only other species but itself.

. . . the enemy is not industrialism but its side effects in permitting human weedism; the real conservation problem is the problem of population. . . . Edward Hyams defines the human race as a disease of soil, and sees its future as identical with that of a colony of bacteria planted in a dish of agar. When it reaches the edge of the dish it must either die of starvation (Malthus) or strangle in its own wastes. And we are getting ever closer to the edge of the dish.

The dish—at least until we learn how to climb out into the solar system—is limited to our earth with its land, water and air. Although the land is great and the waters deep, we can no longer sweep our dirt under the rug in the blind faith that it will decay and go away. The major difficulty with solid wastes is that their disposal, by nature and quantity, generally results in polluting some other portion of our precious natural environment. If you burn trash, a common practice in thousands of town dumps, it pollutes the air. If you bury it improperly, it pollutes the land. If you dump it into a river, you help destroy the river.

"The well-known capacity of the modern city to drown in sewage is more than matched by its talent for smothering under a blanket of garbage and refuse," the Public Health Service commented in 1966. "The volume of solid waste has grown more rapidly than the population. At the same time, available economic space for waste disposal has declined. The consequence is that the garbage can, refuse pile and junk heap have moved out of the individual back yard, garage or attic into the major public charge."

Almost no part of the earth is free of man's rubbish, including many of the deepest parts of the ocean. In 1966, Andreas Rechnitzer, chief scientist of the North American Deep Submergence Systems Division, warned that we must stop using the ocean as a permanent rubbish dump. He says that almost any place you dive to the ocean floor, you can find junk (he calls the objects "artifacts"). Rechnitzer, down there, has seen bedsprings, shell casings, unexploded projectiles, beer bottles, wash tubs and cans, as well as wrecked ships and automobile carcasses.

One time, seven thousand feet deep off the Marianas Islands in the western Pacific, he came within a foot of an unexploded five-inch projectile. "We decided it was an American shell because right next to it, in fact leaning on it, was a beer can," Rechnitzer commented with a smile. Another time he thought he had found a new spiral form of marine life capable of withstanding high pressure. It was a bedspring.

The millions of tons of military supplies and equipment which have been left to rot and rust after our wars is a story of its own, but the empty beer can and wrecked automobile have become symbols of our dirty age. During World War II at least one recreation island, a tiny piece of Eniwetok Atoll in the western Pacific, was protected against the rolling windward sea by a mile-long breakwater built entirely of discarded beer cans. This breakwater was the trace left behind by thousands of soldiers, sailors and marines who had been allowed ashore for a few hours to swim, play baseball and drink beer under the shade of a tropic palm.

Each time a modern housewife empties a vacuum-cleaner bag and her husband or son brings the family trash barrel to the street curb, they are contributing to the pollution of our land. In fact, every American (on the average) throws away 4.5 pounds of junk every day—paper, grass, brush cuttings, garbage, ashes, metal and glass. That is about 1600 pounds, almost a ton, per person each year. The current national production of solid wastes amounts to more than 877 million pounds per day—125 million tons per year.

John W. Gardner, Secretary of the Department of Health, Education, and Welfare, estimates that this total will rise to *three times that amount* by 1980. "Although local governments and industries are spending more than \$3.8 billion annually for collection and disposal of solid wastes," Gardner said, "existing practices generally are creating health hazards causing environmental blight."

That's another way of saying that junk and rubbish is piling up faster than it can be removed without making an uglier spot somewhere else. In recognition of this, Congress passed the Solid Waste Disposal Act, which authorizes grants to states and interstate agencies to help with the problem. The grants, as a first step, would pay up to 50 percent of the cost of surveying solid waste disposal problems and developing plans for abatement. Gardner has asked the governors of each of the fifty states to designate agencies to work with the federal government in carrying out provisions of the law.

Obviously, new directions are necesary if we are already spending \$3.8 billion per year—more than two-thirds the amount devoted to America's entire space flight program—*without* solving the problems of our cluttered land. Where does all this trash come from?

During 1965, the American Paper Institute published some facts and figures in support of the world's papermaking industry, which is much maligned for devouring the world's forests and polluting streams with its stinking chemical refuse. The Institute's ad man wrote:

Suppose, as you slept last night, some evil genie had withdrawn paper from the earth and blighted the forests which are the primary source of paper. . . .

The sunlight would glare through shadeless windows and bounce off empty picture frames on paperless walls. You could reach for the morning newspaper to discover there was no morning newspaper. And if you prayed, not even a bible would have survived to help you.

Need a cigaret? There remains only a pile of loose tobacco on the floor. Breakfast? Orange juice and milk spill out of the refrigerator door. Loose cereal tumbles from the cupboard shelf. . . . No point in sending the kids to school, because what is a school without books and paper and lunchbags.

What, for that matter, is civilization as we know it today

without paper which separates us, as much as anything else, from the upper Pleistocene? Without paper there would be no commerce, no industry, no banks, not even a government, which does not really run on red tape, but on tons of paper.

That writer might also have pointed out that authors of books such as this one would be forced to ditch digging or farming as a livelihood. Without question, paper is more responsible for the forward movement of civilization than any other single product devised by man, but it also is a major component in our family trash barrel. According to the environmental pollution panel of the President's Science Advisory Committee, paper and paper products account for *45 percent* of all municipal solid waste matter. Aside from obviously beneficial uses of paper (such as books and money), we have, as a by-product of our modern demand for sanitation, moved into a wrapper-happy age. The days when you could stand as a child amid the wonderful odors of a grocery store and buy crackers and pickles from a barrel or candy from a glass display counter are virtually gone. Now every grocery store item, and half of those in a modern hardware sctore, are encased in paper (and plastic) so complex that in many instances the wrapping is more expensive than the product it contains! This is particularly true of the cereal box fetish which delivers to our youngsters a penny's worth of rolled, baked, sugared and odd-shaped cereal grain in a three-cent cardboard carton at a ridiculous retail price of thirty to forty cents. Likewise, potato chips, crackers and powdered soft drink mixes—considering the food substance alone—probably are worth less than their gaudy packages. That's only one example. The industry itself boasts that Americans are using more than 100,000 different paper and paperboard products, probably all of which are convenient but many unnecessary.

As might be expected, the United States uses more paper than any other nation in the world, 46 million tons per year, 479 pounds for each man, woman and child. By comparison Sweden and Canada each consume 300 pounds per capita, Russia 42, and in China, where it all began with the discovery of the papermaking process in the first century A.D., the average person uses six pounds per year. As an indication of anticipated growth, the paper industry is spending more than one billion dollars a year on new research, experimentation and mills for production. Of all paper used, not more than one-third is reclaimed and remade into paper products at the present time. The other two-thirds goes to city dumps to be buried or burned.

Despite the vast quantities, paper at least is easily burnable, and if not burned, will decay and return to the soil in a reasonably short period of time. Grass clippings, brush and garbage will do the same, but not so with the hard junk.

Each year in America we must get rid of 48 billion tin and aluminum cans (250 per person), 26 billion bottles and jars (135 per person) and more than half a billion dollars worth of miscellaneous packaging material. Metal and plastic bottle caps alone amount to 65 billion per year, 338 for each person. At the present time in America, glass and ceramics account for 6 percent of our municipal trash load; metallics 10 percent; ashes 10 percent; garbage 12 percent; grass, brush and cuttings, 15 percent, second only to paper which accounts for 45 percent. The remaining two percent contains miscellaneous material such as rubber, fabric and a growing quantity of plastics. As one newspaper reported: "Americans last year bought and presumably squeezed 1,244,126,428 metal squeeze tubes, half of which contained toothpaste" and all of which ended up in the junk pile.

The garbage can has been part of the American home for so many years that very few people think beyond the garbage truck to the mountain of rotting refuse which piles up across the nation. As a partial solution to this problem, the home garbage grinder has been one of the great inventions of our century. Because solids normally make up not more than one percent of the liquid flowing in city sewers, it is obvious this water flow also can disperse a great amount of garbage if it is properly pulverized so as not to clog the pipes with whole tomatoes and lettuce leaves. The garbage grinder, however, is far from universal in use, and millions of tons of food wastes still are heaped on slow burning fires which blacken the sky with foul-smelling smoke. In New York City, for example, more than thirty-five tons of cooked garbage is belched into the sky each day from eleven city incinerators. These garbage burners have no air pollution control equipment except for coarse screens on tall smokestacks to keep the larger chunks from spewing out. That city's garbage disposal system is judged to be twenty to forty years behind the time, but at least temporarily necessary because hauling all such waste matter out of the city would cost from twenty to twenty-eight dollars per ton. Even so, New York's incineration methods are modern when compared with the thousands of this country's communities which burn their garbage in open city dumps, to the detriment of land values on that side of town.

While the city of New York worries about the age and inefficiencies of its garbage disposal system, many parts of the city remain as filthy as they were a century ago when the Board of Health first went to work. The Board in 1966 conplained that city-owned tenements were violating health, safety and housing regulations. Hallways were obstructed by garbage, tin cans, and plaster gouged from inside walls. The smell of urine pervaded the squalid rooms, and interior court-yards were shin deep in "air mail garbage"—garbage tossed from windows. As will be shown later this garbage actually could be quite useful in several ways, some of which offer intriguing methods for solving a great share of our solid waste disposal problem.

Although the horse has dwindled in both use and numbers since its displacement by the automobile, farm animal wastes still cause a considerable problem of land pollution. This is particularly true with modern feed lots, where thousands of cattle and hogs are fattened for slaughter, and poultry farms where millions of turkeys and chickens are raised by new force-feeding methods. Most of this waste, obviously, is usable fertilizer but the problem lies in the economics of processing and packaging these manures for sale. In southern California and a number of other areas feedlot steer manure is baked at high temperature to remove moisture and kill weed seeds and bacteria, then profitably sold for lawn and garden enrichment.

The average individual seldom thinks of it, but vast quantities of solid waste material results from mining. In the United States, during 1963, more than 3.3 billion tons of waste rock and mill tailings were discarded near mine sites. In addition, the refining of ores, combustion of coal, and the production of metals and nonmetallic materials result in building vast mountains of slag, ash and other waste material. At the same time, enormous scars are slashed in the earth by strip mining, which leaves ugly gaping holes and raw gullies where land and woods once offered sweeps of calm, natural beauty.

American industry contributes vast quantities of scrap materials to the nation's solid waste totals, while at the same time helping to conserve useful raw materials. Industrial scrap is generated at a rate of twelve to fifteen million tons each year.

Another growing source of solid waste is the construction industry, particularly in the demolition of thousands of homes and other buildings to make way for urban renewal projects and new miles of superhighway. Much demolition material is burned on the site, but this complicates the air pollution problem. In Los Angeles County some five thousand *tons per day* of demolition material is going into sanitary landfills. Philadelphia reported disposal of fifty thousand tons of demolition waste in this manner in 1964.

The complexity and interrelation of pollution problems was shown in December 1965 when the New York City Council prohibited open burning of waste lumber. Wood began piling up at construction sites all over the city and Abraham Dollinger, attorney for the Wrecking Contractors Association of New York, cried: "This is the death knell of our industry." Before January 1, four city burning sites had accepted an average of 485 truckloads of demolition wastes per week. The ban on burning required the wrecking contractors to cut the waste lumber into three-foot sections and pack it solidly to eliminate holes where fires could start and rats could live in the sanitary landfill sites. In the first week following the ban, only 331 truckloads of debris were hauled to the landfill areas. On the site of the old Savoy Plaza Hotel on Fifth Avenue small mountains of splintered wood were growing. "Our problem is that we're choked up with lumber," commented an official of the wrecking company. "I have no idea what to do. It's tough to cut up everything here on the site because of nails." H. Earl Fullilove, chairman of the board of the Building Trade Employers Association, expressed the bitterness of wreckers who were hurt by the city's action. "It seems they singled out this industry," he said. "Everyone can see that the air pollution lumber creates is infinitesimal compared to other sources."

His comment is typical of every company and every individual who is against pollution of all kinds, but resents any control upon his particular contribution to the problem.

Crumbled masonry and splintered lumber is one kind of solid waste; radioactive residue in the nuclear age is another.

In April 1966 a ship docked at Charleston, South Carolina, bearing five thousand steel drums filled with Spanish soil. From there the barrels were hauled to the Atomic Energy Commission's Savannah River plant at Aiken and buried under ten feet of Carolina clay. The soil was scooped up from the surface of farm fields near Palomares, Spain, where a B-52 bomber crashed on January 17 and scattered plutonium fuel from two of the hydrogen bombs the plane had been carrying. A third bomb dropped into the Atlantic Ocean off the Spanish shore. Three months of worldwide suspenseful attention accompanied heroic U.S. naval efforts to recover the third bomb, but the story of the radioactive soil was less thoroughly told.

When the plane crashed after midair collision, the bombs fell and were blown apart by TNT charges designed for exactly that function. Some radioactive dust was scattered over the adjacent tomato fields, although not enough to endanger anyone in the area. Despite this fact, and because of the superstitious fear of radioactivity which has existed since the end of World War II, the U.S. Air Force dug up the contaminated soil, shipped it to America and buried it. Disposal of the fifty-five gallon steel drums of earth and tomato vines under three feet of earth would have been sufficient, but the Department of Agriculture required the trenches be dug seven feet deeper to guard against possible spread of fruit and vegetable pests imported from Spain. The people of Palomares knew a good thing when they saw it and sued the U.S. Air Force for $200,000 in damages for lost crops, profits and wages. Hundreds of acres were closed to harvesting and cultivation for two months. Business came to a standstill in Palomares and nearby fishing villages. (After it was all over, one bartender commented: "We are praying for another American bomb, but we want it right here on Main Street.")

The Palomares bombs only illustrate what promises to be a growing land pollution problem, not from bombs, but from the increasing production of electric power by nuclear energy in the years ahead. Much of the partially consumed waste products from a nuclear reactor are highly radioactive and remain so for many years. Already the United States has stored underground at Savannah River and Richland, Washington, *seventy million* gallons of radioactive material, buried in steel and concrete tanks. By 1970 it is predicted the U.S. will produce forty thousand gallons of such waste per year, with three million per year by the end of the century. AEC laboratories are studying many methods for disposing of these wastes, including injection into bedrock more than 1000 feet in the earth, or storage in the mined-out salt mines.

Whereas some land pollutants, such as radioactive wastes, are potentially harmful to man and other living organisms, most solid wastes are simply displeasing to the eye and are the residue from our increasingly complex technological civilization.

"I am concerned that just because we can build almost anything, we do build almost anything and usually with little or no thought to the side effects which these innovations produce," said Professor Hubert Heffner, Stanford University researcher. "Then when we find that new engineering advances have created social problems or political problems, or health problems, we seem to accept them as though they were completely inevitable."

One such engineering advance which today seems "completely inevitable" is the automobile, and the dead carcasses of this metal monster provide one of the ugliest blots on the American landscape today. More than five million cars and trucks are consigned to the junk heap each year. Most of them, after they are stripped of usable parts, remain there. Every American city has one or a dozen auto graveyards, such as one outside Baltimore which covers many city blocks with hulks stacked four and five high.

> The unsightly picture currently presented by junk cars has become of major national significance within the past decade [wrote the President's Science Advisory Committee in November 1965]. The negative reactions can be attributed to increased accumulations of hulks in scrap yards or scrap storage areas, and a "king size" litterbug tendency to abandon useless hulks on the streets or highways and in the farmyards. Essentially, the reason for the accumulation and casual discard of old automobiles is that although nominally a source of valuable metal, junk cars are now in surplus commodity.
>
> A number of influences are acting to interrupt a normal recycling of scrap from old cars back into steel furnaces. The cost of collecting, processing, and transporting auto hulks is high and the price of the product is low compared to other more desired forms of ferrous metal scrap; changes in the steelmaking process require less scrap than formerly; and closely paralleling the rapid increase in motor car production, the number of automobiles junked each year is steadily increasing.

The survival curve for passenger cars shows that about 50 percent of a given model will have disappeared from the roads in about ten years. Begining at the age of five years, the rate of disappearance accelerates. This explains, in part, the tremendous increase in scrapped cars during recent years, because autos built in the high production years of the 1950s are now reaching the scrap pile in enormous numbers. These numbers in turn may be expected to increase because U.S. automobile production now is running between eight and nine million per year. Interior Secretary Stewart L. Udall estimates there are now 40 million junked cars rusting around the country and within another generation "a trash pile or piece of junk will be within a stone's throw of any person standing anywhere on the Amercian land mass."

In the fall of 1965, Herman Streur, a resident of Bellflower, California, was moved to write the editor of the Los Angeles *Times* about the ugliness he observed on the road: "This spring and summer," he wrote, "I made a tour from Los Angeles to Florida, then to New York, Michigan, and then crossed into Canada. Of all the states and Canada, California has the worst littered highways. . . . Between litter on the highways, automobile graveyards, and sign boards, we have the worst looking highways in the nation."

Californians have an eye for beauty and it is doubtful that that state has any monopoly on the hideous eyesore produced by the automobile, but it sometimes seems worse because the automobile population is so high in that Western state. Los Angeles County, for example, because of its air pollution problems has been forced to prohibit burning of car seats, tires and other flammable waste from scrapped vehicles. As a result, the burning problem has moved to the high desert east of Los Angeles and has become so severe that it is jeopardizing flying safety around Edwards Air Force Base, one of the nation's most vital airfields. Colonel Donald E. Ewing complained in December 1965 that smoke from burning car seats, tires and wiring insulation, one-half mile from the base, often threatens cancellation of important test flights.

There are few places left in America and the world where garbage and trash may be dumped in the open without offending nearby residents, and we must stop throwing our trash into the sky.

New Brooms

*The time has come when man can no longer
continue using the land, sea and air as his "trash
basket." We must find ways to cycle wastes
back into the economy.*

National Academy of Sciences Report, 1966

ON APRIL 21, 1966, MRS. LYNDON B. JOHNSON RECEIVED THE
George Foster Peabody award for a television program in
which she campaigned for national beautification. The award
was but a symbol of the outstanding work Mrs. Johnson has
done, lending her name and work to the national drive for a
more attractive America.

Her husband, the President, commented: "The fact that
there is family representation among your honorees has not
entirely escaped me. I hope you will agree that my pride in
your recognition of Lady Bird's efforts is justifiable. But
beyond this is the pride that her drive and her work to help
make this a lovelier land are having tangible results."

47

Mrs. Johnson would be the first to admit that she has had help. In October 1965 Congress passed the highway beautification law, which called on states to set up controls to ban billboards and junk yards along the 41,000-mile interstate highway system and 225,000 miles of primary roads. The measure prohibits billboards within 660 feet of main highways built and maintained with federal funds. Junk yards must be a thousand feet away, or at least screened from view with something more attractive than a wrecked automobile. States which fail to comply could lose 10 percent of their federal highway aid funds. As a carrot to offset the whiplash, states are given money equal to 3 percent of their aid funds to be used for "scenic enhancement."

The citizens of Palmdale, California, took scenic enhancement seriously and sent Mrs. Johnson three hundred lilac plants to help beautify the city of Washington. These were planted around schools, public housing units and recreation areas. Lady Bird thanked the officials of Palmdale and said some residents in Washington "will be seeing their first lilacs because of the kindness of your city."

Every major issue also has its moment of laughter according to the American way of life. In Laramie, Wyoming, a group of residents spoofed Lady Bird's beautification program by erecting a billboard, replete with lavender trimming, at the western edge of town. "Help beautify junk yards," the sign reads. "Throw something lovely away today."

In Laramie the wild Western lands may still appear an endless dumping ground, but so do the miles in outer space, and some people already are concerned about the new junk yards we are creating out there. Hilliard W. Paige, head of General Electric's Missile and Space Division, warned in 1966 that a rubbish removal program will be necessary beyond the earth's atmosphere by the year 2000. At the present time, only ten years after the beginning of the space age, there are more than one thousand tons of satellites orbiting the earth. Paige predicted there will be *one million* satellites in orbit by 1990 weighing a total of 100,000 tons. Obviously, if a manned spacecraft should collide with a piece of this junk, it would be just as fatal to the astronauts as an auto crash on the New Jersey Turnpike.

The problems of cleaning away scrap metals, including junk cars, would be much greater than they are if it were not for the thriving salvage industries. Despite the number of automotive carcasses now visible, an average of 26.6 million tons of scrap iron per year was purchased in the period 1958 to 1963. This represents a fairly large portion of the new steel production in the United States. Nearly 100 percent of nonferrous scrap materials are salvaged for reuse. About 957,000 tons of copper were recovered from scrap in 1963, some 40 percent of the total supply of copper that year and 80 percent of the amount produced by domestic mines. Lead recovered from scrap amounted to 494,000 tons, almost double the 253,000 tons produced in U.S. mines in 1963. The annual volume of aluminum scrap is about 25 percent of the total supply. Reducing the remainder of the automobile to new material is strictly a matter of economics answering to the law of supply and demand. At the present time, it is still easier to obtain steel from the ground than from available scrap.

> The junk automobile problem [wrote the President's Science Advisory Committee] does not appear to be a technological matter, but rather one of management and incentive for disposal. The principal eyesore results from storage of automobile hulks which have been or still are being processed for removal of spare parts until such times as the scrap steel market makes it profitable to sell them. These hulks are in private ownership on private lots and there is very little in the way of a health or hazard problem to generate action. The problem is sufficiently widespread, however, to make it a public issue.
>
> The basic short range problem is how storage of automobile hulks can be changed to reduce the number and screen the necessary remnant. . . . The automobile is processed for its parts and the dealer makes sufficient profit to enable him to store the hulk as a dead item. It is not certain, however, that the cost for the ultimate disposal of the hulk can be absorbed by the junk auto processor. Steel is a valuable natural resource and part of the total question should be its conservation. . . .

One difficulty in reducing junked cars is matching still usable parts with automobiles that need them. One solution has been found by Arthur Jordan, owner of J & W Auto Parts on a highway south of Richmond, Virginia. Jordan grossed $100,000 in 1965 by way of a telephone hot line that plugs him into the auto market at 109 points between Buffalo, New York, and Jacksonville, Florida. Jordan's system brings together the junk yard that has a radiator for a 1949 Buick and the customer who wants one. His regional sales network started with a teletype machine. Now it has graduated to a telephone link which is heard over loudspeakers in the more than one hundred junk yards hooked into the system.

In England the disposal of a mounting volume of abandoned automobiles is complicated by legal rulings which award ownership of the useless hulks to owners of property where they are found. Thus, anyone trying to get rid of a junker might just leave it on his neighbor's property, and the neighbor inherits the problem. Finding the spare part for a used car, or vice versa, also is an occupation, hobby or disease, depending upon how you look at it, which is not limited to the United States.

Not long ago when Derek Taylor, twenty-five, of London, needed some spare parts for his car he went to the police station and asked the desk sergeant if he could get them from an automobile which had been abandoned on the street.

"Of course not," said the sergeant. "Even if the car's been abandoned, you would still be guilty of stealing, so forget it."

"But it's been there for months," protested Taylor.

"Can't help it," said the officer. "The law's the law."

Two hours later Taylor was back with the car in tow.

"I found this car," he told the same sergeant. "Please put it in your lost property department." The law again being the law, the sergeant was compelled to do so. British law also says that if no one claimed the car in two months it would be Taylor's.

"I will then take the car home and get the parts I need," he said. "I also like its body. I might put that on my car too."

When all usable parts finally are stripped away, however, the hulk remains, and that is a heavy, bulky item which seems to defy, at least for the present, economical methods of returning it to the raw material mainstream or storing it in a compact and not-unattractive manner. One answer was suggested by Senator Clifford P. Case of New Jersey. He asked Senator Carl Hayden of Arizona, chairman of the Senate Interior Appropriations Subcommittee, to allocate $400,000 permitting the Sandy Hook, New Jersey, Marine Laboratory to build an artificial reef of junked cars in the Atlantic. The reef would serve as a fish sanctuary.

Senator Case's suggestion opens up the possibility that a number of reefs and breakwaters could be built, using millions of junked cars, along both the Atlantic and Pacific coasts. These could serve to establish sheltered coves where exclusive housing and marinas could be built. The junked cars could be covered over with rock and earth above the surface of the shallow water and beautifully landscaped. Thus the junk dealer who is stuck with ten thousand dead automobiles, which are doing nothing except utilizing valuable storage space, could receive a medium return for his junk and the old cars could finally serve a useful purpose. Another possibility suggested by some engineers and scientists is to run the junk autos through a giant hammer mill, reducing the iron and steel to shreds the size of sand and gravel. The resulting raw material could be used to build roadbeds.

New York Governor Nelson Rockefeller's ambitious proposal in 1966 to extend Manhattan Island by filling in ninety-eight acres of the Hudson River offers another possibility for utilizing a mountain of scrapped automobiles. As visualized, a new "coordinated community" of offices, light industry, housing, and commercial and recreational facilities would be built on the new land created to replace old piers on the river from the Battery to Chambers Street. To be known as Battery Park City (if it comes to fruition), the project would cost an estimated $600 million with the state of New York putting up $138 million to build 7500 units of middle- and low-income

51

housing. The city would provide services such as schools, and private promoters would pay the remainder. New York Mayor John V. Lindsay indicated approval of the idea, pointing out that renovation of the semi-blighted area of the great metropolis would increase the city's annual tax from the area from one million to twenty million dollars. In this project, and wherever major landfill operations are necessary, it might be cheaper to utilize scrapped automobiles than to quarry rock and dirt, which in turn would leave new scars on the land.

Altering the storage of junk automobiles is compounded by a number of economic and legal considerations [according to the Science Advisory Committee]. The auto wrecking and scrap business is a multi-billion dollar industry serving a useful purpose. Action that might eliminate or materially reduce the effectiveness of this business would probably compound the problem. . . .
Some relief can be expected now that the industry is conscious of the problem and is aware of the bad public image created by junk automobile yards. Possibly more important, the industry already feels and can foresee restrictive repercussions. . . .

Which is another way of saying that if industry, automotive and otherwise, doesn't do something about the mounting mess of junk automobiles, the government probably will.

Here are some of the things that are being suggested:

1. Design automobiles so they can be more easily cannibalized.

2. Increase the interchangeability of auto parts among various manufacturers.

3. Improve salvage by the reverse production line technique, including super centralized scrapyards.

4 Send cleanup trains to collect auto hulks from outlying villages and farms.

5. Compress auto hulks in as small a package as possible, then stack millions in an artificial iron mountain as a source of raw material for the future.

No one in government or industry yet has suggested the

ultimate way to eliminate junk automobiles, which is to re-move automobiles from society entirely. Obviously, this is not immediately possible without disruption of the world econ-omy, but the days are numbered for the individual automobile with an internal combustion engine.

Cars, however, although perhaps the ugliest, are not the largest part of the solid waste problem. More than 100 million tons of other junk and trash per year must be put somewhere so that nature eventually can absorb and reuse it. Unofficial dumping grounds, in the country as well as the city, are among the most unsightly and unsatisfactory of all. One such is Flatlands Industrial Park, a ninety-six-acre tract in the borough of Brooklyn. Seven years ago, amid considerable fan-fare, the city administration announced that this area would reclaim a blighted area, reverse the outward migration of in-dustry and provide thousands of jobs. In 1966 it was inspected by New York's new mayor, John Lindsay, who was forced to climb over mountains of junk to see it. Political and legal machinations have prevented development of the area, now covered by heaps of moldy mattresses, unsprung sofas and debris ranging from dressmakers' models to the bowling pin. "It's quite a lover's lane at night," commented a guard, "but my, you should see the rats. They're as big as cats."

People thus find an easy way out of their individual prob-lems of dumping unwanted articles in the most convenient place. On the other hand, individual people sometimes find new ways to help solve the general junk disposal problem. Henry Soto is a Los Angeles landscape architect who drove several miles each day to his office, and each day passed a forty-foot-deep abandoned gravel pit. Then came the bright idea. Soto rounded up several partners, purchased the pit, and converted it to a private garbage and trash dump. The com-bine charged trash haulers $8 per truckload to use the dump, a low price in the Los Angeles area, and covered each day's collection of refuse with a layer of earth according to ap-proved sanitary landfill practice. Soto also set out a living bamboo fence to screen the dump from the highway, and planted a border with flower beds and palm trees. The area was so attractive that new customers became confused and drove on by until Soto put up a sign which read "Disposal Gardens." When the hole is filled, Soto plans to build a swimming pool and tennis courts on the new level ground, then charge admission to his private recreation area.

Document Disintegration, Inc., of Los Angeles is a unique business concern. It deals entirely in top secret documents generated chiefly by the aerospace industry of southern California. Such papers, when no longer useful, must be carefully destroyed to insure complete destruction. Burning is not sufficient and also is not consistent with city air pollution regulations. Each Thursday morning, the D.D. Inc. forty-ton truck goes around to the various industrial establishments, collects the documents, and under scrutiny of a security guard grinds the paper to powder with a giant hammer mill which can devour eight thousand pounds an hour. The chewed-up material now goes to the city dumps, but it is expected soon that the new "compost" may be used as mulch in the fruit orchards.

According to the U.S. Department of Health, Education, and Welfare, less than half of the cities and towns in America, with populations of more than 2500, dispose of community refuse by approved sanitary and nuisance-free methods. Open dumps still flourish, contributing to air pollution and serving as feeding and breeding places for disease-carrying rats and flies. Yet a proper burial ground for rubbish, known as sanitary landfill, actually is a method whereby waste can be converted to new, more attractive, reclaimed land. John R. Sheaffer, resources planning officer of the Northeastern Illinois Planning Commission, told the National Conference on Solid Waste Research in 1965 that he had yet to meet a city official who knew the difference between a sanitary landfill and an open dump. The technique consists of putting down layers of garbage and refuse, with proper engineering method and supervision, and covering each layer with an appropriate layer of earth. The only hill in Evanston, Illinois, was built in this manner. It rests on the site of a former refuse dump, rises seventy feet high, and is composed of tree stumps, rough concrete, rubble, bottles and anything that wouldn't burn in the municipal incinerator. The mound was covered with clay, dirt and sod; and now, in place of an unsightly dump, Evanston has an attractive hill with toboggan runs, sled slides and a stairway.

In San Bernardino County, California, refuse was used to build a 1400-foot levee along the Santa Ana River. The compacted landfill is 250 feet wide at the base, 35 feet high and capped with concrete.

Neighboring Los Angeles County is using the same method on a far grander scale which may set the pattern for eliminating health hazards and unsightly dump sites through the nation. The county (almost solid city) produces twenty thousand tons of solid waste matter each day. It is being used to develop two thousand acres of desolate canyon land into flowering parks and recreation areas. Up to ten thousand acres of wasteland ultimately may be developed into new golf courses, botanical gardens and other recreation areas on top of three hundred- to four hundred-foot-high rubbish landfills.

Frank Bowerman, the sanitary district's assistant chief engineer, said that in New York, Chicago, Philadelphia and Detroit it costs from five to twenty dollars per ton to dispose of trash and garbage by incineration. The Los Angeles operation, building new land in useless canyons, charges $1.25 per ton, and Bowerman says, "We're making a handsome return over all costs, including administrative. We take twenty-five cents a ton profit and put that in a reserve fund to buy more sites and to build parks." The district, with a six-million-dollar annual budget, now has five sanitary dump sites and hopes to acquire three thousand acres in the Santa Monica Mountains to serve as a fifty-year answer for the county's rubbish disposal and to preserve land for park development.

As examples of the Los Angeles work, a three hundred-acre park is being created in Glendale's School Canyon. Rubbish is covered daily, and although the landfill continues on adjacent land, baseball diamonds and other facilities are already in use. Rubbish is likewise being compacted in an abandoned open-pit mine on the Palos Verdes Peninsula to make a new 180-acre park.

"A landfill used to be finished out table-top level," Bowerman said, "and then sanitation agencies would find out if somebody wanted it. Here the stuff can be dumped, compacted and covered with dirt—one foot of solid earth for every four feet of rubbish—and molded to fit the need, including contours for a golf course. Wedges of earth may be left as a foundation for any desired buildings." The difference, according to Bowerman, is dumping according to a plan so that the new reclaimed land is immediately useful and at a small fraction of the price a city would pay for prime park land. Bowerman said the Detroit area now is studying the Los Angeles sanitation plan for eighty cities in that area.

"There has been no problem with rodents, odors, or dust," he said. "Every night when the crews leave, you can't even tell where anything was dumped. This is something that will always be beautiful. It has been an asset and will be for years to come.

"You don't have to make a mess out of a rubbish disposal site. It can be clean. It can be dust free and odor free, and you can do it right next to homes. The refuse does give off gases, mainly carbon dioxide and small amounts of methane, but these are all contained with the body of the fill and they diffuse out to the surface very, very slowly."

In this manner most of the nation's solid refuse could be hidden away in old gravel pits, open pit mines, and canyons. Bottles, cans, metal and concrete building refuse would become part of the soil. Organic material would gradually decay through the years and eventually go back into the earth from which it came.

Fire is a quicker way to do the same thing, but one of the blights on America today is the enormous quantities of black, noisome smoke belching into the air from open city dumps and simple incinerators. It does not need to be that way. One of the finest contrasts to New York's eleven dirty city incinerators is the Oceanside incinerator on Long Island. This unique incinerator, which opened last year in Nassau County, burns garbage to produce steam and electricity, a system used in Europe since the end of World War II. But it goes one step further. It produces fresh water from sea water drawn out of Hempstead Bay.

Designed to burn the refuse of half a million people in the Hempstead area, this incinerator simultaneously produces three thousand kilowatts of electricity, steam heat, and 460,000 gallons of fresh water each day. The huge plant is equipped with the latest cyclone-type equipment to remove soot, ash and chemicals from the stack exhausts. In addition, the salt-free water which it produces is used in scrubbers and to help clean up the smoke from the plant. The water is used only in the station, but it adds that much more to Long Island's limited water supply. Officials estimate this refuse incinerator could produce as much as two million gallons of water per day in an emergency.

In nearby New York City, where thousands of buildings spew smoke into the sky from furnaces and garbage burners, one thirty-seven-story building has no chimneys at all. The structure is Mayfair Towers, a bright new apartment building. Its owner, paradoxically, had considerable conflict with City Hall in getting permission *not* to pump garbage into the city's air.

The luxury apartments were completed in November 1964 with a garbage compression system. It utilizes stainless steel chutes to pack refuse into private trucks that carry the refuse to landfill areas on the outskirts of the city. The building is heated by steam purchased from Consolidated Edison, New York's power-producing utility.

"We found the garbage collection and compression system better in every way than an incinerator," said Michael Lee, chief maintenance engineer in the biulding. "We're not only keeping pollution out of the air, we're keeping it out of the building. Even the best incinerators let smoke into apartments. We've also eliminated the danger of fire and, on an over-all

57

basis, this system has cut our costs way down." Ironically, New York has an ordinance which requires apartment buildings to have incinerators and the construction company argued with the city for several months before obtaining permission to try the experiment.

With the Mayfair Towers system, apartment residents simply throw their refuse through a door in the wall. The waste matter falls down chutes into large iron cars. These are collected daily, the refuse is compressed into private sanitation trucks, and then hauled to landfill areas in Brooklyn and Queens.

Ultimately, the true answer for the disposal of our solid wastes is to channel them back into the economy. America is well known as the most wasteful nation on earth. It is still easier to chop down trees than to remove ink from used newspapers so that the newsprint may be reused. It is still easier to strip iron from our rich mines than to put the dead automobile back into the smelters. On the other hand, the nation's industries which deal in scrap metal recovery do an annual business amounting to nearly $10 billion, and the sales of agricultural by-products total some $2.5 billion each year. We are on the right track, but we need millions of dollars' worth of basic and applied research to show how we can do a better—and economical—job of recovering our solid waste products.

"The waste of organic materials is as serious as squandering water," commented Frank M. Stead, chief of the California State Health Department's environmental sanitation division. "We waste organic matter by burial, burning and discharge to the ocean. Our free ride on the indiscriminate use of resources is nearly over."

One case where squandering has stopped and secondary use of former organic wastes has proven profitable is the utilization of peach pits from canning factories to make charcoal briquets for home barbecueing. Another is crushed walnut shells impregnated in rubber to assist the automobile driver to negotiate snow-covered and icy streets. Food scraps put to work also include the oil squeezed from the outer part of an orange peel. It seems to have some benefit in treating strains and bruises. "We don't know for sure yet," said Arvil Smith, an officer of Sunkist Growers, Inc., "but there's some university experimentation being done to find out." Sunkist, in fact, derives nearly $45 million per year in sales of citrus by-products, mostly oils which enhance the flavor of products ranging from cattle feed to soft drinks or even catsup. Pectin, made from citrus oils, is used to make jams and jellies. Lint from cotton goes into photographic film, pens, pencils, smoke-less powder, cellophane and sausage casings.

These are only samplings of what a little ingenuity will do when someone tries seriously to make something useful out of an item of waste. Such ingenuity long has been a hallmark of America and offers great promise for the future if enough research money and time are spent on the problem. Such ingenuity also produced a bold new concept of garbage and trash reclamation, utilized in a plant built for the city of St. Petersburg, Florida, by Westinghouse Electric Corp. and International Disposal Corp. of Shawnee, Oklahoma.

Each day the St. Petersburg rubbish trucks pull into a white concrete building located on the north shore of Lake Miggiore, and loads of refuse are dumped onto a moving conveyor belt. As the belt moves along, metal, glass, paper, rubber and rags are picked out automatically and deposited in metal boxes. Later in the day, other trucks drive in and take away the boxes to factories that pay for the scrap material. The remainder of the dumped garbage moves along the conveyor for six days until it has become compost, a harmless grainy material used as a soil conditioner and mulch. On the sixth day, another truck picks up bags full of the compost to be sold to farmers and home gardeners. There, in one continuous operation, trash and garbage are disposed of, usefully, without smoke, stink, rats, or pollution of any kind.

The St. Petersburg City Council awarded a one-million-dollar contract to the Oklahoma firm in 1964 to build the disposal plant designed to handle one hundred tons of refuse a day. The city pays private contractors $3.25 per ton to haul garbage to the plant. International Disposal earns its profit by selling the scrap material and fertilizer. The plant is the first full-scale garbage reclamation operation in the nation. It is so quiet and clean that it could be located in the heart of any residential district in the nation.

Composting has long been known as one of the best methods for digesting sewage, but normally the process takes much longer than the six days required in the St. Petersburg plant. The garbage moves along the conveyor into a five-story "digester" tower where it is ground up, pulverized and moistened as it moves. Generating its own bacteria, the garbage odorlessly ferments into compost and the final product is 20 percent of the volume of the original refuse. A planned refinement of the process is to use sewage sludge as the moistening agent, thus reducing another main polluting agent.

"The technology of trash management, generally speaking, is in a primitive state," commented the President's Science Advisory Committee in 1965. "There is need not only for improvement of components in the existing systems for handling trash, but also for a careful look at new systems. It is necessary to stimulate regional authorities to bring political units together for management of solid wastes, and to consolidate waste management systems having to do with all pollution matters. Planners should recognize the importance of waste disposal systems. Land beneficiation should be a goal to be achieved through designs for the ultimate disposal of trash."

From the minds of planners, scientists and waste management engineers must come the new brooms which will sweep away our growing mountain of solid waste matter and put it back to work easing the drain on our natural resources.

Dead Water

Till taught by pain, men really know not
what good water's worth.

Lord Byron

KILLING THE WATER IN A SPARKLING LAKE OR RIVER IS A LONG
and laborious process requiring many years of conscious or
unconscious effort. It is not easy, but the dirty animal which
destroys forests and throws beer cans out of car windows is
an expert in such matters.

A lake, formed perhaps by the grinding edge of an ancient
glacier, will age and die naturally with the passage of centuries. First, sediment from streams settles in the quiet water,
and as the lake level shallows, growing plants accumulate.
Next, an outlet stream cuts a new way out and drains away
the water. The lake becomes a swamp and finally dry land.
In this slow but dynamic process of nature, the United States
has lost perhaps half of all the lakes it had twelve thousand
years ago.

Today one of the continent's Great Lakes—Lake Erie—is in its death throes, not by natural process but by the work of man. The death weapon, quite simply, is an indigestible dose of sewage, industrial chemicals, detergents, shipping oil and sludges, the myriad of slops and substances which men discard while booming along on the greatest wave of population growth and industrial progress in the world's history.

The critical illness of this once-beautiful fresh-water lake might have been ignored for at least another decade except for a five-year period of below-normal rainfall. In 1965, Erie's water level was at the lowest point since 1860. Cargo vessels in this and other of the Great Lakes for years had been forced to lighten loads to avoid being stuck in mud. Beaches once fit for swimming were corrupted with sludge, chemicals and the rotting residue of algae and other water plant life. The breeze blowing gently off Lake Erie no longer smelled of sweet water but carried the rank odor of half-digested sewage, and with good reason. Lake Erie is the heart and blood of possibly the heaviest concentration of people and heavy industry in the United States—and Canada. Beginning with Detroit, Michigan, major cities in Ohio, Pennsylvania, New York and the province of Ontario butt up against this huge but shallow body of water and utilize it as a gigantic cesspool.

A year ago the Michigan Water Resources Commission reported that the Detroit River flows into Erie with 1.6 *billion* gallons of industrial and municipal wastes *each day*, including seven million pounds of alien chemicals. Twelve American cities and three in Canada dump their sewage into this one body of water. The U.S. Public Health Service estimates the daily flow of waste matter into Lake Erie at seventeen million tons. The lake, through its natural digestive system of wind, water, plants and marine animals, simply cannot cope with this vast load of foreign material. It is dying, as a human being would die, by its inability to eliminate an overdose of food and poison.

A primary measure of life in water is the amount of oxygen it contains, and this determines how much waste matter can be harmlessly digested by a lake, pond or stream. In turn, a primary gauge of sewage is its *biological oxygen demand;* in other words, how much oxygen is needed to convert the waste matter to harmless form. Lake Erie has been robbed of its oxygen supply.

Preposterous as it may seem, most of the municipal sewage which drains into Lake Erie has been given only primary treatment; that is, only the solids have been removed and the remaining liquid sometimes chlorinated to kill some of the most harmful bacteria. Add to that billions of gallons each year of chemicals ranging from steel mill acids to the effluent from paper plants. Then add the pollution of soluble salts, heat from industrial cooling processes, and the solid residue from meat and vegetable processing plants. Finally, among the hundreds of individual water pollutants, are phosphates resulting from the use of detergents, and nitrates from industry and fetrilized farm lands. Phosphates and nitrates in particular have set up a chain reaction which is hastening the rate at which Lake Erie's water is dying. These two substances are basic plant fertilizers and cause an abnormal growth of slime, algae and inferior species of fish and worms, while killing off valuable game fish in the lake.

Dr. George B. Langford, head of the University of Toronto's Great Lakes Institute, noted recently that commercial fishing on Lake Erie has almost entirely disappeared. "They used to catch whitefish and pickerel, which were much sought after and valuable," he said. "Since the pollution has become severe, these fish have disappeared. They have been replaced by perch and smelt and coarse fish which have much less market value. This has almost killed the fishing industry on Lake Erie.

"I hope," Dr. Langford added, "that we can stop the spread of pollution, but it's getting worse at an alarming rate. In 1956 the commercial catch of valuable blue pike in Lake Erie was 6,855,000 pounds. In 1963, only 200 pounds was caught."

Fish are not the only sufferers. C. W. Northington, head of a U.S. Public Health Service team seeking a solution, reported that 2600 square miles of the lake|bottom had lost almost all of its oxygen. This was primarily due to the growth of algae which dies and sinks to the bottom. The process of putrefaction uses up the oxygen. In the summer of 1965, a patch of algae covering 800 square miles was found in the center of the lake. The algae washing ashore disrupts commercial use and recreation, affects water supplies, and piles up in windrows twenty to fifty feet wide on the beaches where the rotting mess discourages all but the hardiest swimmers. Lake front property has dropped in value. Keith Krause, a Public Health Service expert, said "a glass of water taken from the central basin of Lake Erie looks like thin green paint." Whenever a swimmer dares to try the water, he emerges with a coating of algae over his body and perhaps bloodsucking leeches as well. In 1965 hundreds of sea gulls died along Lake Erie and neighboring Ontario, believed victims of eating fish contaminated with DDT. Mink ranchers stopped feeding perch from Lake Erie because they feared the fish had picked up something from the water that makes mink sterile.

At the upper end of Erie lies Niagara Falls, renowned through generations of newlyweds as one of the most beautiful scenic spots in the Western Hemisphere. Now Niagara stinks. Arthur B. Williams, general manager of Niagara Frontier State Park, said pollution has been growing for several years. A recent inspection showed that streams of raw sewage were pouring over the U.S. section of the Falls and gushing from a large sewage main near Rainbow Bridge. Williams said the sewage comes from the city of Niagara Falls (which paradoxically thrives on tourist dollars which the Falls provide) and chemicals from the International Paper Company. On the Canadian side, the Falls are stained with brown foam and lumps of solid matter typical of paper mill effluent. It smells like rotten eggs.

The other Great Lakes, for various reasons, are not quite as severely polluted as Lake Erie. Ontario receives the drainage from Erie, but it has fewer municipal and industrial centers and empties on into the St. Lawrence River. Huron and

Superior are the cleanest because they are comparatively free of large cities and industrial plants. Lake Michigan is in danger because it is a cul-de-sac with no major stream draining out of it. It is helped by the fact that Chicago draws its water from the Lake but drains sewage into a tributary of the Mississippi River.

The amazing thing about the story of Lake Erie is that a multiplicity of city, county, state and industrial officials could be so collectively blind that their greed and short-term saving of money would permit destruction of their most valuable resource—fresh clean water. Some officials fear that the death struggle of Lake Erie and its neighbors cannot be reversed. Others believe more optimistically that it can be done, but only through expenditure of billions of dollars over several decades to buy proper treatment of municipal sewage and stop the indiscriminate dumping of industrial heat, waste and chemicals into the lakes and their feeding rivers. The alternative should be obvious to all but the lowest of political hacks and the greediest of industrial tycoons. In the words of Murray Stein, chief enforcement officer of the Public Health Service: "If the Great Lakes go as a source of fresh water supply, the blow to the economy of the area will be devastating and will change the whole economic life of the country. If a realistic pollution abatement program isn't launched immediately the rapidly receding lakes may offer a solution to many municipal parking problems."

Happily, the alarm bells are beginning to awaken the sluggards and the recalcitrant, as will be subsequently shown. It may be many years before Erie returns to a semblance of health, but regional concern, under the prod of federal intervention, is beginning to turn it away from its apparent fate as a "noxious swamp." In 1965, the Michigan State Department of Health listed nineteen industrial concerns, some of the nation's leading corporations, which had been advised to improve their waste disposal during the preceding three years. Ten did, nine did not. All had been cited by the Public Health Service for causing excessive pollution. The reason why the nine didn't is obvious—the cleanup would have involved installing waste treatment facilities costing a total of $100 million. One-third of the Detroit River's pollution comes from Detroit sewage, which receives only primary treatment. The city, in the past, has resisted installing secondary treatment facilities costing $109 million. A Public Health Service official, in pinpointing the sources of Lake Erie's pollution, commented drily that big corporations comprise a multi-billion-dollar concentration of industry which "exerts a pronounced influence on public affairs." That was a gentle way of saying that at least until recent years, most industries have dumped their waste materials into the handiest and cheapest body of water or air with unconcern for the resultant damage, not only to the public but the long-term welfare of their own business. There has been a great unwillingness to take steps toward pollution abatement wherever such steps take a nibble out of corporate profits. Most industrialists shudder at the implication in the words of Clarence Eddy, geologist for the Michigan Department of Conservation: "We believe," Eddy said, "that the concept of disposing of wastes by committing them to lakes and streams ultimately must change."

Every lake and stream in America is suffering from corruption to some degree with the possible exception of high mountain creeks and rivers where water comes directly off the melt of last winter's snow. Even there, high in the Rocky Mountains or the Catskills, it is difficult to find a rivulet without its quota of beer cans and scraps from last week's picnic. One beer can and one partially cleaned chicken bone seems unimportant to the person who left them there, but when scraps and sewage are multiplied by the growing millions of people, the result is almost unusable water everywhere.

"Pollution touches us all," wrote the President's Science Advisory Committee in November 1965. "We are at the same time pollutors and sufferers from pollution. Today, we are certain that pollution adversely affects the quality of our lives. In the future, it may affect their duration."

The late Albert Schweitzer stated the problem more grimly

and succinctly. "Man has lost the capacity to foresee and forestall," he said. "He will end by destroying the earth."

It is difficult to believe that at least seventy million people—more than one-third of the total U.S. population—are drinking water which contains remnants of someone else's sewage and discarded chemicals. This is what the Public Health Service terms "secondhand water." It is the content of a river which has received the partially treated, or even raw, sewage from one city and then is used again as the water supply for another community downstream. Many millions of people are receiving *fourth-* or *fifth*-hand water in their dinner glasses, water which has been filtered and chlorinated just enough to forestall an epidemic of disease.

"The growth and spread of urban and industrial communities is bringing continually closer together the sewage outfall of one community and the water intake of the next one downstream," commented Stewart L. Udall, Secretary of the Interior. James M. Quigley, assistant secretary of Health, Education, and Welfare, points out that "treatment processes in use today were designed for the wastes of forty years ago. For larger cities they will prove inadequate in a growing number of instances."

Quigley was speaking of the purity of water for drinking purposes, an area in which the United States long has held the most prideful reputation in the world. Yet danger signals already are running in outbreaks of infectious hepatitis from water in New York, and in New Orleans, where it was traced to shellfish taken from contaminated water. In 1965 eighteen thousand people in Riverside, California, contracted a bacterial infection traced to city water. Four died. In addition to the vast and undigestible quantities of common wastes which pour into our lakes and streams, another big problem lies in the multiplicity of new chemicals and chemical combinations which are being dumped. "We have a backlog of ignorance when it comes to these things," Quigley said candidly. "We don't know how dangerous these waters are. We don't know how to detect them, or remove them."

The discharge of sewage and other organic wastes by the

67

year 1980 will be sufficient to purge the oxygen from all twenty-two of the nation's chief rivers during their dry season flow, according to a special waste management study conducted in 1966 by the National Academy of Sciences for President Lyndon Johnson. Dr. Athelstan Spilhaus of the University of Minnesota, chairman of the study committee, stated flatly that "the situation is unprecedented and becoming desperate. The massiveness and urgency of the problem justifies large-scale experiments, even in new experimental cities or in urban redevelopment plants."

The severity of America's water pollution problem was pointed up by President Johnson when he delivered his conservation message to Congress in February 1966.

A nation that offered its people a century ago uncharted forests, broad sparkling rivers, and prairies ripe for planting, may have expected that bounty to endure forever.

But we do not live alone with wishful expectations. We live with history. It tells us of a hundred proud civilizations that have decayed through careless neglect of the nature that fed them. We live with the certain future of multiplying populations, whose demands on the resources of nature will equal their numbers.

We are not immune. We are not endowed—any more than were those perished nations of the past—with a limitless natural bounty. Yet we are endowed with their experience. We are able to see the magnitude of the choice before us, and its consequences for every child born on our continent from this day forward.

Economists estimate that this generation has already suffered losses from pollution that run into billions of dollars each year. But the ultimate cost of pollution is incalculable. We see that we can corrupt and destroy our lands, our rivers, our forests and the atmosphere itself—all in the name of progress and necessity. Such a course leads to a barren America, bereft of its beauty, and shorn of its sustenance. . . .

A prime example of "America bereft of its beauty" is the Hudson River rolling through the majestic green hills of New York State toward its juncture with the sea at Manhattan. At Newburgh on the Hudson a graceful arching monument marks the place where George Washington established his headquarters during the Revolutionary War, but only a musket shot away, six-foot cast-iron pipes protruded in 1966 from the shore, spewing raw sewage into the rippling river. When he left Newburgh, Washington admonished the residents to "change nothing until I return," and since then the people have taken him literally in many respects. The lower half of the monument is hidden behind heaps of junked automobiles on the shoreline below. Dozens of shabby factories and buildings share the waterfront with broken-down piers. A number of industries empty their wastes directly into the river. Others have deluged once-lovely Quassaick Creek, which is partly in and partly out of Newburgh's borders. Below Quassaick lies Moodna Creek, just outside the industrial city of thirty thousand people. Moodna trickles down for thirteen miles from its source above Purgatory Swamp past scatterings of new houses where it picks up sewage and ground seepage. It reaches the Frost White Paper Mills relatively clear and still capable of supporting fish. It leaves the mill stained and ugly with the varicolored dyes used in making paper. After another twelve miles the stream "improves" to dishwater gray, then trickles sluggishly into the Hudson. For nearly a half century the city of Newburgh took virtually no steps at all to cleanse itself, and since 1957 the town fathers had fought off court orders which demanded the construction of a sewage treatment plant. It was not until late 1965 that government pressure, emanating at state level, moved the council to plan a three-million-dollar sewage treatment plant and a thirteen-million-dollar riverfront renovation. As with thousands of other communities throughout the nation, Newburgh residents and their governmental representatives believed in the principle of pollution abatement, but did nothing out of procrastination. Other problems seemed more pressing. River pollution, to an individual town or city or industry, always appears to be a secondary blight and somebody else's problem. After all, wastes are carried downstream and building a sewage treatment plant does not benefit the residents of a town that owns one. Besides, the town upstream doesn't build one either—until forced to do so by higher authority.

If Newburgh were an isolated example, it would be unfair to single out this community for its failure, during the half century when much should have been done, to do nothing about the filth it dumps into a river. Hundreds of cities are in the same predicament, always postponing the costly construction of waste treatment facilities until suddenly *their* sewers—the rivers at their door—run sluggish with an undigestible load of chemicals and organic corruption. The Hudson River is not alone.

The deep, rich Columbia alive with salmon now runs to the sea with an extra burden of heat and radioactivity from the Atomic Energy Commission's Hanford, Washington, plutonium production plant. The mighty Mississippi, accepting the raw sewage of river cities from Wisconsin to the Gulf of Mexico, now bears more sludge than mud. The once sparkling Milwaukee River is overlaid with bubbly slime; gone are the gay throngs of swimmers that once crowded the mill race, or fishermen proudly bearing long strings of pike and bass. Philadelphia reported in 1966 that the lack of dissolved oxygen in the Delaware River, only starting to recover from five years of drought, had blocked that year's run of shad. A recent water sample taken from the Cuyahoga River flowing into Lake Erie from Akron and Cleveland showed a bacteria count four times as high as that in a stream of raw sewage. The north branch of the Potomac River, near the nation's capital, is loaded with sulfuric acid that corrodes boats, bridges, even dams; and on the Potomac itself, more than 65 million cubic feet of silt is deposited each year, gradually smothering the estuary. The Connecticut River has not been safe for swimming for fifty years. The same is true of the Merrimack River in Massachusetts, and shellfish areas at its mouth have been closed since 1926.

The Mahoning River in Pennsylvania actually steams with the heat from coke ovens and bubbles with acid and other corruption from the crowd of industrial giants on its shore.

70

In the summer of 1965, the river ran low with water temperatures as high as 105 degrees. So serious was the condition of this stream in Ohio that new firms hesitated to move into Trumbull and Mahoning counties and the bustling cities of Warren and Youngstown were threatened with economic suffocation. Finally, in desperation, the region pooled its resources to build an earth-fill dam on the west branch of the river to hold part of its water at flood time for discharge during the low stream-flow summer months. The cost of preventing the immediate death of the Mahoning, as far as useful purposes are concerned, was sixteen million dollars, which will provide 32 million gallons of extra water per day during the summer to help flush out the stream. Unfortunately, this solution can be compared with giving a blood transfusion to a dying cancer patient while doing nothing at all to cure the disease.

All of these streams could have been saved, long ago, if a persistent and logical—albeit expensive—program had been followed to prevent pollution at its multiplicity of municipal and industrial sources. Yet city councilmen and their counterparts in industry are not entirely at fault for their sloth and reluctance to spend money on treatment facilities. Their problem is complicated by the fact that most streams, particularly in the eastern half of the nation, rise to flood every spring. When streams are full, the sewage and waste are diluted and washed away. With enough dilution a stream can even clean itself, in time. But when water is low, as it has been through most of the northeast since 1960, rivers such as some of those in New Jersey consist largely of undiluted sewage. From those same rivers come the waters which somehow must be purified enough to suit the needs of the same people and industries that supplied the corruption.

Each summer, and other seasons as well, Western highways swarm with carloads of Easterners seeking the wide outdoors, a few days of respite from the stink and corruption of the metropolitan melee, seeking a blue sky and a lake so clear the trout are visible on the bottom. There are not many such left. For years Lake Tahoe, high in the Sierra Nevadas, had been one of the world's clearest bodies of water. The azure pool, twenty-two miles long and twelve miles wide, lies in a forested basin a mile down from the crest of the mountains. The cool climate and Tahoe's depth inhibit the growth of microscopic plant and animal life, giving it a clarity which scientists say is matched only by Crater Lake in Oregon and Lake Baikal in Eastern Siberia near the Mongolian border. Unfortunately, during the past several years, Tahoe has suffered a surge in growth of both algae and plankton, threatening its blue clarity forever. Fortunately, the tourist dollar is so important in that area that the governments of both states, as well as bordering counties and communities, assigned immediate engineering studies to determine the cause. The answer has two parts: nitrates and phosphates seeping down through the ground and ultimately into the lake from a multitude of cesspools, and the sewage treated by six small utility districts in the area. To prevent this destruction of Tahoe's beauty, sewage treatment officials had been careful not to run their effluent into the lake but instead had sprayed the nutrient-rich fluid over the forests in the adjacent basin. Despite this care, however, the by-products of sewage are getting back into the lake. The only solution is to "export"— physically haul out of the basin—all of the sewage produced by a population which in the summertime numbers in the hundreds of thousands. Pipelines over the mountain ridges to disposal points in California and Nevada will cost about fifty million dollars.

"Water has become the nation's most important natural resource problem," the American Public Health Association's *Journal of Public Health* stated in December 1965. "Not only is there an acute shortage of potable water in many parts of the country, there is also serious threat to many water supplies from municipal, industrial and other sources of pollution. Current and planned programs to combat water pollution show promise of overcoming the more serious problems, but there is growing concern over the adequacy of present water purification measures to protect the public against multiple hazards to health traceable to contaminants reaching waterworks. The Association urges substantial expansion of federal, state and local effort, including necessary financial support, to devise and use improved water purification and distribution methods."

During recent years, many industries, such as textile mills, have moved from New England into the southern tier of states. This is partially to escape high labor costs and taxes, but also to find vital sources of good fresh water so necessary in virtually every industrial process. Many Southern streams still run fairly pure because population is low, cities small, and industry—until now—relatively light. Soon, if the trend is not somehow halted, the South in its greed for new industrial dollars, jobs and skilled people will follow the same polluted pathways pioneered so effectively in the North.

In microcosm, the children of Biloxi, Mississippi, offer a case in point. There on the Gulf of Mexico the white sand beaches provide a wonderful playground where children splash in the warm bay water and play leapfrog over a series of great conduits that emerge from under the highway and cut across the sands into the water. Out of the pipes pours green and black slime into which the youngsters dig their toes with glee. A nearby filling-station operator, unconcerned, described the outflow as "just drainage."

"You mean those are sewage outlets?" he was asked.

"Oh," he answered, "I imagine a little sewage here and there, but it flows away fast. Nothing to worry about. It's the best beach in the country—and you should see the crowds of kids on a hot day."

A little sewage; nothing to worry about—this phrase very nearly sums up the attitude of most people in the United States, officialdom and otherwise, as they watched or failed to watch through the years of changing political administrations, growing population, and burgeoning industry while the lakes and streams grew murkier and the nostalgic "old swimming hole" exuded a stench intolerable even to the hardiest

73

of young boys. Even today, in areas where the full scope and consequence of water pollution are well known, understood and deplored, there remains great reluctance, political and otherwise, to do something about it. In New England, for example, where America's Industrial Revolution was born and flourished, a federal cleanup program is running into trouble. The six-state region has some of the worst river pollution in the nation and is falling into a backwash of growth, partially because of it and partially because of efforts to do something about it. Conservative New Englanders thus are rendering little more than lip service, if not open hostility, toward a series of programs described as "Orwellian" (not calculated to produce results before 1984).

More than eighty years ago, Massachusetts passed a health law which became known as the charter of sanitary engineering in the U.S. A research laboratory designed to devise new and better methods of eliminating stream pollution was established at Lawrence on the Merrimack River. New England was the cradle of the nation's industry and today is more dependent upon it than ever before, but only one year after this enlightened health law was passed—in 1887—the Merrimack River itself, a major servant of industry, was *exempted* from the pollution regulation and remained so until 1946. Federal abatement proceedings now have been brought against the Merrimack, as well as the Androscoggin (choked with pulp and paper waste), Blackstone and Connecticut rivers. Thirty-four such federal actions have been started throughout the country, but New England has stubbornly fended them off.

"We've proceeded on the principle of making a stream suitable for what it is to be used for," said Worthen H. Taylor, chief engineer of the Massachusetts State Department of Public Health, "*not* to provide the highest water quality possible. Somebody tried to make one stream suitable for swimming. Well, the damned place wasn't good enough for swimming. There were stumps in it. Our theory is that you don't provide the quality of water in these places for uses it

74

can't be used for." Taylor added, with a touch of irony, that in the past seventeen years organic pollution from industry in the Merrimack River has dropped 70 percent "not because the plants did anything about their waste, but because they moved out to other parts of the country. We lost all the cotton industry and most of the woolen industry." The Merrimack is far from being clean, because industrial sites as well as the cities of Lawrence and Lowell still dump sewage into it. Taylor acknowledges that the river's discharge into the Atlantic Ocean contaminates much of the breeding grounds of Massachusetts' celebrated shellfish. The state now is urging communities to build big enough sewage plants to take care of local factory wastes, but the last state prosecution for polluting waterways was in 1954.

The Massachusetts engineer also points up a serious dilemma facing communities which recognize they must have the labor and tax base provided by industry or stop growing. This is not necessarily bad, but many states, counties and cities have carried the industrial search to such ludicrous lengths as offering free land and special tax benefits to companies which promise to build new plants and employ many people. By so doing, unfortunately, the community has established an untenable relationship with business firms involved. This relationship is that of the young lover who, in his eagerness to please, buys his lady candy and flowers, only to find that all she wants of him is more candy and flowers. The company not only will continue to demand community concessions but lets it be known that any pressure, such as that required to stop water pollution, will not be tolerated. The ultimate threat is that the business, which brought prosperity, will pull up stakes and move out if it is required to help make the community a decent place in which to live.

Sanitation experts say industry is responsible for two-thirds of the nation's water pollution. Yet it is not sufficient to point the accusing finger at presidents of steel, paper and chemical companies. These men, after all, must face each day the alternatives of making a profit or going out of business. They are under unavoidable pressure from at least two directions. First, no industry would be in operation without the growing pressure of population demanding its products. Second, an industrialist is charged with showing profit and dividends for his shareowners, who may number millions in the larger corporations. These same millions are part of the general public which complains that the water tastes evil and the air stinks. Thus, the third pressure now is forcing the corporation president and his board of directors to determine where their operation is threatening the public welfare, and when money must be spent to do something about it. Pollution control is very expensive, and in most cases the expense is a direct drain upon corporate profits. Attacking a man's pocketbook is a blow to the tenderest part of his anatomy and the same is true of a corporation. There is, therefore, except in isolated cases, great resistance to pollution control until pressure is threatened from on high.

In October 1965, this pressure expressed itself at the national level when Congress passed the National Water Quality Act. While signing the measure, President Johnson repeated his earlier statement that "every major river system is now polluted" and cited paper mills, chemical companies, oil refineries and slaughterhouses as the major sources. Cries of anguish were heard throughout the land. At the thirty-eighth annual conference of the Water Pollution Control Federation in Atlantic City, Joseph R. Shaw, president of the Associated Industries of New York State, termed the bill "another law that won't work." (One of its major provisions requires states to promulgate adequate water quality standards by June 1967 or the federal government will do it.) Shaw urged industry to promote the concept that waterway pollution is a relative matter that depends upon desired stream uses. Then he said, cynically: "Industry should propose a crash program to get rid of the *visible* evidence of pollution. If the *visible* evidences are removed, the public notices. If *visible* pollution is not removed, money spent for control is not nearly so effective." What Shaw appeared to say was that if the *sensual* evidence could somehow be hidden from the public, industry could then go ahead and pollute to its heart's content.

The reaction of most industrial leaders was "we can't afford it." During a two-day national conference on water, sponsored by the U.S. Chamber of Commerce in December 1965, George B. Angevine, secretary of the National Steel Corporation of Pittsburgh, said that "if the steel industry were to treat all of its water to standards recommended by the Public Health Service, it would face a 1965 bill of $260 million, or about one-quarter of its net earnings." George Olmsted, Jr., president of the S. D. Warren Co., a Boston paper concern, said the paper industry was "spending fifty million dollars this year" on new waste treatment facilities. "If we're going to shoot for the moon on this whole abatement problem," he added, "then we figure that in the next ten years the pulp and paper industry will have to spend at least one billion dollars to do this job right. That's $100 million each and every year. The industry only makes a profit of about $800 million a year.

"We believe," Olmsted continued, *"there's a social cost involved which should rightfully be borne by the public. We believe the federal government should pay a substantial part of the capital expenditures for waste treatment facilities."* This somehow seemed a strange thing to hear in a meeting of the U.S. Chamber of Commerce, which has long fought government subsidies, intervention in the sacred realms of American business, and the corporate income tax.

A more rational approach was voiced by Herbert S. Richey, president of the Valley Camp Coal Co. of Cleveland. "We in industry," he said, "have invited our share of this plague on our own house through an attitude of waiting for the other fellow to develop water pollution control processes."

Dayton H. Clewell, senior vice president of Socony Mobil Oil Company of New York, told the meeting that the petroleum companies of the nation are spending about thirty million dollars each year on waste water treatment with facilities valued at more than $250 million. John O. Logan, executive

77

vice president of Olin Mathieson Chemical Co., said the chemical industry in 1966 would spend 2 to 5 percent of all its new invested capital on pollution control facilities, representing a minimum outlay of fifty million dollars a year. "But to maximize the effort toward pollution elimination," he said, "will require that tax or other incentives be granted."

James M. Quigley, assistant secretary of Health, Education, and Welfare, placed the matter in perspective, at least from the federal government's point of view. "You must accept and act on the principle that the cost of pollution control from now on is part of the cost of doing business," he said. "If and only if the American business community acts on this principle can we be certain that American business and America's communities will have the abundant supply of clean water we need."

The National Association of Manufacturers, while pointing out that many industries "can't afford" the cost of waste disposal facilities, reported that 2800 leading companies spent $100 million on the pollution problem in 1965 "but touched only a fraction of the problem." Ronald Sadow, pollution control engineer for the Monsanto Company, said in 1966 that the chemical industry has "generally accepted the fact that pollution control is a necessary cost of doing business." He estimated that the industry in general now operates waste treatment facilities costing forty million dollars and involving 1700 full-time employees. As an example, six treatment systems are used on a 2200-gallon-per-*minute* flow of wastes from Monsanto's petrochemical plant at Chocolate Bayou, Texas. To meet the sewage specifications at the Anniston, Alabama, site of a new Monsanto parathion (insecticide) plant, an experimental waste treatment facility has been built at Nitro, West Virginia, to pioneer new disposal methods.

In that state, Bern Wright, water resources director, said a program to achieve a 40 percent reduction in pollution of the Kanawha River has nearly been completed. The cost was thirty million dollars, including twenty million dollars from industry. "We will be the first to admit that the Kanawha is still polluted," Wright said, "but we will also insist that we have a sound program which will get the job done. Patience is in short supply these days on pollution abatement programs and extensive periods of time to correct them are a thing of the past. Public demands will be met." Wright did not mention the obvious corollary that if industry and governmental units had cooperated in an effective program many years ago, the cost would have been less and the outraged voice of the people would not have been heard at all.

This single fact, though it is now an immensely complicated one, is truly the heart of the matter. The nation's dirt, both municipal and industrial, has been swept under the rug for so long that now the rug must be renovated or replaced. The total price tag, which once might have been relatively small, now is of staggering magnitude. The backlog of work is so immense nationally that it can be estimated with reasonable accuracy only on a piecemeal basis. The New Jersey State Department of Helath in 1966 guessed the cost would "run into the millions" just to start cleaning up the highly industrialized Raritan River Basin. Affected industries would include the American Cyanamid Co., Johns-Manville, Union Carbide, National Lead, Hercules Powder, and Du Pont, some of the most famous names in the growth of the nation. The estimated expense, to industries alone, of cleaning up Lake Michigan is expected to reach $100 million.

Late in 1965 Governor Nelson A. Rockefeller used all his political and personal charm to gain passage of a one-billion-dollar bond issue to help pay for a six-year water cleanup in the state of New York. He utilized to good effect the fact that two youngsters died of typhoid fever after eating a watermelon dredged out of the East River where it flows sluggishly past Manhattan. In a publicity campaign, he gathered a number of other youngsters around him, at the river's edge, and referring to the danger of typhoid said, "This is what happens from the pollution of our rivers."

"Someday," Rockefeller told the children, "we want to have swimming here."

Dr. Hollis Ingraham, state commissioner of health, said that eleven children actually suffered typhoid after eating the contaminated melon. An average of fifteen cases of the disease, transmitted through bacteria in human feces, are reported in New York City each year. When the threat is this apparent, one billion dollars to help clean up the state's rivers does not seem exorbitant. Under Rockefeller's plan, local communities and industry would pay 40 percent of the cost, the state 30 percent (one billion dollars) and the federal government 30 percent. Into the total pot would go more than three billion dollars; but no one, including the governor, pretends that this would return New York's beautiful rivers to their original and natural clarity. As regions assess their problems, the price tag goes up. Conferees met in August of 1965 trying to decide what to do about Lake Erie. John W. Gardner, secretary of Health, Education, and Welfare, estimated it would require at least *twenty billion dollars* to clean up all the Great Lakes.

These enormous figures keep slipping up and up on the engineering slide rule because the problem, when seen over-all, is one of managing the nation's supply of water so that it will continue to be satisfactory for the uses demanded of it. These vary from irrigation in the West to industrial processing in the East, and human consumption everywhere.

We are now faced with a difficult problem in the East [Lt. Gen. William F. Cassidy, Chief of the Army Engineers, stated recently]. Basically there is sufficient water in the East—both surface water and ground water. But some of the sources have become heavily polluted and are no longer usable. There is pollution by industry, pollution by municipalities, and there is salt-water pollution . . . from Boston down to Norfolk.

Proper water management is the key. That means many things: pollution control and pollution abatement to protect the quality of water; transfer of water from one river basin to another; storage of heavy run-offs so that we prevent floods and save water for future use.

Cassidy said that between now and 1980 it will cost fifteen billion dollars *only to provide "dilution" water throughout the United States.* "It's the cost of storing water," he said, "so that it can be released during low-flow periods to carry away the waste that man will put into rivers *even after 90 percent treatment*. On top of this there's still another great cost in treating the water before it's returned to the stream."

It becomes apparent with each passing month that thirty to fifty years of sloth and ignorance have complicated the water management problem beyond belief. For example, even in cites which have excellent sewage treatment facilities there is no way to make adequate disposition of a surge of water which falls during a heavy rain or thunderstorm. In most cases, storm water flows through the same municipal system as household sewage. When it does, it simply overflows the sewage treatment plant and goes rushing into the river carrying the raw sewage with it. Now, across the nation, there lies waiting a thirty-to-fifty-year job which grows greater with each new day. In 1960—almost a decade ago—a U.S. Senate water study committee pointed out that water is taken for granted until there is too much of it, too little of it, or when there's too much filth in it. At that time, the committee estimated *eighty billion dollars* would be required to catch up with the *backlog* of needed waste treatment facilities for cities and industrial plants.

Such figures certainly are enough to wring sobs of pain from the profit-conscious industrialist. At the same time, he is a man who knows quite well that his roof has been leaking for many years; now it has caved in. There should be consolation in the fact that some people in authority finally have measured the magnitude of the water pollution and made a realistic estimate of what must be done. Beyond that, no one expects private business to pick up an eighty-billion-dollar bill overnight, or in a year or in five years. The cost will be shared, over half a century, by city and county governments, regional authorities, state legislatures and certainly by the federal government. Even if this were not so, the pain of lost profits is not so severe as the business community would have us believe. In 1965, corporate profits in the United States totaled more than $75 billion, or a more realistic $46 billion (after taxes). It is easy perhaps to discuss ways of spending another man's hard-earned dollars, but it would be no severe hardship for industry to kick in one billion dollars a year to the task of pollution abatement. This would amount to no more than one or 2 percent of profits, and the public relations value to be derived from an *honest* cleanup program might well exceed the cost through the years. Finally, an obvious question is whether it would be better for industry to cleanse itself or allow an inefficient government to do it at an even greater cost in taxes.

Several years ago, the Wisconsin Board of Health reported on the Mississippi River a "wall of foam 35 feet wide, 300 feet long and 15 feet high." It was the mark of household detergents in sewage effluent, a mark which by its visibility hastened the nation's awareness of its water pollution problems and finally moved industry to its most significant solution to date of a waste treatment situation. The now-familiar sight of huge banks of white suds on creeks and rivers near sewage outfalls was first reported on March 31, 1949, at Mogden, the largest air-blown sewage treatment plant in Great Britain. "It was observed," a sanitation expert commented, "that sales promotion campaigns for household synthetic detergents were invariably followed by exacerbation of the foam problem." Throughout the industrialized part of the world, from the Neckar River in Germany to water wells on Long Island, the "foam problem" bubbled up around sewage disposal plant operators, who found themeslves helpless to dissipate it.

Prof. Hubert Heffner, Stanford University researcher, in 1966 cited detergents as an outstanding example of the world industry's tendency to push new products into the hands of the public without consideration of peripheral consequences. "While solving certain laundry problems," he said, "detergents have polluted virtually every stream and river in the thickly settled parts of the country." Heffner added that detergent manufacturers should have foreseen the effect fifteen years ago. During those fifteen years, however, television helped soap manufacturers sell vast quantities of detergents as the magic answer to every household cleaning chore. In 1965, more than four billion pounds of packaged detergents were sold in the U.S. California housewives, for example, used 385 million pounds, of which 80 million pounds found its way into septic tanks and sewer lines.

The difficulty with the "old" detergents was the fact that these substances (alkyl benzene sulphonate) are extremely difficult to break down by bacteria and other microorganisms. As a result the residue persists for long periods of time in the nation's waterways. One part of detergent per million parts of water is sufficient to cause foam. In this case, *visibility* of the pollution truly resulted in its answer. Recognizing that it could not live long under the fire of concerted public criticism and the threat of Congressional action, the soap industry launched a massive research program. Within relatively little time, chemists came up with the answer, a closely related detergent formula but one which breaks down more quickly. Part of the chemicals now degrade on the way to the sewage treatment plant. When 90 percent of other sewage is consumed, a similar fraction of the new detergent disappears. The last of the old detergent went out of production in mid-1965 and already the head of foam is disappearing from lakes, creeks and rivers. The changeover cost $150 million but it is doubtful that anyone in the soap industry regrets the action or the expenditure.

The message is becoming clear to more and more segments of American industry. W. W. Hopwood, president of Calgon Corporation of Pittsburgh, told the security analysts of New York that industry must take the initiative in water conservation and pollution control or face federal policing and taxation. Mr. Hopwood is in the business of developing and producing water purification equipment, but his point is well taken. He said the United States does not have a national water shortage, but conservation and pollution problems on many local watersheds are serious. He pointed out that there is currently much confusion because of "eager beaver" tactics by politicians and other advocates of pet schemes. Another Calgon official, Edgar G. Paulson, said that if industry and local politicians do not work vigorously to solve the pollution problem, Congress ultimately will step in "with a manner that is both expensive and onerous." He warned that Congress might require every plant in the land to install electronic instruments to measure water pollution, with policing by federal inspectors. Paulson predicted that if cities and industries do not get together to solve their own problems, both will be heavily taxed to pay for building and operating huge federal water treatment plants for protection of the rest of the country.

Philip H. Abelson, editor of *Science* magazine, placed the matter in even better perspective in his May 1966 editorial. He referred to the fact that the soapmakers, under the whiplash of threatened federal action, had managed to remove the detergent foam from the country's waterways. "Now our people and Congress," Abelson wrote, "can turn to the substantive problems of water pollution. Only a minor fraction of the sewage from towns and cities is fully treated. Upstream communities show little enthusiasm for spending money for the benefit of communities farther down. Even in those cities that have 'full treatment' performance is often poor . . .

"The problems of water pollution are many and complex," he concluded "The greatest present difficulty is that, while the public favors pollution abatement, only a few politicians are providing imaginative leadership."

Imaginative and courageous leadership must be brought to bear if our dying waterways are to be recalled to life.

Living Water

My object all sublime
I shall achieve in time—
To let the punishment fit the crime—
The punishment fit the crime.

Gilbert and Sullivan, The Mikado

IN APRIL 1966, WHEN SPRING WAS BEGINNING TO BURST WITH the joy which follows winter in the eastern United States, two hundred men, women and children of Mamaroneck, New York, spent a day collecting beer cans, bed springs, bicycle tires and chunks of rusted metal out of the river for which their town was named.

The action started with a seventy-year-old housewife, Mrs. Raymond T. O'Connell, who perhaps typifies the town "busybody," the man or woman whose nagging, plaintive voice is heard at town councils decrying the destruction of trees, pleading for preservation of flowers and forests, praying for a small measure of beauty in our ripped-up land. For more than twenty years Mrs. O'Connell had tried without success to marshal community effort toward cleaning up the Mamaroneck, ever since "our perfectly lovely river became a local dump after World War II."

Finally the fire of her words struck a spark of action and a day was set. The Camp Fire Girls promised cupcakes and coffee to the workers. The local civic association offered manpower. The town fire company lent ten pairs of fire boots. Mrs. Vito F. Luceno, chairman of the river cleaning project, met commuter trains with a decorated white station wagon soliciting people to give a few hours of help.

The two hundred men, women and children set to with a zest which can be found only at family reunions or when a group of people feels it is doing something tangible and worthwhile. As youngsters hauled pieces of slime-covered junk out of the river, village trucks hauled away loads of tin cans, machine parts, abandoned toys and Christmas trees. Chuck's mobile lunch wagon served free food.

By noon, the job was almost done. Three fingers had been cut on tin cans. The coffee was getting cold and the ducks, disturbed by the unprecedented flurry and splash of human toil, returned to swim across the clearing water. Mrs. O'Connell, her red leather jacket and flat suede shoes stained with mud, paused to catch her breath.

"I'm so excited I can't stand it," she said, her eyes sparkling with pleasure. "It's all come true. Now that we've got it clean, we can keep it clean and make the whole river area into a pretty park, with flowers and paths, so people can be enjoying Mamaroneck long after I'm dead."

The mayor, Arthur C. Phillips, Jr., climbed up the riverbank and wiped his hands on water-stained trousers. Despite the unaccustomed labor, his face wore an expression of calm satisfaction.

"The idea is involvement," he said quietly. "These people out here today are working hard. Then the next time they see someone else start to throw paper into our river, they'll say, 'What are you doing, we have to keep that river clean!' "

86

Involvement *is* the name of the game. Community action by these townspeople was a small thing, really, when measured against national and world pollution problems. The amount of work actually done probably was insignificant. Yet Mamaroneck's day at the river symbolized most clearly the simple fact which must be faced by all of us: Every individual has contributed to pollution; every individual, through work or money, must help clean it up. It is even better if the corruption can be halted before it begins, but this apparently is contrary to the basic, careless nature of the dirty animal. It is almost universally assumed that we will eat the dinner and that someone else will do the dishes. As a bachelor will allow dirty dinnerware to accumulate in his kitchen sink until the supply of clean utensils has been exhausted, the heavily populated, densely industrialized nations of the world—particularly the United States—have used up their clean lakes and rivers. Now comes the accounting at the kitchen sink.

As the Industrial Revolution came first to Europe, so came also the earliest major concentrations of people and industry in metropolitan centers with the contingent unsanitary conditions and accumulation of wastes on land, in air and in the water. Because Europe has lived longest with high population confined within small land areas, that enlightened continent, despite its predilection for wars, was forced earlier to solve its most serious water problems, and thus offers some practical guideposts to America. This is particularly true in England, where centuries of persistent work have produced gradual results, and in the Ruhr industrial region of Germany, where a modern-day crash program of great practicality has been put into force.

In the year 1065, King Edward the Confessor issued a decree concerning the four royal rivers in England, the Thames, the Severn, the Trent and the Yorkshire Ouse. He ordained that "mills and fisheries be destroyed, the *waters repaired* and the tribute to the King be not forgotten." This royal order, issued nine hundred years ago, is the first government regulation of clear record against stream pollution in the history of the modern world. What happened to the mills of that century is not known but in the words of the Thames Conservancy, modern watchdog of that fabled river, "many have sprung up since and even today the interests of navigation, the mills and the head water they want, the drainage of the land and the anglers on the river do not always harmonise." Until 1350 it was the king's prerogative to manage the four royal rivers, but in the year 1191, King Richard granted a charter to the Corporation of the City of London to control the Thames up to Staines, Middlesex. Six years later, in 1197, Richard I sold his rights in the Thames to London to finance his Crusade in Palestine.

The Thames River is a magnificent stream which has witnessed the birth, life and death of more commerce and industry than most other watercourses in the world. It rises out of hundreds of tributaries, serving even a greater number of British communities, and flows its many-branched and winding course through beautiful country, past London and then to the sea. Over the centuries, scores of locks were built on the river and its many feeders. Although constructed in the interest of shipping, these served also the finer function of controlling flood waters and holding high water tables in the land upstream so that a consistent supply could be furnished to the city of London. Few, if any, watersheds in America have received such careful conservation and control, measures which obviously are basic to abating pollution. Those who have become conscious all at once of the need for instant pollution control should listen to the history of the Thames and the attention paid to it through the years.

Magna Carta alluded to the Thames [the Conservators' historian writes] and said "Let all kiddles be abolished." The kiddles were primitive weirs of stakes and brushwood put up to keep a head of water for the millers, and large quantities of small fish were caught in them. The peasants who looked to fish for some of their food were upset and in one petition it was complained that mill owners caught the fish and fed them to swine, which was "against the Will of God."

By the early seventeenth century the navigation had got into a bad state. There were no railways and roads were bad and the Thames was an important means of communication. There were no pound locks as we know them but only the flash locks which were weirs and gates at the end of long reaches and a whole reach had to be nearly emptied to let traffic up and down, and progress was very slow.

In 1605 and 1624 King James I appointed Commissions above Staines and they built the first pound lock at Iffley, but otherwise did not do much. In 1751, after a bitter fight with the Corporation of London, the Thames Commissioners, 600 in number, were appointed to manage the river above Staines and they gradually built the pound locks above Staines, whilst the Corporation built those below.

It was interesting to note that as long ago as 350 years, management of the Thames was undertaken, not from the viewpoint of each village, town or city along its course, not by individual industrial plants, but according to a plan encompassing the entire stream and its tributaries, the entire watershed. Only now in the United States are regional water control agencies being established under the stimulus of federal pressure. The Thames historian points out that "every lock and weir from Lechlade downwards is of importance. They hold up the water in every reach to a certain height and this in turn holds up the water in thousands of acres of land adjoining the river . . . It is the vast amount of water held up in the land by the weirs that is important. This gradually seeps out in the summer and helps to keep up a reasonable flow. If it were not for the weirs, the Thames would be a raging torrent after rain and a mere trickle in dry weather, and London's water supply could never have been kept up."

The essential point about the Thames is not the *amount* of water management practiced through early centuries but the fact that someone in power and authority recognized the value of the river as a natural resource which must be protected and retained in useful condition. Genuine pollution control on the Thames, again coinciding roughly with the upsurgence of the Industrial Revolution, dates to the year 1857, when the Thames Conservancy was formed. This group, including representation from the city of London, consists of twelve board members or conservators. These men and their successors were (and are) charged with prevention of pollution in the river's entire catchment area, incorporating 3845 square miles from its rise in Gloucestershire County to a boundary line between Teddington and Twickenham in the area of the Greater London Council. The conservators, in 1857, found they had a mess on their hands.

> The Thames within their jurisdiction [a spokesman relates] was in a foul and offensive state due to the enormous quantities of refuse and sewage passed through canals and sewers communicating with the Thames. . . . The proper remedy appeared to be prevention by statutory powers of the discharge of noxious refuse into any watercourse or sewer communicating with the river. However, the Conservators made every effort to prosecute the proprietors of several chemical, gas and other works for allowing offensive and injurious matter from their factories to flow into the river. In 1863 two Inspectors of Nuisances were appointed to help maintain the rigid inspection and checking the practice of discharging mud and other deleterious matter into the water.

Legal and political problems then were little different from what they are now. In 1865, the conservators sued in court for an injunction to stop the Kingston-upon-Thames Corporation from "passing their entire drainage into the Thames." The case was lost, but the war against water corruption had only begun. In 1866, the conservators assumed the task of "scavenging" the river "which meant that the lock-keepers and workmen were required continually to remove from the stream dead animals and other injurious substances floating on it." Records show that in 1867, one hundred years ago, the Thames authorities started issuing notices to cities and industries to stop pouring sewage into the river. "Owners of paper mills on and within three miles of the Thames were notified to stop the practice of passing liquid matter produced in the manufacture of paper into the river." By 1880, through the conservators' work and persistence, most communities on the upper reaches of the river had completed sewage works to divert raw waste away from the stream, but the Thames near metropolitan London "still provided reason for frequent complaint; especially during hot weather when there had been little rainfall, when pollution was indicated by the offensive odour and highly discoloured state of the water." By the turn of the twentieth century, even the city of London was hauling away its sludge by ship instead of dumping directly into the river.

> The Conservators' attention [the record relates] then was specially directed towards the discharge of cargoes of rubbish (and bilge water) from vessels into the river in its lower reaches and proceedings were taken before the Magistrates in a large number of cases against the owners of offending vessels. They also took measures for preventing pollution by the discharge from houseboats and steam launches. . . .

Aside from the fact that the Conservancy's efforts have prevented the Thames from turning into a noisome and continuous swamp of sewage and debris, as it might well have done in a half century without proper attention, the last major flood on the river occurred in 1894 after a rainfall which averaged thirty-two inches over the watershed. Nine years later, after more than forty inches of rain, the river's flood was much less severe due to the holding of water behind locks and in the land upstream. In 1905, the conservators reported that "works for the purification of drainage were then in operation at nearly all the towns and centres of population on the Thames Watershed and, generally speaking, at the few remaining places where pollution still reached the streams, sewage disposal systems had been carried out and all that remained to be done was the connection of premises with the new systems."

Because the work of the Conservancy had been consistent and persistent through the years, budgeted with fair adequacy, and armed with regulatory power, the waters of the Thames remained alive. During World War I "the large number of military camps and other establishments which were set up in the Watershed necessitated a constant watch by the outdoor staff for ensuring that the drainage disposal systems were effective, and in view of the constantly changing population of the camps continuous inspections were necessary to obviate pollution by misuse of the surface water systems." In the decade between 1920 and 1930, management of the Thames waters was achieved with an annual budget of some £150,000, on the order of $500,000. Control was achieved by a system of careful water inspection and fines levied against offenders, the entire procedure backed up by successive acts of Parliament. During World War II, the Thames, as did all of England, carried a vast load. There were small resources available for keeping sewage treatment plants up to date and the river was clogged with the by-products of overworked industry, not to mention the millions of soldiers and ships which gathered there to carry the final victory to Europe. After the war, however, the methodical care of the river was resumed.

In accordance with the Rivers (Prevention of Pollution) Acts of 1951 and 1961, all discharges into the Thames and its headwaters require the consent of the conservators, who limit effluent to 30 milligrams per liter of solids and biochemical oxygen demand to 20 milligrams per liter.

"The effect of our endeavours for the control of pollution," said G. E. Walker, secretary to the Conservancy, "is that on chemical analysis the River Thames water continues to be generally satisfactory, and the importance of this work cannot be too strongly stressed when it is realized that approximately two thirds of the total quantity of water supplied daily to London is taken from the River Thames within the Conservators' area."

The Thames is only one river, yet it is a model of what might have been accomplished on the more heavily populated watersheds of America. It is a model of farsightedness which has kept a tremendously vital stream of water alive instead of permitting it to die through greed and carelessness. The Thames Conservancy also represents one strategic technique feasible for controlling stream and lake pollution on a major scale—halting corruption *before* it reaches the water by controlling the effluent from each individual industry and town in the watershed. The other technique, applicable in the desperate situation now approaching most U.S. streams and rivers, is construction of giant disposal and purification works financed jointly by the industries and communities which contribute to the pollution—each paying the cleaning bill in proportion to his share of the dirt. The outstanding example where this has been done is the Ruhr Valley in Germany.

The Ruhr is a name which rings through history with the sound of iron and steel bending to the will of warfare. The word and what it stands for was the only thing in Germany that Nikita Khrushchev feared. President Franklin D. Roosevelt, visualizing the end of World War II, once considered dismantling the vast industrial complex and turning the valley back to pastureland under international control. The word Ruhr is the sound of great wheels turning to work of the devil, evoking a mental image as hellish as Dante's variegated Inferno. For almost a century the ground has been black with soot from rich coal veins torn out of the earth, the sky brown with rolling smoke shot through with tongues of flame from the steel mills, the water frothing with heat, acids, chemicals and sewage from the profligate outpouring of nature's resources to shape the metal muscles of men.

Today the new Ruhr again beats with the pulsation of Germany's industrial might, but it has cast off its old, menacing image. Instead of guns and tanks, its plants now ship cars to the U.S. and Africa. The old Ruhr continues to hiss and roar with tonnages of coal and steel, but a new Ruhr operates as quietly and efficiently as an engineer's brain. Through the heart of the valley runs a river which long ago should have been completely destroyed by the work of men.

"That river today would be 110 percent solids," a U.S. Embassy scientific aide at Bad Godesberg commented recently, "if the governments and industry had not cooperated for a practical solution."

The question was simple, though stupendous. The river was

there from the beginning, but how do you ensure its continuing sufficiency and quality to serve six million people *and* Europe's greatest industrial complex? The answer began more than fifty years ago when it was determined that coal mine seepage was polluting the Ruhr River and interfering with its flow. In 1913, a federal law created two public corporations to correct the situation. Both have been in operation ever since. One is the Ruhr Reservoir Society, charged with the business of providing *enough* water for industry and individual consumers. The other is the Ruhr Association, responsible for maintaining water *quality*. As with the Thames conservators in England, the Ruhr Association must assure month after month, year after year, that the water in the Ruhr remains pure enough for its people and industry to use over and over again. Thanks to this efficient and enlightened arrangement, the river is the cleanest major stream in West Germany. It is far less contaminated than the Rhine, the Danube or the Elbe, none of which carries a load nearly so large.

The Ruhr complex begins, as any such system must, with an adequate water supply. Six reservoir complexes with a total capacity of 116 billion gallons have been built to feed into the Ruhr and its tributaries. The biggest of these, accounting for a third of the total capacity, went into operation in 1965. In addition nine repumping stations are located at the point where the Ruhr meets the Rhine. Thus, in case of drought (which seldom occurs in this part of Europe), water can be drawn from the Rhine to replenish the Ruhr.

The valley and its vast complex of industry and people covers an area smaller than the state of Delaware. Sewage from the entire basin is directed into the Ems, another river which bisects the triangle of blast furnaces, steel mills and coal mines between Düsseldorf, Dortmund and Oberhausen. One hundred and four sewage treatment plants are spread throughout the 1700 square miles of the Ruhr's drainage area. In addition, the stream has been widened at four places by dredging to create the equivalent of four shallow lakes to expose more water to the atmosphere for aeration and recharging its oxygen content. A number of the largest industrial firms also operate their own purification systems, cutting down the amount of corruption discharged into the river.

These measures are practical and impressive, but the heart of the region's water health is the Ruhr Association. By law, every municipality and business using water from the river must join this group, which now has 250 municipal and 220 industrial members. All are voluntarily "punished" according to their "crime."

"To start with," an official of the Association explained, "members are forced to join. But once they're in, it really becomes quite democratic with government interference at a minimum. Every member votes, but on a weighted basis. The vote is weighted according to what the member pays as his share of the Association's budget.

"You pay according to how much water you take out of the river and how much you put into it in the way of pollutants. In other words, the more water you use and the more you dirty the river, the more you pay."

Computing what a city or town must pay is based upon relative population. With industrial firms, a formula of payment has been devised on "population equivalents." It is possible to calculate that a given factory is corrupting the river to the same extent as a town of ten thousand or twenty thousand and the company pays accordingly. The total bill of keeping up with the river's problems is about ten million dollars a year, a trifling sum compared with the billions which are needed to clean up the more severe water messes in America. Private firms contribute about $2.8 million, municipalities and governmental bodies a similar amount, and the balance is contributed by about a hundred waterworks which use the river as their source of supply.

"The success in cleaning up the Ruhr shows what can be done," one official commented, "when determined people band together and operate relatively free of government interference."

During the past five years, the pattern in the Ruhr has attracted a great deal of attention in the U.S. The technique is most attractive because it is now generally recognized that a lake or stream cannot be managed, or kept alive, by the uncoordinated effort—or lack of effort—of hundreds of industrial firms and piecemeal governmental units. All of the water polluters on a given watershed must be brought together in a unified program, but until now it would appear most would prefer government interference.

In June 1966, Dr. James J. Flannery, chief economist for the Federal Water Pollution Control Administration, told officials attending a University of Buffalo water symposium that the Ruhr plan should be followed in the Great Lakes area with municipalities and businesses required to pay for the pollution they cause. The proposal first was made early in the year by President Johnson's Council of Economic Advisers, but at that time it was resisted on the grounds that such charges might come to be regarded as "a purchased license to pollute" and that high charges would be a poor substitute for regulation. Dr. John E. Wood, director of the Manufacturing Chemists Association, pointed out that thirty-one state governors opposed the idea, five questioned it and eight approved in a recent Congressional survey.

"Most businesses," Dr. Flannery countered, "have a wide range of choices to reduce their wastes" other than costly outside effort. These, he said, include more careful management, changing manufacturing processes or product composition, or discharging wastes at different times or places and installing treatment facilities. The nation, according to this economist, suffers *$12.7 billion* in water pollution damages each year. The cost of corrective programs by 1972, he said, could range from eight to twenty billion dollars.

To corroborate his massive money estimate, Dr. Flannery said that 118 million Americans are served by 11,420 community sewer systems, but the sewage of 11.3 million in 1342 communities *"receives no treatment prior to discharge."* He added that the sewage from another 16.8 million persons in

1337 communities is "inadequately treated" before it is dumped into the nearest watercourse. As for industry, he said, only *20 percent* of the water used by manufacturing concerns *receives and treatment before disposal.*

Dr. Luther L. Terry, former Surgeon General of the United States, said in Chicago that the country is "at least ten years behind in terms of controlling the pollution of our environment.

"Water is the most serious problem, in terms of running into shortages of even drinking water," Dr. Terry declared. "It is obvious that we need more research in learning better techniques of handling waste. Water purification techniques that are used today are twenty to thirty years old. To say the least we have not done enough research.

"We are either going to do something about the pollution of the water and the air," Dr. Terry said, "or we literally are going to drown in it. I think in the past there has been too much tendency on the part of industry to be almost oblivious to any responsibility in this direction. In recent years much of industry has assumed a more responsible attitude. They are beginning to do research. Though they have done relatively little in the immediate past, we now are getting some response. But it is awfully late, and we are going to need a lot more cooperation from industry than they have put into it thus far."

What industry must put into it is perhaps best illustrated by what industry has been putting into our lakes and rivers for more than half a century and what we may anticipate in the future. In 1900, according to the U.S. Public Health Service, waste flowing into streams from cities and towns equaled the raw sewage from 24 million people; that from industry equaled the output of 15 million people. Sixty years later, the figures had jumped to 75 million and 160 million, with organic wastes from industry amounting to more than twice the sewage production of populated communities. By 1970, the Public Health Service estimates, municipal wastes will equal raw sewage from 85 million people, while industrial wastes will jump to the equivalent of that from 210 million. Although these are gross figures, they demonstrate that both municipal governments and industry have a stupendous job to do, not only in cleaning up the mess which has been permitted to accumulate, but in keeping up with the anticipated growth in waste production. Equally clear is the fact that cities, counties, industries and states must meet together, face their joint problems realistically, and share in paying the price of water purity. Part of the task will be done according to the Thames River method of policing individual polluters and abating their output. Part will be accomplished eventually in the manner of the Ruhr Valley, particularly in those U.S. districts where population centers and industries have reached a stage of density and maturity making ultimate cooperation possible.

Although America's waters appear to be a foul and dismal mess, the pendulum already is beginning to swing away from careless and indiscriminate pollution toward awareness, concern and action. Even now nearly $600 million a year (one-sixth of it federal money) is being spent to build local sewage-treatment plants. New York State is well into a $1.7 billion dollar stream-cleansing program. The primary impetus for the work under way now was the Pollution Control Act passed by Congress in 1956. Many cities and industries launched abatement and purification programs then, but others lagged and thirty-seven enforcement actions were started under that law. The first major interstate cleanup program was aimed at the Missouri River. Until 1957 every city along that stream dumped raw sewage into it. Now all those cities have treatment plants or are preparing to build them. The Mississippi now is on the active agenda. All cities on the banks of the Father of Waters throw raw sewage into it. By the time the great watercourse reaches New Orleans, it is carrying the equivalent of raw sewage from twenty million people. New Orleans now is planning a treatment plant and other cities upstream are beginning to fall into line.

"You probably could provide treatment plants to clean up

city and industrial pollution in the nation's major watersheds for about thirty billion dollars over a ten-year period," according to James M. Quigley, assistant secretary of Health, Education, and Welfare. He is the overseer of new federal antipollution programs.

Communities and federal government would need to spend about one billion dollars each year. Industries would have to spend two billion dollars a year.

On top of that, you have the problem of a great many cities where storm sewers and sanitary sewers are combined in one system. If you can imagine tearing up all of the streets of these cities and laying new sewer systems over a period of ten years, the cost would be around twenty to thirty billion dollars. We are hoping that some other way can be found to deal with this problem.

We have established a beachhead in our fight for clean water. We have not made spectacular progress, but I hate to consider what shape we would be in now if we had not made the effort we have in the past eight years.

Bright spots of hope and beauty are breaking out here and there across the land. In Chicago residents complained for years about the noxious smell, bad taste and cloudy appearance of their water. Now good water emerges from the city's new Central District Filtration Plant, largest in the world, which serves 2,700,000 people on the North Side. Costing $105 million, the plant occupies a sixty-one-acre man-made peninsula in Lake Michigan and treats 1.7 billion gallons of water per day.

New York City is nearly two-thirds of the way done with a $700 million program which began in 1931 to clean up harbors, bays and waterways. Twelve sewage treatment plants now are in varying degrees of operation, and Public Works Commissioner Bradford N. Clark said recently that a total of eighteen plants will be processing 1.8 billion gallons of sewage per day by the year 2000. New York sewage plants now are treating 800 million gallons per day. In addition the city is spending $175 million to insure safe bathing at present and proposed new city beaches.

It is difficult for a city to justify spending its taxpayers' money for new or improved sewage treatment facilities when an old, obsolete plant may not yet be fully amortized. Likewise, industry's problem, when it comes to pollution abatement, is that it may be impossible to adapt an old plant to waste disposal methods without prohibitive cost. Therefore, it is only in recent years that pollution control has been taken into the profit-and-loss capital accounts when new facilities are contemplated.

In beautiful Shasta County, California, fifty-pound salmon today leap in the waters of Sacramento River 250 miles up from the Pacific despite the fact that a new pulp and paper mill discharges ten million gallons per day of waste-processed liquid into the stream. Of all known industries, papermaking discharges perhaps the ugliest, most noxious waste matter at the end of its process. Fifty thousand gallons of fresh water are required to produce each ton of paper. Wood chips are cooked with sodium sulfide and caustic soda to separate fibers, then are bleached with sulfur dioxide, sodium chlorate, hydrogen peroxide, sulfuric acid and sodium hydroxide. Corn starch and clay are added to provide body to the paper. Residual fluids called "black liquor" and "white liquor" spew out of the mills. Scores of major rivers along both the east and west coasts of the U.S. have been spoiled by papermaking. For decades the major corporations have retained lobbyists in Washington to forestall and ameliorate Congressional action, which is threatened periodically as outraged citizens speak and write against pollution of their water. It is understandable then that the new Kimberly-Clark Corporation plant at Anderson, California, is hailed as the "pattern of the future."

The pulp and paper mill cost twenty million dollars—including 10 percent devoted to waste treatment. Built according to strict California stream clarity regulations, the Kimberly waste treatment system is large enough to serve a city of 100,000 people. Waste fluids go into a series of outdoor basins which hold one million gallons each. The solids settle out and are buried. (Such wastes amount to as much as 50 percent of the effluent from paper mills which do not incorporate sewage treatment.) In the second step of the Kimberly purification process, the partly clarified liquid is churned and aerated in a second series of basins containing plant organisms which digest much of the organic pollutants. Finally, the effluent, now almost entirely water, goes to a third tank where it flows slowly over sawtooth metal "weirs" which strain out the finest sediment. At this point, small amounts of the treated water are diverted to a laboratory tank containing newborn salmon. If the baby salmon live, then the processed water is sufficiently clean to go into the river. By the end of the Kimberly waste treatment cycle, the biological oxygen demand of the polluted fluid has been reduced by 90 percent. "The BOD [biological oxygen demand] of our discharge is in the range that would be in the river if we weren't here at all," one official commented. The paper mill's effluent finally is pumped four miles to the river and diffused underwater from sixteen vents. Part of the flow is diverted to a thousand-acre experimental farm exploring the possibilities of widespread use of waste water in agriculture.

There in California is a perfect example of what industry can do to keep our waters alive, but it must be remembered that the Kimberly plant was a new one with pollution control built into the original plans. Applying the same waste treatment system to an already existing paper factory might be prohibitive in cost. The *New York Times* commented editorially on this situation:

> It is easier and cheaper to do what is being done in Shasta County, California, if the new technologies in waste control are built into an industrial plant from the beginning. Much of the pollution still caused by the pulp and paper industry in New England and other places comes from old plants now barely competitive because of obsolete equipment and methods. The same situation prevails in other industries. Companies saddled with this problem need help.
>
> A new law in New York State meets this problem by allowing a company to deduct [for state income tax purposes] the expenditures it makes to install or improve waste treatment

facilities. The law also exempts such facilities from real property taxes.

States that have not granted this kind of relief ought to follow the New York lead. More important, because it would help eliminate competitive disadvantages between regions and states, Congress should write similar incentives into the Federal tax laws.

The nation's economy would benefit; so would its health.

The sweet of tax credits to offset the sour of government regulation has come to sound more and more logical concerning the massive problem of water pollution control, particularly since passage of the Water Quality Act of 1965, which puts more teeth into the enforcement process. It could be argued that all industries should have foreseen the consequences of their own corruption and planned for it in advance, but few of us are that perceptive in our affairs. It is not the intention of the U.S. government, as it moves forcefully into the abatement of water corruption, to run industries out of business. Therefore tax incentives as a reward for compliance may play a major role in our national cleanup program. On the other hand, it is quite possible that the addition of pollution prevention systems may actually improve some industrial processes and, consequently, their profit picture.

One such case was demonstrated in 1966 within the Greater Pittsburgh industrial complex by a major steel producer which moved voluntarily to halt its share of the tremendous quantities of waste going into the Ohio River. This company's pair of five-stand tandem steel mills were arranged to apply river water as roll coolant at the rate of five thousand *gallons per minute* and then dump it back into the river with an accumulation of rolling oil, iron residue, oxides and other mill sump wastes. The net result, in the understated words of a company executive, was "an effluent discharge of highly undesirable character."

To change its habits, the steel company called upon the Dravo Corporation of Pittsburgh for a major design, engineering and construction program to equip the mills with a water recirculation system along with devices to separate out the rolling oil and other waste products. Some of these were found to be reusable.

> Before incorporation of this recirculation system, [wrote H. E. Riester of the Dravo Corporation,] the source of water for direct application was the river itself. This introduced variations in temperature and water quality and, with other contaminants, led to difficulty in maintaining an equilibrium of quality control. With the new closed recirculation system, makeup water comes from potable water service and steam condensate. Thus, the uncertainty in river water supply is eliminated.
> Pollution abatement regulations are being met by this new system. Besides benefitting the public and meeting his civic responsibility, this steel producer has, in turn, achieved significant economies of production and obtained the means for achieving consistent product quality control.

A single paper company and a single steel company certainly are not enough to demonstrate methods which would work for all of industry, yet it is precisely leaders such as these which will point the way out of the bad waters, to the public's benefit as well as their own.

Another example is the Xerox Corporation, which has joined forces with the city government of Webster, New York, to tackle their combined waste problems. The Xerox plant is the main reason for prosperity in the city of twenty thousand people, but at the same time its processing operations were overburdening the municipal sewage facilities. Xerox and Webster now have agreed to share cost in building a new fifteen-million-dollar sewage disposal system.

"We decided that we would assume this responsibility and help Webster to cope with the sewage and pollution problems," commented Sol Linowitz, chairman of the Xerox board of directors. "Our company feels it has an important social as well as economic role in the community, so to become involved in its effort to keep industrial waste from spoiling the local streams and Lake Ontario was a very natural thing." Walter W. Bradley, town supervisor, termed the joint venture "an excellent example of the kind of industry-government cooperation needed to put into effect Governor Rockefeller's Pure Water Program."

Industry-government cooperation is beginning to coalesce in more and more areas as the way to accomplish pure water programs. The Pittsburgh steel company's enlightened action was part of work undertaken in 1948 by the Ohio River Valley Sanitation Commission, an agency created under an act of Congress by the states of Pennsylvania, West Virginia, New York, Ohio, Kentucky, Indiana, Illinois and Virgina. With a structure reminiscent of the Thames Conservancy in England, this agency includes three commissioners from each state. Their task is coordination of a regional crusade to eliminate existing river pollution and "place the waters of the Ohio basin in a satisfactory condition for public and industrial water supply, recreation and maintenance of aquatic life." By the end of 1966, treatment facilities were in operation serving 99 percent of the people living along the main stream of the Ohio.

In 1965 W. J. Conner, attorney for the Du Pont company, told a group of industry and local government officials that individual states have only a short period of time in which to clean up their lakes and rivers if they want to avoid federal "domination of the whole pollution picture."

"There is a serious proposal," he said, "to place all water resources of the nation under a federal commission modeled after the Federal Power Commission." Conner added that if states start making real progress in improving their water resources they should be able to do the job without referring the "whole problem to Washington to solve." Washington, however, had waited too long. Less than a year later the new Federal Water Pollution Control Administration was in operation in the Department of Health, Education, and Welfare. U.S. officials moved with new authority, prodding industries, municipalities and other governmental units into cohesive and meaningful action.

In August 1965, conferees on dying waters of Lake Erie

met at Cleveland and Buffalo and agreed that the lake was subject to federal enforcement under the Water Pollution Control Act. Representatives of Michigan, Indiana, Ohio, Pennsylvania and New York agreed that waste discharged into the lake was endangering the health and welfare of people living in the region. An abatement program, they agreed, would be drawn up and approved. In November 1965, John W. Gardner, Secretary of Health, Education, and Welfare, accepted conferees' recommendations for controlling pollution on Lake Erie and the Mahoning River. Emergency measures to start the waters back toward health included a plan to operate waste treatment plants at full capacity in the communities of Warren, Niles, McDonald, Girard, Youngstown, Campbell, Struthers, Lowellville and Mahoning County. All industrial plants in the region were directed to provide adequate effluent disinfection and secondary waste treatment with new construction to be completed by April 1969. Pollutant discharges from industries in this entire region are being sampled regularly by federal officials to measure abatement progress.

The U.S. moved just as rapidly to halt the deteriorating water situation around the entire southern tip of Lake Michigan. Early in 1966, following a year of negotiations under federal guidance, Indiana, Illinois and the Chicago Sanitary District along with steel, petroleum and chemical companies rimming the tip of the lake reached agreement to meet strict new standards of water quality by the end of 1968. Some industries already have spent millions to purify the water and waste they dump into the lake, but public health officials estimate industry must spend at least $100 million more to assure meeting the goals on Lake Michigan.

At the end of a five-year study, it was determined that thirty-one industries and twenty-one municipalities were dumping thousands of tons of waste matter into the sluggish end of Lake Michigan, endangering the health of eight million people. Six beaches were virtually unusable and one at Hammond, Indiana, had been closed by pollution. The Michigan agreement, which also takes in the Little Calumet and Grand Calumet rivers, thus includes one of the world's largest concentrations of steel plants, as well as oil refineries, chemical plants and other industries. Murray Stein, enforcement officer for the Federal Water Pollution Control Administration, said there now are "good prospects" for ending pollution of the southern end of the lake.

"We are optimistic," he said, "that we are facing a landmark case in which, for the first time, representatives of the federal government, states, the city of Chicago and industry have sat down together to devise a pollution program acceptable to all.

"We have achieved," Stein said triumphantly, "what many of us through the years believed impossible. The honeymoon with industry is beginning." The agreement, reached through a year of negotiations, is so strict that it "may be a blueprint for what water pollution control will look like throughout the country.

"Lake Michigan, perhaps, cannot be returned to conditions of the Indians and Fort Dearborn," Stein added, "but it will come pretty close. I hope that when we get the lake cleaned up we will be able to utilize it for all the water uses which the Indians had, including the same kind of fish." Stein was optimistic that by the end of 1967, considerable improvement already would be apparent in the cul-de-sac southern tip of the lake.

In a democracy—and a corporate structure arising out of America's free enterprise system is the highest form of democracy—a problem must grow to pressing magnitude before the pendulum begins to swing ponderously toward a solution. Thus the Lake Michigan agreement may well be the beginning of the pendulum swing toward the regional attack on water pollution. In the East, PennJerDel is an excellent case in point. The name itself demonstrates that three states—Pennsylvania, New Jersey and Delaware—have gotten together at least to define the magnitude of work necessary to restore the lower end of the Delaware River Basin to reasonable water quantity and quality. The area contains 377 municipalities in eleven counties in three states. The 1960 population was five million, and the 1985 projection is eight million. The Penn-JerDel area (the Delaware River Basin) contains more than one hundred major industrial plants. Water available in the entire region totals 3.5 billion gallons per day and 2.9 billion already are used. The President's Science Advisory Committee in 1965 predicted a *threefold* increase in water use in the next thirty to forty years, with a 50 percent increase in anticipated water pollution. "Two points are illustrated," the Committee wrote. "First, the rates of pollution are increasing more rapidly than the population. Second, control of water pollution probably can be handled in such areas only by such forms of interstate cooperation as river-basin compacts." PennJerDel at least has taken the first steps. This region and others obviously will press on from there or face a near future with people and industry moving out, the consequences already being felt in New England. The greater reality exists that few places remain where people and industry can find unused fresh water. They must turn back to the restoration of the water they have used.

Pressure was finally applied by the 89th Congress after most cities, states, counties and industries waited until that pressure was required. The Water Pollution Control Act of 1965 authorized quality control standards for interstate waters and offered new, federal resources for treating wastes. Pressing forward from that point, President Johnson, in his February 1966 conservation message to Congress, stated:

> I propose a new kind of partnership, built upon our creative Federal system, that will unite all the pollution control activities in a single river basin. Its task is to achieve high standards of water quality throughout the basin. . . .
> Where it does not already exist, a permanent river basin organization must be created to carry out the plan. It must represent the communities and the states. It must work closely with the Federal Government. The organization must be prepared to revise the plan as conditions require, so that new threats to the quality of the river may be turned back.

Communities must be willing and able to contribute funds necessary for constructing facilities. They must be prepared, with Federal help, to levy charges for their use—charges adequate to maintain, extend and replace them when needed. . . .

The program has one ultimate goal: To clean all of America's rivers. This year we shall start with those few basins whose states and communities are prepared to begin. As additional organizations are formed and their plans drafted, more basins will qualify [for Federal guidance and financial assistance].

If that message was not clear enough, Interior Secretary Stewart L. Udall made it so in June 1966 when he addressed the Manufacturing Chemists Association at White Sulphur Springs, West Virginia. He told the chemists at their own party that the federal government would step in if the industry does not hasten to clean up its own waters. He assured the executives that the government "will invite and exhort" but added that "the Water Quality Act of 1965 puts an additional responsibility on the Federal branch—the responsibility of control."

Anticipating Udall's remarks, the association had previously announced a new environmental health program, with annual expenditures of $675,000 per year. John O. Logan, executive vice president of Olin Mathieson Chemical Corporation, said one of the program's aims was the "minimizing of excessive governmental harassment."

Udall, in turn, reminded his audience that Logan had recently declared that almost 95 percent of the chemical plant locations were complying with existing regulations.

> Within the truth of that statement [Udall said] lies the crux of our water problem. From its truth springs the indictment of all existing regulations. One whiff of our nation's water makes it obvious that these regulations are hopelessly inadequate.
>
> The same chemical industry spokesman told the national water conference that he endorsed appropriate control programs, or control agencies at the regional, state and local levels, with emphasis on the lowest capable of doing the job.
>
> The underlining of the words: "capable of doing the job," was done by your own man [Udall emphasized], and in effect,

this advice was heeded by the United States Congress. After assessing the job that has to be done and after looking at the quality of water sludging through our riverbanks, the Congress concluded that the lowest level capable of doing the job is the Federal level.

Udall concluded by congratulating the chemical industry for setting up committees to look into the water quality problem. He did not comment on the comparative relationship of a $675,000 annual expenditure with the multibillion-dollar cleanup job which must be done.

Later in 1966, Udall served notice before a conference of state representatives in Cleveland that Lake Erie, where the waters are dying the fastest, will be the main battleground in the nation's stepped-up war on water pollution.

"This is our best test case," he said. "If we can lick water pollution here in the next few years, then we can lick it in the country at large. If not, we are in trouble."

January 1, 1970, is the target date for having abatement facilities in full operation around the lake, but some states expressed concern that they could not complete new disposal plants by then. Udall answered grimly that cities and industries which refuse to cooperate in the program should be subjected to the "glare of fearless publicity."

"We will consider announcing a list of filthy American cities, and filthy American industries," he said, "to let the people know the troublemakers."

Udall's message got through. In October 1966 he announced that all fifty states in the union had filed letters of intent with the Federal Water Pollution Control Administration to set their own water quality standards rather than have standards imposed at the federal level. Expressing his pleasure that the individual states had taken the initiative, Udall said: "The program is beginning to roll. Perhaps two or three years from now we will begin to reduce pollution instead of just holding our own."

While placing the monkey on the back of municipalities and industry, Congress also recognized that the federal government must help support the monkey. In a Senate and House conference agreement, a $3.6 billion, five-year program was established to help clean up the nation's lakes and streams.

To help cities pay for new sewage facilities, the law provides that the federal government will pay up to 30 percent, regardless of the magnitude of the project. Encouraging state-municipal-industrial cooperation in building waste treatment systems, the federal government will pay half the cost of any river basin program crossing state lines. States involved would put up 25 percent with cities and industry making up the other 25 percent.

Under the bill, regional commissions are to be set up to establish and enforce water quality standards approved by the Interior Department. States failing to establish suitable criteria by June 30, 1967 are subject to federally-imposed standards. With $3.6 billion as the initial five-year federal contribution to cleaner water, the program is expected eventually to reach $12 billion including state, city and industrial expenditures.

Whether the total cost be $12 billion, or $50 billion, or $100 billion over the next 20 years, America's waters are beginning their long convalescence from death to life.

New Water

We see that there is another course—more expensive today, more demanding. Down this course lies a natural America restored to her people. The promise is clear rivers, tall forests and clean air —a sane environment for man.

President Lyndon B. Johnson, February 1966

In practical quantities, there is no such thing as new water.

Virtually all of the precious fluid around us, on land or in the sea, fresh or salty, clear or contaminated, has been on earth for millions of years. This universal solvent is not only vital to man, animals and plants, it is indeed the primary reason why living creatures were able to evolve and multiply on this planet. The oceans are full of it, enough that if it were distributed evenly water would cover all of the world eight hundred feet deep. During all of the millennia that

111

water has existed, nature's sublime pumping system also has been at work. Each day the sun boils off billions of tons of water from the ocean surfaces, leaving the salt behind in the sea and lifting the sweet water vapor into the sky. There cooler air condenses it into clouds of ice crystals which grow with time and multiply until the pull of gravity draws them to earth again as raindrops, snowflakes, or pellets of hail and sleet.

Snow which falls in the mountains may remain there for years before melting. Glaciers may stay frozen for centuries. Rain that seeps through the ground into basins of underground rock may flow back and forth through hundreds of miles of its aquifer for thousands of years. Finally, however, the rain which falls returns again to the sea. Day and night, throughout all ages, this magnificent pumping system works without interruption, never depleting the sea but always washing some portions of the world's land masses with clean, fresh water. The fluid you drank for dinner yesterday might have bathed the feet of a dinosaur and flowed again past the pyramids of the Nile. It may have pushed gobbets of meat down the gullet of a king, irrigated farm land in India, and helped float a barge down the Mississippi River. The water of the earth, virtually all of it, is very old. Some, if not all, has been used in various ways many thousands of times.

Water may be *new* in the relative sense, however, when it becomes possible to tap a fresh source of supply where none existed before, or when used water is recovered and cleansed sufficiently for use again. The latter process occurs, of course, whenever a city draws water into its purification plant from a lake or stream where another city has dumped its sewage. The content of our major rivers thus has been used many times on its way to the sea, but in its apparent plenty, America for two centuries has used up its water and carelessly abandoned it to nature's remarkable pumping system for ultimate renewal. When we become alarmed about water pollution, then, we are not really talking about the dirt, but how to separate out the dirt so that enough fresh water remains to wash the face of a nation which grows bigger and dirtier every year. With cost estimates ranging from twelve billion to eighty billion dollars, and armed with new federal laws and enforcement procedures, the U.S. is beginning to clean its waters. It will be a long, slow process. In the meantime there is growing alarm that the *total* fresh water supply available across the land is not enough to meet the needs of the future. Many authorities argue that this is so, others contend that if we make proper use of what we have, there is no water shortage at all.

Proper conservation and use is the short-term key, along with the ability of politicians and engineers to cope with nature's unequal distribution system. An Eastern river may destroy cities as it runs to flood while the Midwest suffers under a crop-killing drought. A metropolitan center such as New York City may shudder before pending disaster when a nearby reservoir runs low while the arid Southwest thinks nothing of reaching three hundred, five hundred, or a thousand miles to tap a dependable water supply.

Over the entire United States, the solar pumping system drops an average of thirty inches of rain and snow each year. This amounts to 4.4 *trillion* gallons per day, but only one-fourth of it stays around for men to use. Three-quarters of it—3.3 trillion gallons per day—is evaporated back into the atmosphere or absorbed by growing plants. The 1.1 trillion gallons left is a tremendous amount of water, but this is a deceptive figure because it includes that which filters into underground aquifers and flows back to the sea.

Dr. James J. Flannery, chief economist for the Federal Water Pollution Control Administration, said in 1966 that the nation's daily consumption of water now includes 22 billion gallons for municipal supplies, 160 billion for manufacturing, and 141 billion for irrigation, a total of more than 320 billion gallons per day. This appears to be only one-third of the total amount available, but once again, the 1.1 trillion gallons is only the *potential* the United States has at its demand *if* every drop could be held in storage until it is needed.

Obviously, this is impossible. All the money in the annual budget could not build enough dams and reservoirs to hold the floodwaters of our major rivers. Therefore, we are forced to consider only the *dependable* fresh water supplies. Flannery estimates that total will be 355 billion gallons per day in the year 1980. At the same time, he said, the nation will be *using 600 billion* gallons per day. The unpleasant disparity between these two figures, he believes, can be erased only by cleaning and reusing our waters over and over again. That, in turn, requires the water to remain *where* it is needed. Ten cities may use Mississippi River water as it moves downstream, but when it reaches the ocean it is irrevocably gone until the big pumping system brings it back as rain or snow.

The relationship between water available and water used is expressed in other terms by the National Academy of Sciences in its 1966 pollution report to the Federal Council for Science and Technology. In 1954, the study shows, 300 billion of the 1.1 trillion gallons available was withdrawn daily while 190 billion gallons of polluted water was returned to the nation's streams. By the year 2000, the amount of polluted water returned will amount to 889 billion gallons per day.

"Thus," the study states, "whereas in 1954 withdrawals amounted to less than a third and waste-ridden returns less than a fifth of the total; in 2000, it is predicted, withdrawals will be a little over four-fifths and polluted returns about two-thirds of the entire U.S. stream flow." Five basic categories of water use included irrigation, municipal consumption, manufacturing, mining and steam-electric power cooling.

The U.S. Public Health Service estimates that by the year 2000 some 95 percent of the nation's population of 280 million people will live in urban areas. Wastes discharged through municipal sewer systems will average some 132 gallons per day per person. During the same brief years, wastes produced by the large water-using industries are expected to increase *seven times over.*

These residues [according to the Academy of Sciences report] will be extremely variable in character and will contain oxygen-consuming ingredients as well as the complete range of industrial chemicals. It seems likely that the total quantity of pollutants in these separately discharged wastes will substantially exceed those originating in industries that discharge into the municipal sewage systems.

The major withdrawal of water will be for steam-electric power generation. It will be returned practically undiminished in quantity but at appreciably higher temperatures. This thermal pollution can have serious effects on the ecology of streams. . . .

Each bank of earth thrown up to build a farm pond, each town reservoir built or enlarged, each multimillion-dollar dam stretching its geometric splash of concrete across a Western canyon adds a measure of "new" water to the nation's available supply. Each of these, from the Iowa pond with its few thousand gallons to Lake Mead with its millions of acre-feet of blue mountain snowmelt, represents water which was restrained from running to the sea before it could serve a human purpose. That purpose may be as modest as holding moisture in the subsoil of a forty-acre field or grandiose as the irrigation of desert areas in Arizona and California.

It is not possible to conceive a dam built across every tiny trickle, every rivulent feeding the tributaries of our great rivers, yet in essence this is what has been done on the Thames River, holding the water back from flood, holding it to ensure a steady feed downstream to London in the dry months. This also is the heart of the living waters in the Ruhr flowing down from mountain reservoirs to ensure a *dependable* supply. The beavers did this sort of thing most effectively before they were chased out of their mountain lands. Forests and grass also were excellent water conservators until they were chopped down to build houses and plowed under to make wheat. Men learned the lessons of denuded watersheds the hard way when torrential rains fell, the soil stripped downslope and ran away from the land in muddy flood.

Floods taught the nation that rivers do not respect the artificial boundaries of cities, counties or states, and the Bureau of Reclamation learned to build dams. Once the breakthrough had been accomplished with this new toy, the Bureau along with the Army Corps of Engineers and logrolling congressmen went on a dam-building binge. White water roaring down from the mountains in spring stopped for a time in giant new reservoirs, not only to quell floods but also to generate electric power and irrigate arid lands of the West. Here, above all, in the half of the United States which stretches from the Missouri River to the Pacific Ocean, men learned the treasure of "new" water held back from the sea in flood, loosed gradually to the land in blistering summer to drench new fields of corn and wheat, melons and cotton.

The Rio Grande River yielded before the cement stoppers engineered by man. The Owens River in California, as early as 1913, sent its water through a 238-mile aqueduct to quench the thirst of booming Los Angeles. That same thirst was a major force which, in conjunction with urgent demands for irrigation in Arizona and southern California, led to the harnessing of the rich Colorado River for new water and power. Hoover Dam, creating the largest man-made lake in history, was completed in 1936 at a cost of $160 million, in the midst of America's Great Depression. Lake Mead backs up behind a 726-foot-high dam, filling the barren, rocky canyons at the Arizona-Nevada border with 32,471,000 acre-feet of water at its peak in summer. (An acre-foot contains 325,851 gallons, enough for one day's use by 1800 average American city dwellers.) The great bulk of this "new" water serves irrigated farm lands reclaimed from barren desert, but one billion gallons per day, 1.2 million acre-feet per year, flows from the Colorado to the Metropolitan Water District. This agency, formed around the core of Los Angeles, now serves more than seventy California cities. Population in the area numbers some ten million now and is expected to reach seventeen million by 1990. If new water had not been created by dams across the Colorado, the population, industrial and agricultural growth of southern California would have come to a halt many years ago. As early as 1953, this great metropolitan center contained half of California's people but less than *1.5 percent* of the state's natural water.

Other great dams grew on the Colorado and on the Mississippi in Montana and the Dakotas. More concrete spanned the Cumberland, the Red, the Sacramento, Green, Feather, Savannah, and dozens of other streams which sparkle with the history of a nation bursting with growth. In 1966 the U.S. Bureau of Reclamation listed more than eighty American man-made reservoirs, each impounding more than 1.2 million acre-feet of water. These range from the San Carlos Reservoir established in 1928 on the Gila River in Arizona (1,210,000 acre-feet) to Lake Powell, the newest, with capacity of 28 million acre-feet behind the Glen Canyon Dam completed in 1965 on the Colorado River at the Utah-Arizona border. Eighty-three major dams impound 325 million acre-feet of new water which, if it were used exclusively for personal drinking, washing and sewage removal, would be sufficient to serve the entire population of the country for more than six years. According to the Public Health Service, the average person uses 180 gallons of water per day; but, as we have seen, personal consumption accounts for only 22 billion (less than 7 percent) of the total water demand in the nation each day. Fully half of it goes to wash down the hot wheels of industry and the remaining 43 percent drenches parched land to grow food and fiber.

Without these vast sources of new water developed in the first two-thirds of the twentieth century, most of the farm land in the West would be fit for nothing but buffalo grass and cactus. Industry, except for a few benign areas along the Pacific Coast, could not have expanded to any major degree west of the Missouri River. Yet each new dam and reservoir has been created laboriously, at great cost in labor and money after convulsive years of political infighting, legal battles between states and regions, and the anguish of conservationists who suffer when they see the dirty animal spreading his filth ever outward into the beautiful wilderness areas of the land. The battle for new water and power, it appears, must always be fought across the chasm which separates the ideal of retaining natural beauty for the relatively few privileged to see and enjoy it and the equally pressing ideal of building new utilitarian services for an expanding population. Arbitrating these opposing poles must lead to a compromise in which the original beauty of nature is sustained around the new reservoirs, the new lakes being created by men for men.

In learning to build dams, the civil engineers also learned that a stream can be completely dried up, as witness the tiny trickle of the Rio Grande River where it passes between El Paso, Texas, and Ciudad Juárez, Mexico. This tendency for a once rich river to become a dry water hole now is becoming apparent on the Colorado as Arizona claims its right to water which has been used for years by southern California. Within twenty years, the waters in the lower Colorado will be completely used up; yet still more dams are being planned, two of which have been the subject of bitter controversy over threatened destruction of the natural beauty of the Grand Canyon. These are the Hualapi and Marble Canyon Dams, one or both of which eventually probably will be built to provide desperately needed water and power for the booming Tucson-Phoenix areas of Arizona.

The struggle over the Grand Canyon reclamation projects is a game of tic-tac-toe compared with the war now shaping up between the water-hungry Southwest and the water-rich northwestern section of the nation. California, recognizing that the Colorado River is rapidly approaching its end as a dependable water hole, moved in 1960 to draw a new supply from the Feather River in its northern half and ship it south in a project costing more than two billion dollars. Starting in 1970, this mammoth system of dams, concrete canals, and pumps to lift over the Tehachapi Mountains will deliver two million acre-feet of new water to the southland per year. This will satisfy the region's water needs, however, only until the year 1990, so Governor Pat Brown ordered a seven-year study of other northern California rivers, which uselessly dump millions of acre-feet of water into the Pacific Ocean each year.

These streams are mere trickles, however, against the mighty Columbia River, which carries to the Pacific each year

170 to 190 million acre-feet of water, ten times the flow of the Colorado and more than all the water now being used for irrigation in the West. The Columbia is an obvious target of the thirsty Southwest, but Oregon and Washington, whose borders share the major bounty of the river, are telling their neighbors to keep hands off. The Department of the Interior has been conducting a gradual softening-up process for some years now, especially since Arizona's rights to the Colorado were upheld in the courts and it became apparent that stream will soon run dry. Nearly forty bills were introduced in the 1965 session of Congress dealing with southwestern water development. None specified the Columbia but all were aimed indirectly at that goal—how to pull water one thousand miles south to replenish water holes, the underground aquifers and rivers which now run only part of the time above ground. The battle lines are engaged in Congress, and William E. Folz, head of agricultural economics at the University of Idaho, recently sounded the war cry: "You wealthy states who have grandiose plans for your own future growth . . . had better give serious thought to the more modest aspirations of your less fortunate neighbors. For if you don't, we will find some way literally to shut off your water!"

"Our water supply is assured through the year 1990," California Governor Pat Brown commented, "but after that, whether we bring it from the Snake, the Columbia or the Volga, we will have to have it." Arizona's Governor Sam Goddard issued a more poignant plea before a meeting of the Inland Waterways Association in Portland in 1965. "Arizona faces disaster unless water from outside the Colorado River Basin is found. We do not covet one drop that you [Northwesterners] can ever use—only some that you can never use."

Officials responsible to the people of Oregon, Washington and Idaho are just as adamant that they will need all their own water in the near future to wash down the refuse of growing cities, industries and nuclear plants. Washington's Senator Henry M. Jackson, chairman of the Senate Committee of Interior and Insular Affairs, argues that even now the wealth of Columbia water flowing into the Pacific is not wasted. Without it, he says, fisheries and navigation would suffer; the channel, now scoured by the huge volume of water, would have to be dredged; and pollution on the lower Columbia, already a problem, would become more serious.

Most ambitious of all the Roman aqueduct schemes to build reservoirs and siphon new water into the American system of lakes and rivers is NAWAPA, the North American Water and Power Alliance. Conceived by the Ralph M. Parsons Co., a Los Angeles construction-engineering firm, this colossal plan proposes to reach *through* Oregon and Washington, on through Canada and Alaska to the Yukon, almost to the polar icecap itself. Cored around a series of dams across the Susitna, Copper, Tanana and Yukon Rivers, NAWAPA would divert *33 trillion gallons of water per year* from Alaska and northern Canada. This gigantic artificial stream would be pumped in stages one thousand feet uphill, then fall naturally into the Rocky Mountain trench, a five hundred-mile natural gorge which now carries the Columbia, Fraser and Kootenay Rivers into northern Montana.

From this trench, the water would be diverted outward to benefit the arid Southwest, thirty-six other states, and part of Mexico. This monument to all the world's past thinking in dam and aqueduct building would irrigate forty million acres of land in seventeen Western states, while yielding 100 million kilowatts of electricity, seventy-five times the output of Hoover Dam.

A generous new flow of water such as this, if it could be brought to bear immediately, would solve many of the nation's stream pollution problems. Among other benefits seen from NAWAPA is the possibility of opening a canal from the St. Lawrence River to the Pacific Ocean with enough water to flush the corruption out of the Great Lakes and bring them up from the subnormal levels they have held in recent years. Unfortunately, even if political conflicts could be settled between states, regions and nations, it still would cost $100 billion and fifty years to build NAWAPA. America's polluted lakes and streams cannot wait that long for a flushing of new water.

Although municipal and industrial sewage are the main causes of concern in the East, the Western U.S. is plagued by the oldest of all forms of water pollution—chemical salts. From ancient times, many of the world's great agricultural areas died of salt accumulation from irrigation water. This, in turn, has become a growing and persistent threat in the Southwest as the great reclamation projects bring more thousands of acres of arid, alkaline land under cultivation. The process by which fresh water turns salty is as old as rain. Pure distilled water falls from the sky, then as it runs down the land it leaches out chemicals and finally reaches the sea where the average salt concentration around the world is 35,000 parts per million parts of water. For drinking purposes, water should contain no more than five hundred parts of salts per million of water (ppm), and most agricultural crops will be stunted or fail to grow entirely if the salt concentration builds up to more than 1500 ppm. Irrigation water, such as that from the Colorado River, may be relatively sweet when it is first poured over the land, but as it drains off and travels downstream to the next user, it has picked up a lot of salt as well as excess fertilizer, insecticides and weed killers. Although the water may still be bright, clear and free of disease-bearing bacteria, it is as corrupted for its intended purpose as though it contained a load of industrial sewage.

Such salt contamination, occurring in the lower reaches of the Colorado River, nearly caused an international incident between the U.S. and Mexico before the problem was circumvented in 1965. Under a 1944 treaty the U.S. guaranteed 1.5 million acre-feet of good water annually to Mexico's cotton farmers living in the rich Mexicali Valley. Colorado River water normally contains no more than 900 ppm of salts but in 1961 the content jumped to 3000 ppm. It came from water pumped out of deep Arizona wells, used for irrigation and then drained into the Colorado. Before the problem was solved, more than four hundred Mexican farmers were being driven out of business per year as their land became salt-laden and their crops died. The international issue was temporarily solved in November 1965 when a thirteen-mile diversion channel was opened at a cost of five million dollars. The new canal permits the Mexicans either to accept the water for irrigation, if it is diluted enough, or reject it to run on into the Gulf of California.

When the greatest floods in the history of the region swept through the below sea-level Imperial Valley of southern California in 1906 and 1907, residents considered it a catastrophe. That unprecedented flood, however, created the Salton Sea, which remains the only sizable lake in that part of the Mojave Desert. With booming population and the growth of American leisure time, the Salton Sea is now rapidly becoming a major inland recreation area with considerable renown for sports fishing. At the same time the sea serves as the drainage basin for agricultural waste water throughout the region. During 1965, the Salton Sea hosted thousands of visitors and the recreation business was estimated to net $25 million annually for local residents. In 1966, Dr. Richard Pomeroy, a Pasadena water specialist, warned that increasing salinity in the sea could damage the recreation and fishing by 1970 and completely destroy both by 1985. "The situation is getting worse much faster than had been anticipated," Dr. Pomeroy said after an eighteen-month study. "Salt in the Salton Sea is increasing at the rate of ten thousand tons per day." He recommended a $22 million remedy which would include evaporation ponds to concentrate the accumulated brine and a pumping system to remove it to a disposal area.

Since 1950, California cities and industries have spent more than one billion dollars on new sewage treatment plants and disposal systems. Now it appears that $200 million worth of work designed to prevent pollution of San Francisco Bay may be canceled by a $54 million 228-mile drainage canal from irrigated farmlands of the San Joaquin Valley. Plans for the gigantic drain were drawn up as part of California's Feather River water diversion project, but without consulting Bay Area officials who had been struggling for years with their own pollution problems. The influx of agricultural waste water, it is feared, will bring into the bay a flood of plant nutrients—nitrates and phosphates leached from the farmland —as well as pesticides and weed killers. In such fashion, a bonus of "new" water from dammed rivers may become the pollution problem of another region. California is studying the feasibility of a huge state sewage treatment plant which would handle 40 percent of all the wastes now draining into the bay. Plans, when complete, may also provide methods for reusing the treated water.

Salt pollution also is a problem along the coastlines of the nation where the ocean seeps under the land to fill deep fresh-water aquifers as they are pumped out to irrigate coastal farmland and serve growing communities. In San Luis Obispo County, California, hydraulic engineers report fresh water wells have dropped thirteen feet since 1954 and sea water is creeping in. The same is true in Los Angeles, Orange and Ventura counties where truck and citrus farming accounts for a major portion of the local economy. In one area, one thousand users have agreed to reduce their well-water consumption by 20 percent in order to stop the salty intrusion. In others preventive measures include the drilling of a line of salt-water wells to stop the forward advance of the sea. The idea of these wells is to pump out the salt water and pour it back into the ocean faster than it can seep into the underground aquifers.

President Johnson, in 1966, threw the full prestige of his office behind a ten-year accelerated research program to develop new ways to reduce water shortages and halt pollution. The program called for research spending to increase from $91.9 million in 1966 to $199.3 million in 1971. "The growth of our population and industry," Johnson said, "has placed new demands on our water supplies. We are confronted with water shortages in many sections of our country. Today, virtually every river system in America is touched by pollution. This menace grows more serious each day. We must continue our search for bold new ideas."

Among the bold new ideas put forth by the President was

the suggestion that Arctic icebergs might be towed south through the Pacific Ocean to bring new fresh water to southern California. "A strong, well-planned program of research now has become a national necessity," Johnson added. "The growth of knowledge in this vital area is important to our future." He handed the new research mandate to Dr. Donald F. Hornig, Director of the Office of Science and Technology.

"A suggestion to supply Southern California with water by towing icebergs from the Arctic finds no home in agencies whose authorized mission is to build dams, canals and pipelines," Dr. Hornig commented. "Some will suggest the idea is impossible—the suggestion of a crackpot, but without evaluation one cannot be sure and even though an idea does not survive evaluation it may suggest other things that are really practicable."

A onetime "crackpot suggestion" which is rapidly approaching the point of being "really practicable" is that of removing new water from the sea itself. The sea contains more than 97 percent of all the water in the world, so it is natural to look to this source for the answer to increasing needs. A majority of all the earth's people live in coastal areas, which means that more than half of the world's major population centers, with their concentrations of industry, eventually can look to desalted sea water to help wash away their accumulated filth. The ocean's salts, however, are held in chemical combination and cannot be removed by any of the standard filtration and other purification methods that are applied to inland fresh water supplies. More than a dozen techniques have been developed for desalting ocean water, ranging from steam distillation to electrodialysis, but all require high energy outlays and until recent years have been too expensive to provide new water at a cost competitive with that drawn from fresh-water streams and lakes. The cost differential now is changing.

For more than one hundred years desalination has provided fresh water for ships at sea. The first land-based distilling plants were built in the late nineteenth century, and since then more than 65 million gallons per day of conversion facilities have been installed around the world. The desert nation of Kuwait uses six million gallons of desalted sea water each day produced by distillation units which are powered almost free of charge by the nation's wealth of oil and natural gas. The island of Curacao depends upon two sea-water desalting plants converting a total of 3.5 million gallons per day (gpd). A number of experimental desalting plants have been built in the United States under direction of the Office of Saline Water. The largest of these distilled more than 1,000,000 gpd of sparkling fresh water for the community of San Diego, California, for several years before it was moved to the Guantánamo naval base to ease the Castro-induced water shortage there. The largest electrodialysis plant (a technique useful for reducing salts in brackish water) operates at 650,000 gpd capacity at Buckeye, Arizona. That state is one of many regions in the Western U.S. which are underlain by alkaline waters with salt concentrations up to 5000 ppm. The electrodialysis process can, at fairly reasonable cost, reduce this brackish water to a salt level at which it can be used for domestic purposes.

Ten years ago, using techniques developed for shipboard and scattered desert areas around the world, desalted sea water cost from $5 to $15 per thousand gallons, a price obviously prohibitive in a nation where most residents pay no more than 30 to 50 cents per thousand gallons. Agricultural water is considered prohibitive when the price goes above 15 cents per thousand. According to the Stanford Research Institute, development of improved desalting efficiencies now has reduced the price to about $1 per thousand in a 1,000,000 gpd plant, and 60 cents per thousand in a 10,000,000 gpd plant.

The Institute predicted in 1966 that desalination capacity to be installed during the next decade will be ten times the 65,000,000 gpd now in operation throughout the world. The researchers added that the free world will spend from $500 million to $700 million on new sea-water conversion plants by

1975, with an additional $350 to $500 million to be spent on steam and power plants built in connection with water conversion facilities.

As a result of the level of research and development going into desalination, the SRI stated, by the end of the decade the cost of converted water may decrease from present levels by about 20 percent for small plants and 10 percent for very large sized plants. Costs of converting sea water will range from 22 cents per 1000 gallons in large scale dual purpose plants to about 35 cents per 1000 gallons in single purpose plants. . . .

The Office of Saline Water, established in 1952 with passage of the Saline Water Act, started with an annual budget of $175,000. By the end of 1965, the agency's research expenditures had totaled $40.5 million, impelled by a nation finally facing up to the declining conditions of its fresh water supplies. In 1965 Congress extended the program through the fiscal year 1972 and authorized expenditure of $200 million more. Another $220 million will be spent by the Atomic Energy Commission between now and 1975 in related nuclear reactor developments which ultimately are expected to provide the extremely large quantities of low-cost power and heat needed to bring desalination into the realm of economic competition. The use of nuclear energy, which now is becoming competitive with conventional fuels for the production of electric power, has given birth to the concept of the dual-purpose very large scale water and power plant. The combination plant would offer full-time utilization of the power- and heat-producing facilities, a condition which is not possible in standard large power plants. Such a plant would produce power as needed for peak loads in large metropolitan areas. Then, when the power demand slackens, the full power could be turned to water desalting.

In 1963 Dr. R. Philip Hammond of the Oak Ridge National Laboratory urged a beginning of new facilities to combine power generation and ocean desalting with nuclear power.

A few tons of natural uranium can be the means of providing a plentiful supply of food, water and electric power anywhere

126

on earth [he said before the Atomic Industrial Forum in New York]. There will be about 10 years before a real crisis in water supply exists, but some means of meeting the crisis must be committed for some years before that.

We now have used up a third of that ten years, the real crisis in pure water has become most evident, and it now appears the first large-scale experiment—combining power generation and ocean desalting with nuclear power—will take place off the coast of southern California.

During the past three years, the Metropolitan Water District which serves Los Angeles and five neighbor counties with a billion gallons of water per day, has joined forces with the U.S. Interior Department and the Atomic Energy Commission to pin down costs and techniques for a large nuclear-power dual-purpose plant. Late in 1966, following a thorough study conducted by the Bechtel Corporation of San Francisco, Southern California authorities and the U.S. government agreed to go ahead with a $434.7 million desalting plant which will be constructed on a forty-acre artificial island, beautifully landscaped, one-half mile off Bolsa Chica State Beach near Los Angeles. This plant will produce 150 million gallons of water per day along with 1800 mega (million) watts of power. The cost will be shared by the Federal Government, the Metropolitan Water District and a number of California utility companies which will buy the power. The resulting water is expected to cost only twenty-two cents per 1000 gallons, and with its distilled purity will be used to sweeten the more salty water coming to the Southland from the Colorado and Feather River projects. Later, as we shall see, the first noble experiment in large scale desalting may guide the nation into truly far-sighted methods of cleaning up its inland lakes and rivers.

While American industry belatedly faces up to the necessity of cleaning up its wastes and purifying its process water for reuse, another way of adding "new" water to the nation's dependable supplies is becoming more and more acceptable. This is the removal of sewage and the return of purified water back into the municipal water system. As distasteful as the thought may seem in fastidious America, millions of people have been drinking reclaimed sewage water for several decades, water which has been emptied into a stream by another community or that which has percolated down to underground aquifers from farm yards and suburban cesspools. The only question is how thoroughly the water is purified and treated with chemicals before it is used again.

Headquarters for the Public Health Service efforts to find economic and foolproof methods of reclaiming the water from sewage is the Robert A. Taft Sanitary Engineering Center near Cincinnati, Ohio. There researchers are experimenting with advanced new methods to remove the most stubborn contaminants from water.

"The ironic thing," one scientist commented, "is the fact that a good many people in the U.S. today—probably a majority—are drinking reclaimed sewage [water] right now. What we're doing is trying to improve its quality.

"Probably 80 percent of the nation's water supply now is taken from lakes and streams which also function as sewers," he said. "It is statistically provable that the main course of many rivers is through people's alimentary canal. In place after place, the bulk of a river's flow measurably consists of the sewage discharge just upstream."

The scientist pointed out that many communities still discharge their sewage untreated. Others apply primary treatment, which means the mere settling out of solid materials. More progressive secondary treatment of sewage consists of forced biological digesting and chemical neutralization of noxious components. The Taft Engineering center is concentrating on *tertiary*, or third stage, treatment, which filters the treated water through diatomaceous earth or activated charcoal to remove final organic material, and applies electrodialysis to remove the final charged, or ionized particles, such as salts. In 1965, Taft engineers estimated that the final tertiary treatment could produce potable water from sewage at a cost of $1.05 per thousand gallons in a plant operating at ten million gallons per day.

"People often ask why, if the sewage situation is so bad we aren't all dead," the Taft scientist commented. "The reason is that more and more complicated and expensive water-supply treatment has kept the quality potable. But nobody knows how long this will be effective as contamination increases."

He pointed out that in New York City, as an example, the water supply is chlorinated, rechlorinated, coagulated with alum, aerated, filtered and treated with lime, and further treated with caustic soda. The growing complexities in the treatment of water mean only one thing—sanitary engineers are becoming increasingly worried about exotic new chemicals which are pouring into our water supplies, not to mention the ever present threat of viral epidemics of hepatitis or meningitis which could break out at any time. Normal purification techniques do not remove viruses from the water.

Direct reclamation of sewage water looms with ever greater importance particularly in the larger metropolitan centers where water use is measured in billions of gallons per day. As a prime example, Los Angeles, which has paid millions of dollars to import its water from the Owens and Colorado rivers, each day throws away 600 million precious gallons. Through a vast network of trunk sewers, this river of water is pumped miles out into the Pacific Ocean far enough that it will not wash back ashore with the tide, and there left to nature's purification system of dilution, aeration, sunlight and biological decomposition. Fresh water, which makes up about 99 percent of sewage flow, is simply dispersed in the sea. The metropolis is not unmindful of the waste. Although reclaimed water is not yet being reintroduced to the city's water system, 24 million gallons per day is being saved and reused for such purposes as golf course irrigation. J. D. Parkhurst, chief engineer for the Los Angeles County Sanitation District, said that the district now operates seven reclamation plants at Whittier Narrows, Pomona, Lancaster, Azusa, Palmdale, Saugus and La Canada. He estimated that four times 24 million gallons of reclaimed water could be saved each day using current methods.

A. F. Bush, of the UCLA Engineering College, said in 1965 that at least half of the 600 million gallons discarded daily could be purified and reused and "it would be cheaper and simpler than desalting sea water." Bush said that the certain removal of viruses is one remaining problem which he is researching now. In a test method under experimentation, sewage goes first into a settling tank where solids sink to the bottom. The remaining water, rich in bacteria and nutrients, is transferred into an activated sludge tank where the bacteria feed on fats, proteins and carbohydrates in the sewage. Bacteria and viruses then, in theory, multiply and fuse together into heavy clumps which sink to the bottom of the next tank. Any viruses that escape, Bush said, are caught in three sand filter traps. After a final check, the water is treated with chlorine and then is theoretically suitable for injection back into the water mains.

Until people become accustomed to the idea of drinking reclaimed sewage water, such water has several other immediate and beneficial uses. In the high desert Antelope Valley above Los Angeles, the community of Lancaster is using reclaimed sewage water to build new fishing and boating lakes filling at the rate of 3.5 million gallons per day. At San Diego, residents approved a $700,000 bond issue for a similar experiment. Faced with the problem of disposing of 1,000,000 gpd of sewage, the city first created a large pond of treated sewage where it stands for three weeks undergoing natural oxidation and plant life purification. Then the water is pumped to the top of nearby Sycamore Canyon into the dry bed of an old river. When the water emerges at the bottom of the canyon, after filtering through the old stream bed, it is absolutely clear and pure. Now five recreation lakes and a swimming pool are supplied with the reclaimed sewage water. The entire project costs thirteen dollars per day less than if San Diego had purchased the right to hook into another community's sewage line for disposal.

In the city of Ventura, California, a 320-acre park is being treated with two million gallons of reclaimed sewage water per day. David Sullivan, sanitation supervisor, reports that grass grows better under this treatment than with water from the city's main system, and in addition sludge from the town sewage plant is being used to fertilize a golf course. In 1966, Ventura County, California, was considering a $137 million forty-year project for county-wide sewerage and water reclamation to serve the 2.4 million people expected to live there by the year 2015. The sewer system would connect every local sewer to divert 210,000,000 gpd of treated sewage four and one-half miles out into the Pacific Ocean. At the same time, the project would reclaim 130,000 acre-feet of water per year at a cost of $21.74 per million gallons.

Still another, and promising, way to use reclaimed sewage water is in the production of food—for livestock if not for humans. During the past two years, North American Aviation, Inc., a leader in the nation's aerospace program, has used space-age techniques to assist the Public Health Service in its advanced waste treatment research program. In this experiment, North American Aviation scientists cultured marine algae in a pool of sewage water and fed the algae to chickens. Scientist Rudolf Mattoni reported that sixty-six chicks grew to healthy adults eating the beefed-up high-protein algae feed as a protein supplement. He said that in four weeks, 150 pounds of algae was harvested from sixty thousand gallons of waste water. It is feasible, Mattoni said, to extract fifty tons of usable algae per acre of sewage, and while serving as animal food, the algae could purify and reclaim millions of gallons of waste water per year.

When all of the efforts to clean up our streams and provide volumes of new and reclaimed water to the nation's storehouse are linked together, they will undoubtedly bring about marked improvements across the land. However, when it is considered that eighty billion dollars may be spent over the next twenty years for elementary sewage treatment facilities which have been needed for half a century, and when it is considered that the federal government is willing to give serious thought to a $100 billion project which would import water from the polar icecap itself, then it is certainly true, as the National Academy of Sciences has urged, that entirely new approaches must be found to attack the water pollution

131

problem. Devices and techniques which will seem startling and revolutionary during the next ten years will form the pollution abatement systems with which we must live for the next half century.

Sanitary engineers finally have begun to shift their thinking toward the massive facilities, energy consumption and money expenditure which will be necessary to do the job right. Among concepts beginning to emerge in research is an extension of the wedding of technologies which now is on the verge of combining nuclear energy with power production and sea-water desalting. The fact is that a plant, such as that planned for southern California, capable of producing 150 million gallons of fresh water from the sea each day, is just as capable of removing the impurities from 150 million gallons of sewage water each day. Instead of dual-purpose nuclear-power plants, the true future of major metropolitan areas is the triple-purpose nuclear plant. With solid materials removed in settling basins, water could pass directly from the city's sewer system into the nuclear distillation plant, with perfectly pure water returned to the city system in a closed cycle. At the same time, huge amounts of electric power could be produced. Such a triple-purpose facility also could be designed to incinerate the solid sewage by-products and in fact use these as a supplemental fuel supply. With roughly $100 billion, the water pollution problems in at least one hundred of America's largest cities could be completely solved while eliminating the scattered energies now inherent in the building and operation of separate sewage plants, separate water plants and separate power plants. As Dr. Hornig so succinctly commented, "Some will suggest the idea is impossible—the suggestion of a crackpot, but without evaluation one cannot be sure. Even though an idea does not survive evaluation it may suggest other things that are really practicable." In the words of Dr. Hammond, "A few tons of natural uranium may be the means of providing plentiful pure water and electric power anywhere on earth."

It is ideas such as these which must be brought to the stage of specific design and economic study to cut through the apathy, sloth and half-hearted solutions to the problem of our polluted water.

The American public has had enough of streams and lakes [Representative Henry S. Reuss of Wisconsin told the thirtieth annual meeting of the National Wildlife Federation in 1966] which stink to the heavens from human wastes, which are gory with the blood of packinghouses, which are sterile from the acids from mines and industries, which are covered with a coating of detergent foam from somebody's laundry, or of cottage-cheese-like waste from some processing plant.

The American public is fed to the teeth with air that is polluted with harmful gases and solids, and we are deeply ashamed with the contamination of our land. . . .

The American public, as it always has, will see to it that the politicians and potentates move off dead center to do something about our dying waters.

Darkness by Day

This most excellent canopy, the air, look you,
this brave o'erhanging firmament, this majestical roof
fretted with golden fire—why it appears no other
thing to me than a foul and pestilent
congregation of vapors.

Shakespeare, Hamlet

IN 1306 A ROYAL PROCLAMATION WAS ISSUED IN ENGLAND forbidding the use of coal for fuel in the city of London. The order was followed immediately by a directive to punish offenders "for the first offence with great fines and ransoms, and upon the second offence to destroy their furnaces."

Six and one-half centuries later, in 1952, at least four thousand Londoners died when a pall of black smoke and chemical fumes settled over the city, turning day to poisonous night, soot and sulfuric acid penetrating homes and into the lungs of the aged, the ill and the infirm. The coal furnaces, if they had ever been destroyed, had been rebuilt. As the woodlands of England dwindled, coal which fueled the Industrial Revolution served in millions of homes to remove the cold from aching bones when chill winter fog crept in to inhabit the land.

It began on a cool, clear December 4 with no hint to Londoners that "this most excellent canopy" was about to change to "a foul and pestilent congregation of vapors." Some weather forecasters may have detected signs of cold and fog in the high-pressure mass of cold air creeping across western Europe toward England, but it was not until afternoon that the mild winter breeze died. The huge mass of cold air settled into the bowl, hundreds of square miles in size, which comprises the Thames River Valley. A temperature inversion occurred and evening brought a dense, cold London fog.

When city dwellers came home from their daily occupations, they heaped soft coal on the small stove fires in every room to chase away the chill. All through the night the coal fires burned, pouring clouds of sulfur dioxide into the atmosphere. When late dawn finally arrived, it was barely visible through the brown pall inhabiting the droplets of fog. Thousand of motorists, trying to grope their way to work, abandoned vehicles by the roadside when it became impossible to drive.

The temperature in London remained below freezing all day and coal burning increased, intensifying the sulfurous smog. On the following day, Saturday, December 6, the visibility was so impaired that all river traffic was halted and on Sunday the lowland areas within a twenty-mile radius around London were shrouded in complete darkness.

Still the air remained motionless and cold, allowing thousands of tons of soot and fumes to build up in greater concentrations. The city suffered hundreds of traffic tie-ups. On Monday, two trains collided in the smog. More than one hundred people suffered heart attacks while sitting quietly at home. Influenza and emphysema sufferers flooded the city's hospitals. The death rate shot up to unprecedented levels.

By the time a breeze cleared away the smog on Tuesday morning, deaths attributed to the smog numbered four thousand with some estimates rising to six thousand. Dr. Ernest T. Williams, head of the atmospheric pollution section of England's Department of Scientific and Industrial Research, believes the number of people who died eventually, because of exposure to the atmospheric plague, totaled as many as eight thousand.

The London disaster shocked the industrialized part of the world into full awareness of how human life can be immediately jeopardized by the profligate and uncontrolled burning of fossil fuels, from which most of the world's energy now is obtained. It was not, however, the first or last such disaster nor was it an entirely isolated case. In 1873, 1150 Londoners had died in a similar onset of smog. Since then more than forty such episodes have caused widespread casualties.

In December 1930 a high-pressure weather system moved into the Meuse River Valley in Belgium, shrouding the area under a blanket of still, silent fog. The narrow valley which extends fifteen miles between the towns of Huy and Seraing contains an industrial complex rivaling the Ruhr in Germany. Along the river are coke ovens, a sulfuric acid plant, blast furnaces, steel mills, glass factories, zinc smelters and a facility producing chemical fertilizer. Added to the array of poisonous fumes belching from those industries was the smoke and sulfur from coal burned to produce electric power in the region. As in the later episode in London, the sun heated the upper level of the pool of air, forming a temperature inversion and trapping the fog and fumes near the ground. After three days of accumulated smog, many residents complained of stomach pains and shortness of breath. Two days later, the weather changed and rain washed away the aerial contamination, but sixty-three persons had died and at least six thousand suffered varying degrees of illness.

In the United States, the classic example where the weather joined forces with the coal-burning powers of industry to cause physical disaster is Donora, Pennsylvania. In October 1948, a high-pressure system moved in over Pennsylvania, Ohio, Virginia and West Virginia, blanketing a thirty-thousand-square-mile area with fog. In most areas, some natural ventilation prevented the smog from building to lethal levels. Donora, however, is a center of heavy industry on the Monongahela River hemmed in by steep hills which, combined with a temperature inversion, held in the smog like water in a closed boiling pot. By October 27, second day of the black smog, soot and chemicals were deposited on the ground as a greasy black coating. Footsteps and tire marks showed up as eerie traces. By the fourth day, it was impossible to see in Donora except by using car lights. Doctors worked thirty-six hours without rest, treating the upsurge of patients suffering from heart and lung disease; fire department inhalation equipment was soon exhausted.

I knew that whatever it was that we were up against was serious [a local physician said later]. I had seen some very pitiful cases and they weren't all asthmatics or chronics of any kind. Some were people who had never been bothered by fog before. I was worried, but I wasn't bewildered. It was no mystery—it was obvious—all the symptoms pointed to the fact that the smoke and fog were to blame.

I didn't think any further than that. As a matter of fact, I didn't have time to think or wonder. I was too damn busy. My biggest problem was just getting around. It was almost impossible to drive. I even had trouble finding the office.

I could taste the soot when I got out of the car and my chest felt very tight. On the way up the stairs, I started to cough and I couldn't stop. I kept coughing and choking until my stomach turned over—I just made it to the office and into the lavatory in time. My God, I was sick!

After a while I dragged myself into the office and gave myself an injection of adrenalin and lay back in a chair. I began to feel better, so much so that I got out a cigar and lighted up. That practically finished [me]. . . .

On the sixth day of the Donora smog, finally, several steel, wire and zinc plants shut down operations to reduce atmospheric emissions. When the deadly fog finally blew away, twenty people had died and 5900 had suffered aggravated illnesses. One-third of all the 13,900 people living in the community developed coughs as a result of the soot, sulfur dioxide and other poisonous chemicals they were forced to breathe.

These three shocking cases demonstrate clearly how contaminated air, once considered to be no more than an eye-stinging ugliness which occasionally alters the blue of the sky, can cause illness and death for thousands. Yet the smogs of London, Belgium and Donora are but symptoms of the growing blanket of air pollution which is altering the atmosphere over much of the world, particularly the heavily industrialized Northern Hemisphere. Every large city in America and many of those in Europe are potential death traps, waiting only for the proper weather conditions to coincide with the heavy burning of carbon fuels to disable more thousands of helpless individuals.

"Millions of citizens are living in an ocean of air that is, on good evidence, unhealthy to breathe," Dr. Herman E. Hilleboe, former health commissioner of New York City, said in 1965. He cited a recent U.S. Public Health Service survey which showed that every American city of fifty thousand or more people has an air pollution problem. Airline pilots before landing at most U.S. airports advise their passengers to expect low overcast, "just plain dirty air." A California scientist, having witnessed nearly a quarter century of effort to curb air pollution, commented pessimistically: "The world's atmosphere will grow more and more polluted until, a century from now, it will be too poisonous for human life to survive." Doctors and public health specialists, although they cannot yet prove it, are coming more to the conclusion that foreign particles in the air contribute to illnesses ranging from arthritis to lung cancer. This is true not just in areas such as Donora where smog reached critical proportions, but in cities where a chronic and growing level of polluted atmosphere has come to be a standard condition of life.

Dr. Richard Prindle, chief of the medical program of the U.S. Department of Health, Education, and Welfare's Air

Pollution Division, warned recently that more temperature inversions and more critical episodes will hit American cities in coming years, but he added that slow poisoning may be a greater danger.

"The more difficult part of the problem facing physicians," he said, "is not to understand and correct these obvious disasters, but to understand and correct a more subtle, but nonetheless significant disaster—the slow ruination of health and life.

"A potential does exist for disaster from air pollution. Such an occurrence can be an unusual, sudden, acute problem . . . or it may be the result of long exposure to low or moderate levels of pollution resulting in biological damage of far-reaching consequences to a city's population."

Contamination of the atmosphere was not invented by man. Dust storms, volcanic eruptions and other convulsions of nature throw certain amounts of foreign matter into the air. Every living plant contributes mold spores and pollen. The dust of animal manures, smoke from forest fires and swamp gas always have mixed with the natural atmosphere, but in ages past the wind and rain always have been adequate to wash the sky blue and clean again. Nature did not receive its overload until the swarming hordes of human beings, growing in prodigious numbers and voracious for energy, began stripping out and consuming the carbon fuels from the world's forests, its coal beds, its deep reservoirs of petroleum. The situation began to reach serious proportions in the nineteenth century with the burning of vast tonnages of coal to run the Industrial Revolution. It has multiplied in the twentieth century as the dirty animal burns more coal and consumes millions of barrels of oil each year.

"With our numbers increasing and with our increasing urbanization and industrialization," President Johnson said in 1966, "the flow of pollutants to air, soils and water is increasing. This increase is so rapid that our present efforts in managing pollution are barely enough to stay even, surely not enough to make the improvements that are needed."

140

Mention of the word "smog" almost automatically triggers the name "Los Angeles" by association in millions of minds. The average resident of the United States probably would assume that the southern California coastal basin, which holds the state's greatest concentration of population, has the most serious air pollution problem in the world. This is only partially true. Linking smog with Los Angeles has come about principally because that city for more than twenty years has made the greatest effort in the nation to solve its air pollution problem. Virtually every major city has an equal or worse smog production problem, and many of them have put up with it for a longer period of time. *Scientific American* of November 1865, for example, was moved to publish the following report:

> In Pittsburgh, Cincinnati and other cities west of the Alleghanies, where bituminous coal is generally used for fuel, the smoke that constantly hangs in the atmosphere is a very great nuisance. The principles of the problem are very simple. The elements in bituminous coal that burn are carbon and hydrogen and the burning is the combination of these with the oxygen of the atmosphere. When smoke is formed, it results from the fact that a portion of the carbon does not combine with oxygen —in other words, is not burned.
>
> One of the successful plans for burning smoke in the furnaces of steam boilers is that patented in England by Charles Wye Williams. The flame and gases resulting from the partial combustion of coal are carried into a chamber behind the grate and are here mixed with a fresh supply of air. The situation of the chamber causes the smoke to be maintained at a sufficiently high temperature to effect combustion.

Although the word "smog" had not yet been invented, scientific attention had been applied to the problem a century ago. Yet Dr. William H. Stewart, U.S. Surgeon General, told the 59th annual meeting of the Air Pollution Control Association in San Francisco in 1966 that the nation's efforts to stem air pollution are "far from adequate."

Of thirty-three states which have air pollution control programs, Dr. Stewart said, "only a half dozen engage in more than a minimal degree of actual abatement activity." He pointed out that twenty-four metropolitan areas in the U.S. contain half of the nation's urban population, but only *five* of these have control programs in keeping with physical conditions of their regions. He identified these as Los Angeles, San Francisco, Detroit, Pittsburgh and Boston. Dr. Stewart added:

> There is little doubt that air pollution is at the very least a contributing factor to the rising incidence of chronic respiratory disease—lung cancer, emphysema, chronic bronchitis and asthma. There is some evidence that certain types of air pollution may even contribute to the common cold. We believe that air pollution also is a health hazard to many people at concentrations which are routinely sustained in many areas of the United States.
>
> I submit that we must do much better. All the trends of growth which have produced this problem promise to increase as the future rushes toward us. By 1975 we can expect that three-fourths of the nation's 235 million people will be living on roughly one-tenth of the land area. Since it often takes years to bring about technical and legislative improvements, government and industry can delay no longer in development of a control effort commensurate with the seriousness of the problem.

The seriousness of the problem, fortunately, is becoming apparent to more and more people who share the authority and responsibility to do something about it. Dr. Albert W. Dent, president of the National Tuberculosis Association, blames smog as a "contributory factor" in an alarming increase in tuberculosis cases in Los Angeles County. "There is growing evidence," he said, "that impurities in the air contribute to respiratory diseases." The doctor added that tuberculosis cases had increased by one hundred to a total of 329 during 1965 in the southern California county. In Buffalo, New York, Dr. Warren Winkelstein, Jr., of the State University of New York, during 1965 conducted the most comprehensive study yet undertaken on the affects of air pollution on health. The physician compared mortality rates of 77,800 Buffalo men between the ages of fifty to seventy. Half of his test cases lived in a high concentration of fumes and soot from steel and chemical plants and oil refineries. The other half lived in parts of the city with relatively pure air. Dr. Winkelstein found that the over-all death rate was nearly one-third higher among men living in neighborhoods where air pollution was heaviest. Deaths from emphysema and bronchitis were three times as frequent in high-pollution areas. On the other hand, his study showed virtually no difference in the death rates from lung cancer.

The British Committee on Air Pollution, acting for the Minister of Fuel and Power, conducted an extensive study of deaths due to respiratory illness in England and Wales as compared with Denmark, Norway and Sweden.

Our report [the committee told Parliament] deals with the consequences of the continuing air pollution that persists year in and year out. There is a clear association between pollution and the incidence of bronchitis and other respiratory diseases. Statistics show that every year the death rate from bronchitis in England and Wales is much higher than in other European countries for which reliable figures are available.

In 1951, according to the study, the bronchitis death rate in Denmark per 100,000 people averaged 2.2 men and 1.9 women. In Norway the rates were 5.5 and 5.8. In Sweden, 5.0 men and 4.0 women died of bronchitis per 100,000 population In England and Wales the same year, the death rates were 107.9 men and 62.7 women.

Not all of the excess can necessarily be attributed to air pollution [the committee reported], since other factors such as climate or housing conditions, play a part, but in general it is the industrial towns liable to heavy pollution that have the highest death rates.

Carrying its statistical evidence against major industrial centers another step forward, the Committee compared death rates in communities of various size, for pneumonia, bronchitis and other respiratory diseases. The figures showed that 120 persons per 100,000 population died in cities of more than 100,000 population. In smaller cities, the death rate dropped to 95 and it sank still farther, to 78, in rural areas of England and Wales.

> Air pollution is clearly most harmful because of its action on the respiratory system [the Committee said], but it is also damaging because it obscures natural light and thus reduces resistance to infection and retards recovery from illness. . . . The psychological effects of reduced light and sunshine may be no less serious than the physical effects.

Across the channel in France, the city of Paris has had laws regulating air pollution since 1917 but this flower of cities suffers, particularly in winter, with smoke from four million chimneys, the exhaust from 1.2 million automobiles, and a moat of factories which rings the metropolis belching smoke and fumes over its 8.5 million people.

The vast complex of commerce, industry, shipping and people in and around New York City has in the past two years earned that metropolis the dubious honor of having what many term "the world's dirtiest air." In 1966 Mayor John Lindsay appointed a ten-man panel of leading citizens headed by Norman Cousins, editor of the *Saturday Review*, to make firm recommendations on ways to clean up the region's soot, dust, smoke and chemical fumes.

"We are now engaged in a race," Cousins said after a preliminary review, "to bring it [air pollution] under control before D-Day—D for disaster. It is quite possible, under certain conditions, for New York to become a gas chamber." The task force chairman said the city now is spending $500 million a year on bad air, a cost measured in cleaning bills, repairing stained and damaged buildings and decay of metal and rubber on automobiles. "The cost of clean air will be a lot less than that," Cousins said. Sanitation Commissioner Joseph F. Periconi estimated it would cost $65 million to rehabilitate the city's eleven trash and garbage incinerators, the source of a great portion of New York's foul air. Ralph H. O'Donoghue, of the Department of Air Pollution Control, set the cost at $100 million.

"And even if you clean up New York," O'Donoghue said,

"the air pollution reading won't drop by much, thanks to the polluted air we get from New Jersey and our other neighbors. There's just no way of building a barrier against polluted air." Cousins disagreed. He stated that "80 percent of the dirt and poison in our city is homemade.

"Suppose," he said, "that we have four or five days in which there is little or no wind. Suppose there is a heavy concentration of pollutants. There is a density of auto traffic, buses are spewing forth their poison into the streets, there is enlarged use of air conditioning and production of electricity with incinerators going all over the city. There would be a large layer of smoke, and that layer would be like a lid. Normal ventilation would be blocked off. If this condition were to persist for say five to seven days, the city could suffer a disaster of substantial proportions."

Cousins' prediction of disaster very nearly came true before the year was out. During a four-day period surrounding Thanksgiving Day, 1966, a stagnant air mass enveloped the Eastern Seaboard and built air pollution to critical levels over New York City and wide areas of adjacent New Jersey and Connecticut. A first stage emergency alert for the area was called by Governor Rockefeller for New York. Residents of the three states were urged to curtail consumption of heating fuel, gasoline and electricity. In New York City, Pollution Commissioner Austin N. Heller urged motorists to use their cars only when absolutely necessary. Owners of apartment houses were urged to shut down incinerators and landlords using fuel oil or coal were asked to reduce indoor temperatures to 60 degrees. By November 27 the temperature inversion changed and fresh air blew into the East, but there was no longer any doubt that air pollution disaster was a very real and immediate possibility.

Contributing to such a disaster would be fly ash and fine sand from Flushing, billowing smoke from the Consolidated Edison power plants, half-burned debris from incinerators, dust from thousands of construction and demolition sites, cement plants and women shaking dust mops out their windows. The amount of particulate matter falling out of the sky on New York City each day averages more than six hundred tons. On a winter day this includes, among other things, 36.6 tons from coal and oil used for heating, 35.4 tons from Consolidated Edison power plants, 35.5 tons from municipal incinerators, 27.4 tons from private incinerators, 21.9 tons from cars and buses, and 6.7 tons from jet planes taking off and landing at Kennedy International Airport. It is no surprise, therefore, that a pedestrian walking across midtown Manhattan feels his mouth and throat continually coated with soot, dust and minute particles of sulfur. Aaron Teller, dean of the Cooper Union School of Engineering, said in 1966 that more sulfur is entering the air from the nation's smokestacks than is being mined from the ground. He added that by 1970 methods may be available by which sulfur can be economically reclaimed from such sources.

From May 1962 until the end of 1964, a team of thirty-two physicians and researchers from Cornell University Medical College conducted a careful study of the health of 1840 families living on Manhattan's East Side while other research specialists kept a careful watch on the levels of air pollution. Among the findings, many of which still are being correlated, was the fact that people otherwise suffering no disease are disturbed physically by air pollution.

"Air pollution is not just affecting people with asthma or people who are already sick and it's not just harmful at extremely high levels," commented Dr. James McCarroll, the project director. "In other words, air pollution is affecting the health of you and me every day in New York." The U.S. Public Health Service put it this way:

"Air pollution . . . contributes significantly as a cause or aggravating factor for the following medical conditions: acute respiratory infection, chronic bronchitis, chronic constrictive respiratory diseases, pulmonary emphysema, bronchial asthma and lung cancer."

The dirty animal sends up clouds of dirt wherever he congregates in considerable numbers. In a midwestern town the city dump may be the offender, sending greasy black clouds of half-burned garbage into the sky. Planes flying out of O'Hare Airport in Chicago top out above a seven-thousand-foot-deep haze of red smoke poured out in layers by the steel and other industrial plants around the southern tip of Lake Michigan. Residents of south Baltimore find the paint on their autos corroded and pitted by the red stench welling upward from the Bethlehem Steel Company. Even the mile-high city of Denver, Colorado, noted for the sparkling clarity of its Rocky Mountain air, is not immune from the scourge of air pollution. On many days it is no longer possible to see the snow-capped peaks of the Continental Divide only twenty miles to the west. At a seminar held in Denver in 1966 by the American Institute of Physics, Dr. James P. Lodge of Colorado said cities will "do well just to stay even with pollution problems." He commented that Los Angeles was able to hold its own between 1953 and 1963 and that was "a tremendous achievement as far as pollution is concerned." Dr. Walter Orr Roberts, director of the National Center for Atmospheric Research and one of the nation's foremost students of solar phenomena, complained as he has for years that astronomers are running out of places on the earth where decent astronomical observations are possible. He has conducted studies for two decades on the top of fourteen thousand-foot Mt. Evans west of Denver and reports that air contamination, although slight at that rarified altitude, still exists around the mountain peak. Dr. Reid A. Bryson of the Wisconsin University Center for Climatic Research stated his belief that dust and jet condensation trails high in the atmosphere may have lowered temperatures and cooled Wisconsin's summers. "I do know," he said, "we'd jolly well better look at it as a possibility. Man is so industrialized, urbanized, mechanized that he has become as important as natural phenomena in the modification of weather. Every city is putting out as much particulate matter as a volcano."

As an example, Chattanooga, Tennessee, with a population of about 130,000, suffers smoke from wire salvage operations;

smoke from burning junk cars and tires; stench from a dead animal rendering plant; dust from a cement plant; odors from a food company; smoke from a brick manufacturing plant; dust from a glass company; smoke from burning wood; ammonium chloride from galvanizing operations; gases from heat treating and annealing; acids and alkalies from electroplating; fumes from a brass foundry; fluorides from an aluminum foundry; acid mist from a battery plant; ferrosilicon, chrome, manganese and tars from an electrometallurgical plant; tars from an asphalt road plant; varnish and oxides of nitrogen from a paint company; foul odors from a tannery; dust from ceramic companies, and miscellaneous burning coal and wood. All of these air contaminants exist in Chattanooga without even considering the unburned gases from trucks and automobiles.

More than one hundred specific substances are identified by public health authorities as air pollutants, but the list actually runs into thousands, including anything that can be pulverized to dust size and smaller. An example of an unusual pollutant is asbestos dust, a substance connected with fatal cancer in one-half of all people who work directly with it but not until recently considered a general air pollutant. However, Dr. Irving J. Selikoff of Mount Sinai Hospital in New York, said recently that asbestos dust may be a potential health hazard for *one-fourth* of the nation's population. He said autopsies of 1100 people in three cities showed 25 percent had asbestos lodged in the lungs. Although normally associated with fireproofing operations, asbestos makes up 50 percent of asphalt tile and is used in dental cement, brake linings, pipe of various types, plastics, beer filters, gas masks and paper. World production of asbestos is up to four million tons per year, and much of it finds its way into the atmosphere whenever millions of motorists apply their brake pedals.

The earth is covered with a layer of air weighing *5.6 billion billion tons*, an average of almost two billion tons per person, yet the part of it available to the earth-bound man, woman and child is an extremely thin layer near the ground. Space probes have determined that some traces of atmosphere exist one hundred or two hundred miles high, but according to the National Academy of Sciences,

the portion of the earth's atmosphere available to dilute air pollution is confined to a bottom layer about six miles thick.

Within this stratum [the Academy states], which includes some 70 percent of the total air mass, are the complex wind systems and other factors that establish ventilation rates and patterns. These are non-uniform in both time and space, varying seasonally, diurnally, and with such local factors as topography, weather and solar radiation.

In the urban areas where the density of pollutant sources is high, there are few data to provide understanding of dispersion and diffusion effects or to assist in planning to immunize against damaging effects. . . . Man began to add significantly to atmospheric pollution as he developed increasingly effective means of extracting energy from nature. And, in contrast to natural sources of pollution, those for which man has been responsible are localized and increasingly concentrated in small areas.

Since the gross ventilation capacity of a region cannot be increased, the result is local overburdening of the air. As sources grow in number and size, overburdening occurs more frequently and may become chronic.

Particles which remain suspended range from a dust mote 1/5000 of an inch in diameter down to gas molecules which may be less than 1/2,500,000 of an inch. An average cubic foot of air contains three million such particles and a man inhales forty thousand to seventy thousand with each breath he takes. A 9 by 12 rug will pick up ten pounds of dust, and a city dweller inhales about 1½ pounds in a year. Although the numbers are large, the amount of pollution we breathe is so small in a day that it is virtually impossible to measure the effect of that day's contamination upon human health. As authorities learned, after publication of statistics linking lung cancer with cigarette smoking, it is difficult to convince the average man or woman that damage is occurring, however gradual it may be. On the other hand, it is only the average man and woman who can bring the forces to bear which will abate and perhaps eventually halt our gravest sources of air pollution.

In 1966 the Public Health Service said that seven thousand American communities face air pollution problems, but not more than 130 city, county and district air pollution control programs are in existence.

> You have to have a public aroused enough to convince the politicians it's something they must act on [a Public Health Service official said]. These two elements, the people and the politicians, are the basis of any effective program. Without them, the best abatement technologist in the world can be completely blocked. Tough regulations mean nothing if there isn't the sentiment to support them. The most elaborate program can be nullified simply by not voting funds for it.
>
> Along the way, industry has to be persuaded. It's a major smog source. It's also a major part of the power structure in most communities. You can't compel industry to do anything—unless it's convinced that it's defying public opinion if it doesn't go along.

It is difficult to marshal indignation of the American public against bad air. Although one day may be dark and gloomy with the taste of gritty particles in the teeth, the next day may bring a clean breeze to wipe the atmosphere clean again. But if Mr. and Mrs. America are slow to be concerned about their health, they usually are quick to ward off attack upon their pocketbook. According to the Air Conservation Commission of the American Association for the Advancement of Science, air pollution costs every man, woman and child in the nation more than sixty-five dollars per year, an annual damage cost of *twelve to thirteen billion dollars.*

Air pollution dissolves clothing, particularly garments made of synthetic fabric. It corrodes metal, disintegrates stone, rots wood and discolors paint. It decomposes rubber and causes millions of housewives to launder drapes, rugs and clothing more often than would be necessary if the air were clean. Smog in more and more parts of the nation is causing immense losses of food crops and other agricultural produce. In California alone, agriculture suffers approximately $132 million in crop damage every year because of smog, including destruction of growing plants, poorer quality, slower growth and less production. Citrus experiments at Upland, California, dramatically illustrate the difference between fruit produced in filtered air and fruit struggling for life in smoggy atmosphere. The smog-handicapped trees were less vigorous with foliage tending to dusty gray instead of the deep glossy green typical of healthy citrus groves. Smog-ripened oranges tended to be pulpy with less juice and poorer flavor.

In New York State, air pollution damage is estimated at $150 million a year, with $100 million of that in New York City. In Chicago the annual bill is judged to be $50 million. One seventy-two-hour smog siege in Los Angeles built up such concentrations that a light-blue acetate garment lost 30 percent of its color. A red nylon fabric turned blue. Runs in nylon hose are caused spontaneously by sulfur dioxide spewed into the air.

A century ago, the 4- by 6-mile valley around Ducktown, Tennessee, was a lush forest area rich in wildlife. In 1847 copper was discovered there. After the Civil War, the largest copper smelter east of the Mississippi was built at Ducktown, producing ten thousand tons of the valuable metal per year. Ore and coal used in smelting, however, poured forty tons of sulfur dioxide into the air every day. By the turn of the twentieth century, the valley's trees, grass, shrubs and wildlife had been completely destroyed.

Located at Anaconda, Montana, is a complex of some of the world's largest foundries producing copper, zinc, fertilizer, manganese, lime and acids. The outpouring of sulfur dioxide from this facility has denuded huge downwind areas of vegetation and left eroded desert land. On windy days, slag piles choke the surrounding valley with dust. Despite the installation of some air-cleaning devices, the company still emits huge quantities of arsenic. Domestic animals show signs of poisoning, arsenic has shown up in milk from local dairies, horses have developed running ulcers in the nose, and 625 sheep, feeding as far as fifteen miles from the smelter, died of arsenic poisoning.

The first crop damage was discovered in California in 1942.

At Temple City, the leaves of petunias showed signs of ozone burns. The Los Angeles flower industry, once worth $14 million a year, now is down to $4 million. Orchid growing has been nearly wiped out by the smog. In 1960 a single day of smog wilted a lettuce crop worth $22,000. Tobacco crops in the East have been damaged by smog; other crops sensitive to air pollution include cotton, buckwheat, wheat, barley, oats, alfalfa, sugar beets and clover. Thousands of eastern white pines are dying of sulfur dioxide exposure near Oak Ridge, Tennessee.

The cost of sandblasting soot-stained and acid-eroded stone and masonry buildings is well known in every major city of the country, but smog causes irreparable damage in more subtle ways. New York art authorities are concerned about the deterioration of stone sculpture and monuments under the sulfuric acid attack from the air in that city. Cleopatra's Needle, the two-hundred-ton obelisk which stands in Central Park, is a prime example. The sixty-nine-foot-tall monument was erected thirty-five centuries ago by Thothmes III to glorify his reign over Egypt. The granite spire withstood the sun and sand of the Sahara for thousands of years, but since it was brought to New York in 1880, the hieroglyphics it contains have been gradually dissolving away.

"The attack of air on buildings, statues and sculpture is a serious problem," commented Joseph Nobel, administrator of the Metropolitan Museum of Art. "What goes is gone, and with art work that's particularly unfortunate. The sulfurous gases in the air form very weak sulfuric acid that coats everything in the city. It just eats away at stone, particularly limestone; marble is etched; granite is attacked, but not as much."

It is no wonder that emphysema, bronchitis and asthma cases are increasing, no wonder the crops die and stone buildings deteriorate when the quantities involved in air pollution are fully comprehended. Foreign particles added to the air over Chicago total *25,000* tons per day. In Detroit it is 4920 tons; Portland, Oregon, 873. Over the nation as a whole, pollutants added to the atmosphere total *125 million tons* each year.

Although there are thousands of substances in this devilish concoction, the main ones result from the burning of coal, oil, gasoline, and natural gas. According to the National Academy of Sciences Committee on Pollution, the chief offenders are carbon monoxide (deadly in small concentrations), oxides of sulfur, hydrocarbons, particulate matter, oxides of nitrogen, and other gases and vapors.

Carbon monoxide makes up 52 percent of the total; it spewed into the atmosphere in 1966 at the rate of 62 million tons per year. Sulfur oxides total 23 million tons; hydrocarbons, 15 million tons; particulate matter (such as soot, fly ash and cement dust), 12 million tons; and nitric oxides, 8 million tons. Other gases and vapors account for about 2 million tons per year.

Where does it come from? According to the Academy study, 18.7 percent—23.4 million tons per year—are emissions from industrial establishments, principally particulate matter and a wide variety of chemicals. The generation of electricity, burning coal and oil, adds 15.7 million tons of air pollution (12.5 percent of the 125 million ton total). The power contribution to our dirty air consists chiefly of sulfur oxides. (Coal, no matter how you burn it, contains from 1 to 6 percent sulfur. Oil is burned somewhat more efficiently and has a lesser sulfur content. Natural gas, where it is available for power generation, offers the greatest burning efficiency and consequently the lowest per unit air pollution.) Heating of homes and other buildings throughout the nation dumps 7.8 million tons per year of soot and other pollutants into the atmosphere. Burning garbage and trash adds another 3.3 million tons. The greatest culprits of all—and this will be treated at greater length in subsequent chapters—are the truck and automobile. They are responsible for 59.9 percent of the nation's filthy atmosphere, 74.8 million tons per year, and virtually all of the carbon monoxide, oxides of nitrogen and hydrocarbons.

Aside from the obvious and increasing damage which our dark and dirty skies are causing to man and his works, these fantastic tonnages of minute particles and molecules represent a complete loss and waste. Due to the careless way in which we use nature's bounty, 125 million tons of carbon fuels, extracted from the earth at great labor and expense, are thrown away each year by our inefficient engines and power boilers. Even if the natural resources of the world were unlimited, which they are not, it does not seem possible that a nation could long tolerate such waste.

The growing and chronic smudge in our skies is apparent when it harms our plants or stings our eyes, but not so apparent is the long-term impact of a by-product of burning carbon fuels not normally considered an air pollutant at all—*carbon dioxide*. CO_2 is a normal constituent of our natural atmosphere in small quantities, normally about three hundred parts per million parts of air. Carbon dioxide is one of the substances by which nature has traditionally maintained the balance between plants and animals on the earth. One acre of beech forest, for example, removes about 2000 pounds of CO_2 from the air each year and returns some 1500 pounds of oxygen. In a year's time, living plants of the world consume 550 billion tons of carbon dioxide and return 400 billion tons of oxygen.

> Throughout most of the half-million years of man's existence on earth [reported the President's Science Advisory Committee late in 1965], his fuels consisted of wood and other remains of plants which had grown only a few years before they were burned. The effect of this burning on the content of atmospheric carbon dioxide was negligible, because it only slightly speeded up the natural decay processes that continually recycled carbon from the biosphere to the atmosphere.
>
> During the last few centuries, however, man has begun to burn the fossil fuels that were locked in the sedimentary rocks over 500 million years, and this combination is measurably increasing the atmospheric carbon dioxide.

The carbon dioxide study for the Science Advisory Committee was conducted by a committee headed by Roger Revelle, director of the Harvard University Center for Population Studies. The group's figures show that in the century between 1860 and 1960, the world had mined and used more than 85 billion tons of coal, 16.6 billion tons of lignite, 16.3

billion tons of petroleum and natural gasoline, and 4.4 billion tons of natural gas. More than *122 billion tons* of carbon fuels thus have been burned in one hundred years, and *more than half of that total has been consumed since 1920.*

It is immediately apparent, then, that our exploding population with its consequent explosion in industrial growth and power generation is burdening our air with staggering volumes of new carbon dioxide. During the twelve years from 1950 to 1962, according to the Revelle committee, 58 billion tons of CO_2 were produced from the combustion of carbon fuels around the world. At the present time, *6 billion tons* of carbon dioxide are being produced by men each year. By the year 2000, our atmosphere will contain 25 percent more of this gas than at present.

Although a great deal of CO_2 is consumed by interchange with the ocean's surfaces and through the metabolism of living plants, man's artificial production of this gas is overwhelming the delicate balance established and held by nature through countless centuries. The result may be a drastic change in the entire earth's atmosphere with disastrous consequences for the dirty animal who has brought the condition upon himself.

Carbon dioxide serves the same function for the surface of the earth as the glass in a greenhouse: the sun's heat waves radiate down through it but are prevented from radiating back out into space again. If no carbon dioxide existed, for example, it is estimated that the average temperature of the world would be 10 to 18 degrees colder. This would be sufficient to discourage animal life in most areas and would lead probably to an ice age of glaciers over much of the northern and southern latitudes. Conversely, if carbon dioxide continues to increase at its present and predicted rates, the temperature of the earth could increase by as much as 7 degrees by the year 2000. Such an increase could cause entirely new balancing arrangements involving water vapor in the atmosphere. Violent storms and climatic changes would result, but the most catastrophic action could be *melting of the polar icecaps.* This, of course, would not happen overnight, but the Revelle committee finds that a 2 percent over-all change in the earth-wide heat radiation balance could occur by the year 2000.

The level of the oceans, under such conditions, could rise as much as a foot per year for four hundred years, flooding out every seaport and coastal city now in existence.

It is apparent then that man has a simple choice: either reduce the rate of consumption of fossil fuels, or find a realistic way to halt the emission of the gaseous and particulate by-products into the atmosphere.

A Break in the Cloud

When the low and leaden sky
presses down like a lid . . .
It brings a black day
sadder than night.

Baudelaire

FOR ELEVEN YEARS THE 1150 RESIDENTS OF SELBYVILLE, DELA-
ware, endured possibly the foulest air in the United States.

It began when the Bishop Processing Company set up
operations only a whiff away from town, but significantly,
across the state line in Maryland. Bishop's business was the
collection of dead chickens, a "by-product" of the mass production poultry and egg business, and conversion of the dead
birds to livestock feed and fertilizer. Out of the steaming
caldrons of the ramshackle facility arose such a damp, miasmic,
daily cloud reeking of rotten flesh that the nearby townspeople found it virtually intolerable.

The residents of Selbyville could do nothing about it because the processing company lay across the Delaware line beyond the jurisdiction of town, county or Delaware authorities.

"In the spring, summer and fall when you open the windows, the odors start coming in," Asher B. Carey said with a sigh. Carey, a dentist and Selbyville's mayor, was frustrated in his inability to throttle the stink which had kept his town from growing for a decade while the rest of the state of Delaware grew by 40 percent.

"The house gets full of this stench," complained Glenda J. Long, another resident of the town, "and you just can't get rid of it."

Late in 1965, inspectors from the U.S. Public Health Service came in to sniff the Selbyville stench. One inspector was so overcome that he vomited on the spot. In January 1966, John W. Gardner, Secretary of Health, Education, and Welfare, signed an order directing Bishop to deodorize its plant. The company was told firmly to "abate the emission of sickening, nauseating and highly offensive odors," and was given a timetable for installing the proper deodorizing equipment. If it failed to comply, the company could be taken to Federal court.

Although Selbyville's problem was small on the scale of metropolitan air pollution, the case was a landmark in the long and generally ineffectual history of governmental efforts to control noxious emissions into the atmosphere. It was the first action taken under the federal Clean Air Act as amended in 1965, which authorizes the Public Health Service to intervene in air pollution situations without the request of local or state governments. More significantly, the Clean Air Act is a step toward *regional* control under federal coordination to regulate dirty air, which has no respect for city, county or state borders. Until recent years, the abatement of smoke nuisances had been attempted in America, England and Europe through a set of generally toothless laws, backed up by such inadequate funds, enforcement personnel, and halfhearted penalties that a large industry could generally ignore the rules. It was particularly difficult, if not impossible, for a community such as

New York City to take any action against the wilderness of heavy industry in New Jersey which sends its sifting of smoke, dust and chemical mists over its neighboring metropolis. Under the Clean Air Act, tools finally are available by which federal pressure can be brought to bear to clean up entire stagnant air basins, which in many cases encompass parts of several states, just as new federal laws provide for sewage abatement in the nation's major watersheds.

Federal laws and enforcement may be the true break in the clouds of atmospheric contamination. They have come in America after a century of effort by a few scattered communities to do something about their own smog. A number of cities have really tried.

St. Louis, Missouri, in the mid-nineteenth century passed an ordinance regulating the height of chimneys, and the first smoke case on record in any U.S. court occurred there in 1864 when a man named Whalen was awarded fifty dollars in damages by a judge who declared smoke to be a nuisance. Through subsequent years the industrial and power complex continued to grow in the St. Louis metropolitan area. Despite some meager attempts to control the major sources of coal smoke and industrial fumes, the pall over St. Louis continued to grow and spread over an entire region on both sides of the Mississippi River in Missouri and Illinois.

It was not until the mid-1940s that the smudge over St. Louis became too much to bear. Then, in a relatively few years, the city enforced the nation's first successful air pollution control program. The burning of coal was virtually eliminated from all major fixed sources, such as industry and electric power plants, and the sky was cleared of most of its soot. St. Louis soon found, however, that coal is not the only culprit. Fuel oil and gas are cleaner, but automobile traffic was increasing along with industrial emissions, and the St. Louis smog rebuilt in almost direct ratio to its economic and population growth.

In 1962 the city was still getting along with only a ten-man pollution control department operating on a minimum budget, but that year marked the beginning of a $200 million redevelopment of the downtown area. Local leaders, worried that industrial pollution would discourage commerce from moving downtown and finally facing the true monetary loss that smog could cause, called upon the Public Health Service for help. John Sadler, a USPHS engineer, was sent to St. Louis and given a sixty-thousand-dollar budget to do a job.

The job, first of all, required a survey of air contamination over the metropolitan area of two million people, then the formation of laws to fit the 150 seperate communities in the area. If he had been left to his own devices, or had met with active resistance, which is the usual pattern, it is likely Sadler could have accomplished nothing, but for once the people of St. Louis were ready to act. A public relations program was launched including press conferences, television shows, speeches, displays at schools and clubs, letters to residents, an annual Clean Air Week, and even a beauty contest to select Miss Clean Air. Behind this essential press agentry, ten local governmental agencies and civic organizations moved in to cosponsor the study. Three universities—St. Louis, Washington and Southern Illinois—began air pollution research. Garden clubs printed and distributed literature. Local citizens sampled air in their back yards or did clerical work. The $60,000 starting fund grew to $750,000, of which at least a third was acquired through public donations. Friendly persuasion became civic enterprise involving all the people of the metropolitan area, and that massive democratic force was the push needed to prove to politicians they must act and demonstrate to industry that it could not fail to act. Today St. Louis remains a bright example of how scores of small governmental units can be welded together for a regional attack against the smoky cloud in the sky.

Thirty years ago it was impossible to hang out the family wash in Pittsburgh, Pennsylvania, without the certainty that it would be black with soot before it could dry. Now it is possible in that metropolis, once known for good reason as the Smoky City, to wear a white dress from morning till night and come home almost spotless. The skyscrapers are relatively clean. People who have grown up since 1940 do not consider it exceptional when they can see the sky on a clear day. The difference did not come easy. It involved the expenditure of millions of dollars and a titanic struggle between the public welfare and the special interests of steel, coal and rails, the kings of this eastern industrial center. For more than half a century these industry and transportation giants, centered at the junction of the Allegheny and Monongahela Rivers, had wielded the power of Pittsburgh, justifying the perpetual pall of smoke by the fact that prosperity depended upon their operations. For more than thirty years it has been and continues to be a bitter, emotionally charged battle to keep the atmosphere pure enough to breathe and clean enough to see through.

The first step in the renovation of Pittsburgh came early in this century when the Mellon Institute, philanthropic arm of the powerful Mellon banking interests, made a comprehensive investigation of the damage caused by smoke in the city. The report showed that the cost to residents, at that time, amounted to fifteen to twenty dollars per person per year in the waste of fuel; extra cost of laundry and cleaning; damage to clothing, furnishings and buildings; damage to merchandise in stores; cost of extra artificial lighting on the murkiest days; and cleaning and refurbishment of civic structures. Men of vision and determination foresaw that Pittsburgh could soon choke itself to death on the smoke and fumes belching from factories, steel mills and locomotive smoke stacks.

Leading executives, including representatives from the steel industry itself, finally sparked action by forming the Allegheny Conference on Community Development, and by 1942, 142 men and women from seventy-one civic organizations formed the United Smoke Council. With World War II in progress, this group shrewdly attacked the smoke pall on the patriotic grounds that control was essential to save fuel needed for war production. The next year an anti-smoke ordinance was passed, providing that before the end of the year all private homes were to burn only smokeless coal, stoker-fed to furnaces for maximum burning efficiency. The effective date later was postponed to March 1945, partly because of opposition from soft-coal interests and partly because in wartime there was not enough of the proper furnace equipment to supply the need.

In the intervening years, however, the Allegheny Conference and United Smoke Council joined forces and carried forth a persistent public information program. In 1945, also, David L. Lawrence, a well-to-do industrialist, campaigned for and won election as mayor, principally on a smoke control campaign. A key factor in his victory was a fact sheet listing the cost of atmospheric pollution. It showed that in 1945 Pittsburgh led the nation in deaths from pneumonia and that forty industrial firms had decided to leave the city because of smoke, smog, impure air and other pollution. A department store estimated that on one winter day smog soiled merchandise and home furnishings so seriously that the loss in cleaning bills and markdowns was $25,000. In spite of these impressive facts, the coal industry and the railroads continued to oppose clean air on economic grounds. The Pennsylvania Railroad, one of the prime recalcitrants, not only hauled but burned coal. Logically, it feared the loss of freight tonnage and the cost of converting coal-burning locomotives to diesel. Unions involved in soft-coal production were enlisted by the clean air opposition on grounds that thousands of coal miners would be thrown out of work.

In 1946, the Allegheny Conference was joined by the League of Women Voters and Pittsburgh Chamber of Commerce to extend the air pollution control efforts to all of Allegheny County. Smog, they had learned, does not respect neighborhood or city boundaries. The entire issue came to a head in 1947 when legislation to permit county-wide pollution control reached a stalemate in the Pennsylvania General Assembly. The law finally passed only after Richard Mellon, most powerful of the city's financial leaders, persuaded the Pennsylvania Railroad to change its position.

Results of previous efforts already were showing up by this time. Visibility in downtown Pittsburgh had improved 67 percent. Under the new ordinance, factories, homes, steamboats and locomotives were required to burn smokeless fuels or install smoke-consuming devices. Riverboats converted to diesel burners. Apartment houses, churches, hotels and office buildings converted to gas fuel. Private homes, however, were exempted for one more year, chiefly because of persisting pressure from the soft-coal interests and associated unions.

Some foot-dragging continued, but the ball was rolling now. By 1952, industry, public utilities, railroads and municipalities in Allegheny County were cooperating in a $200 million air pollution control program. In that year, it was estimated $25 million was saved in Pittsburgh through reduced cleaning bills alone. Visibility had improved 77 percent since 1945. Operators of the 132 open-hearth steel furnaces in the area found new ways to limit smoke, fly ash and dust.

The war in Pittsburgh is not over. Sulfur contaminants, cancer-causing substances and other airborne health hazards are just coming under serious study because removal of the grosser contamination has revealed the insidious growth of other pollution from millions of homes and motor vehicles. The important lesson from Pittsburgh, however, is that a quarter century of unrelenting work was required just to improve the region's atmosphere by a *significant percentage*. If that margin of gain is to be maintained, or improved, it will require perpetual vigilance, struggle and expenditures of money. It is becoming increasingly evident that America's air, as with its water, can never be returned to the sparkling clarity it once possessed. Men at work making the substances and things to satisfy other men will always raise smoke and dust. The best we can hope for is a halt to the explosive increase in pollution and possibly a percentage improvement.

Most authorities recognize that Pittsburgh is a rare exception and a model. Most cities, and their surrounding suburban areas, still do not recognize that they have a situation severe enough to require new laws and action.

Chicago, the nation's second largest metropolis, did not see the light until 1963, but when it did, the city tackled its air problems with surprising vigor. In September that year a Congressional committee, investigating sources of air and water pollution, visited Chicago and found entire neighborhoods of the city's four million residents engulfed in smoke. The health of thousands was obviously endangered, principally by the smudge from steel companies and oil refineries around the Calumet community. In 1963 pollution laws were passed and James V. Fitzpatrick was named director of the Chicago Department of Air Pollution Control. In the first year, Fitzpatrick's department held 2796 hearings, filed 563 pollution abatement suits, handled 4958 smoke complaints and inspected nearly 50,000 furnaces. In addition, twenty rooftop monitoring stations were established to measure aerial contamination.

One objective in Chicago now is to outlaw, by 1968, all improper burning of combustible refuse. This will strike hard at some thirty thousand apartment-house operators who now shovel trash and garbage into coal-fired furnaces, an inefficient process which simply transfers much of the refuse from the land into the air. Chicago's cleanup efforts were assisted by a $357,000 federal grant for research to back up enforcement. The state of Illinois has established an Air Pollution Control Board and the U.S. Health, Education, and Welfare Department is pushing cooperative efforts between Illinois and Indiana. In 1965 a major breakthrough occurred when four major steel producers agreed to spend fifty million dollars by 1972 for equipment to eliminate virtually all their contribution to air and water pollution. All four companies are in the Calumet district and together account for 90 percent of Chicago's steel production. Fitzpatrick estimates these companies have been releasing sixty-thousand tons of pollutants per year, or approximately 40 percent of Chicago's dust fall. It may be five or ten years before Chicago's air is appreciably cleaner, because blue skies do not return overnight, but momentum is building in the right direction.

Down in the Gulf of Mexico, where the old battleship *Texas* sits in an artificial lagoon at rest with history, the famed San Jacinto monument raises its Lone Star crest a few feet higher in the sky than the Washington monument. On many days the star is invisible in clouds of black smoke which boil up from oil refineries and plumes of flame where natural gas is burned off. Only twenty miles away lies the city of Houston, host to the nation's Manned Spacecraft Center and described in a recent Columbia University economic study as "the outstanding boom city in the United States." Now populated by more than one million people, Houston is growing faster than any other American metropolis, but it appears to have its air pollution problems fairly well controlled through judicious application of common-law nuisance provisions. Dr. W. A. Quebedeaux, Jr., director of the Health Department of Harris County, where Houston is located, filed the first air pollution lawsuit in 1956. This resulted in a court order directing that each offending industrial plant must present a time schedule for dealing with the air contamination it causes. Dr. Quebedeaux feels his way of dealing with atmospheric pollution is better than enactment of a strict control code.

"I'm better off without having specified standards," he said. "My standard is the way it affects the neighbors. That way you don't involve yourself in a smoke screen of a highly scientific nature." Dr. Quebedeaux believes that air pollution in his county is becoming less each year and said that as new plants are built or old ones improved, control devices are being built into them.

A different view of standards was taken by Palm Beach Shores, Florida, in September 1964 when the city council of that community passed the toughest air pollution control law in the United States. The ordinance is simple. It charges polluters twenty dollars a ton for the smoke and chemicals they allow to escape into the atmosphere. True, the Florida town has only about one thousand population and very few industries. The only time the ordinance was used in three years was against a motel with a smoky furnace. Before the first fine was due the motel repaired the furnace and peace returned to the town's sunny shores. But this small community has offered leadership in showing how the public good can be served when the punishment is proportionate to the crime.

Across the nation, more individual communities are sniffing the corruption in their air and stirring uneasily before the unpleasant necessity to take action which involves money, time, labor and struggle. These include New York City, which in 1965 was befouled with an estimated monthly sootfall of sixty tons for every square mile. "The air over our city is helping our citizens to shuffle off this planet at a much higher rate than they would ordinarily go," commented Arthur J. Benline, at that time Commissioner of Air Pollution Control, "yet there has not been any overall demand from the public to clean up our dirty air."

Less than a year later, under the vigorous new administration of Mayor John Lindsay, New York and its people began stating their demands loud and clear. Even before the administration change, the New York City Council in October 1965 sounded the war cry by asking for a ban on the use of bituminous coal for all heating, home or factory, within two years. Under the proposed bill the use of coal and oil also would be controlled for other purposes including power generation. Flue-fed incinerators would be barred in apartment buildings. All city garbage incinerators would be modernized within a year and the Consolidated Edison Company, source of New York's power, would be barred from burning coal unless 99 percent burning efficiency could be achieved. Fines up to one thousand dollars were proposed against offenders. It was pointed out that *eight million tons* of sulfur-rich soft coal are burned annually in New York City, including *seven million tons* for power generation. The proposed new regulations could cost Consolidated Edison ten million dollars in new equipment and smog-arresting gear. The New York ordinance also would not permit coal to be sold in the city if it contained more than 1 percent of sulfur. Adoption of the bill, a councilman said, would result in reducing soot by 25 percent in three years and lethal sulfur dioxide by 80 percent in nine years.

"With growing air pollution hazards from increased fuel consumption by Consolidated Edison and property owners and inefficient private and public incineration," he said, "the situation is bound to get worse."

Through the winter of 1965 and into the early spring of 1966, the debate raged back and forth with industry. Utilities and apartment-house owners argued that the new regulations would put them out of business. In March Mayor Lindsay endorsed the council bill. "If the same methods that have been used in the past for providing electricity or burning garbage or heating buildings are going to be used in the future," he said, "we won't be able to build enough hospitals to take care of the people suffering from respiratory illnesses."

The mayor's task force, headed by Norman Cousins, urged the city to install monitoring devices on every smokestack in the city, with five-thousand-dollar fines per day for offenders. Vernon G. MacKenzie of the U.S. Public Health Service said such devices are available. Consolidated Edison reported it had never heard of them. Otto W. Manz, executive vice president, said the utility could not meet a two-year time schedule for 99 percent smoke-arresting efficiency unless the company were permitted to build a new hydroelectric plant at Cornwall on the Hudson River. (This plant earlier had been blocked by conservationists who claimed the facility would damage the Hudson River scenery. Con Ed's previous efforts to obtain approval for a nuclear power generation facility also had been blocked by public opinion.) Representatives from the National Coal Policy Conference argued that medical data indicates it is not necessary to require a sulfur content of 1 percent or less in coal, but they also admitted that 52 million tons of low-sulfur coal is shipped abroad each year.

The city countered resistance by claiming that the changes required for Consolidated Edison to comply with the proposed new code could cost no more than $1.30 per customer per year for proper coal and $0.75 for fuel oil. The delays in air pollution control, a council committee said, were "primarily caused by unfounded fears, lethargy and reluctance of prosperous industrial giants to apply their great technical ingenuity to this area of public interest." It was proposed also that twelve new pollution-control inspectors be added to the air pollution control department, which then contained only 36 inspectors to cover a 320-square-mile area. The council committee pointed out that New York was spending just 16 cents per capita for pollution control, compared with 51 cents in Los Angeles and 31 cents in Chicago.

While the new air contamination legislation was still under debate, Consolidated Edison welcomed the opportunity to use it as a lever to obtain public approval of its Cornwall hydro-electric plant.

> This plant [Con Ed spokesmen said] will make an important contribution to reducing air pollution. It will allow us to retire a large amount of our older fuel-burning equipment in the city and permit more efficient operation of existing plants equipped with the most modern air pollution control equipment.
>
> It will also enable us to use more power from outside the city to meet heavy daytime demands. All of these steps will not only result in improved air-pollution control, but also will contribute to more efficient generation of power for the entire New York–Westchester area.

By mid-1966, New York had its new smog ordinance. It was not as tough as some wanted and too tough for others. The new regulations limit the use of soft coal, make a start on eliminating trash incineration (covering only new buildings) and provide for the gradual elimination of low-grade coal and fuel oil with high sulfur residues. Public health experts said the New York law fell short of being the "toughest in the country," but it shows a new and vigorous resolution to do something. Federal officials commented that it also should have some psychological "rub-off" among the "seven thousand or so" other communities in the nation now facing air pollution problems.

In July 1966, the city appointed Austin N. Heller as its

new Commissioner of Air Pollution Control. As an official of the Public Health Service, Heller had been instrumental in starting Chicago on its way to cleaner air. He announced that he would draw upon the newest automated equipment, both in information collection and computer analysis, to help New York City clear away the smoke. Heller listed plans to establish thirty-four monitoring stations across the city to transmit data into a central computer. The result would be a continually up-to-date "air quality profile" which would permit Heller's department to make twenty-four- and forty-eight-hour predictions of atmospheric purity. "We need to know a lot more than we do now about air quality," Heller said. "Once we get a handle on that, we'll be in a position to determine priority of action." He added that he hoped to have the monitoring system within operation by the end of 1967.

As New York City struggled with its problem, Governor Nelson Rockefeller took a statewide approach. He appointed Dr. Edward Teller (known as the father of the H-bomb and head of the Atomic Energy Commission's Livermore Radiation Laboratories) to head up a committee of distinguished scientists to find new answers for control of dirty air.

The Governor proposed a series of immediate steps to ease the growing problem: (1) strong enforcement of existing standards; (2) tax incentives for abatement of air pollution by industry; (3) maximum use of federal funds for abatement programs, and (4) state aid to communities for planning modern municipal refuse disposal systems.

New York City thus has joined the fight at the municipal level. New York State has attacked at the state level. The next step is regional, and in February 1966 the U.S. Department of Health, Education, and Welfare began discussions to develop binding recommendations to reduce air contamination in a joint effort between New York and New Jersey. The action followed a joint request from Governor Rockefeller and Governor Richard J. Hughes of New Jersey for federal assistance. Two months later, in the first decision of its kind, a superior court judge in New Brunswick, New Jersey, ordered a company to discontinue daytime operation of an iron oxide plant until it stopped violating antipollution laws, Judge David D. Furman gave Stabilized Pigments, Inc., six weeks to install a system to reduce aerial emission of sulfur dioxide. The company installed a sulfuric acid facility which traps the pollutants and turns them back into useful products. New Jersey has a long history of air pollution laws, but an equally notorious record of little but wrist slapping where violators were concerned.

That state's position in the nation's air pollution pattern is unique. With its upper end nestled against the New York City complex to the east and Pennsylvania to the west, New Jersey is the most densely populated of all the states in the union. More than half of its six million people live in the northeastern clump of counties—Bergen, Essex, Hudson, Union and Passaic—and the same region contains two-thirds of the state's fifteen thousand factories. A glance at a map shows quite clearly how the mammoth metropolitan complex of New York City, including Newark and Jersey City, is blanketed with New Jersey's aerial filth by prevailing westerly winds.

"The people of New Jersey are very nice," the New York commissioner of health commented in 1966, "but they're not doing anything about air pollution. As much as 30 percent of the pollutants over New York come from Jersey."

The most obvious question is why New Jersey's people would wait for pressure from outside their state before tackling the air pollution problem. The answer, greatly oversimplified, is that most of the people in the area are employed by the oil refineries, industries and utilities which form the economic base of the region. New Jersey has had an air pollution control code since the legislature acted in September 1954. A commission, charged with the rule-making function, was appointed and took office in February 1955. Since then, it appears, nothing substantial has occurred to appreciably reduce the contamination of the New Jersey atmosphere. The Public Health Service believes the major reason is that five members of the nine-man commission are from industry. In other words, the majority of the commissioners represent the interests which are responsible for most of the pollution.

The State Health Department, responsible for enforcement of the code, reports that since the law was passed an average of two thousand violations have been noted per year. A violation, however, is defined as "an observation or complaint of illegal activity." The maximum penalty, in turn, is referral of a case to the Attorney General, who gives a final warning and then can file a *civil* lawsuit against the offender.

Five cases were referred to the attorney general in 1965. None went to court.

"We're proud of what we're doing," commented William Munroe, chief of the New Jersey Air Sanitation program. "We consider ourselves pioneers." Then he announced a new survey of pollution levels, similar to several studies which had been completed by the Public Health Service 10 years before. State Health Commissioner Roscoe Kandle said: "We need to know the basis of air pollution before we can really begin to fight the problem."

At the very moment he spoke in 1966, a passenger on any Pennsylvania Railroad train, making its final clattery approach on the run from Trenton into Manhattan, could stare idly out the window at plumes of black, brown and tan smoke from power plants; yellow and purple smoke from chemical plants; palls of tan and white smoke from meadowland fires; black greasy smudges from city dumps, incinerators and oil refineries; and black smog from diesel trucks. To the average resident and commuter, it was difficult to see how another study, another survey, could more clearly point the way to better air.

In January 1967 New York and New Jersey, during another conference on what to do about air pollution, heard U.S. experts describe the metropolitan area again as one of the most seriously polluted places in the nation, particularly in the production of sulfur dioxide and carbon monoxide. Amidst name calling and repetition of previously known information, a few concrete suggestions arose to ameliorate New York's smudgy air. Mayor Lindsay asked Consolidated Edison to submit a plan immediately to cut sulfuric air pollution by 30 percent. Austin Heller suggested that Con Ed could provide heating services to municipal buildings, thus eliminating a great quantity of coal and oil burning. Heller also urged the federal government to define and set realistic pollution standards so that adequate regulations could be built around them. While the talk continued, two excellent examples of how to start fighting the problem were near at hand.

For years Staten Islanders suffered under a smudge of chemical smoke wafting over from the U.S. Metals Refining Co. on the Jersey side. This firm is only one among a forest of industrial smokestacks, but in 1966, U.S. Metals spent $500,000 to install a baghouse. The baghouse contains seven thousand twenty-foot-long fiber glass tubes through which the metal-laden smoke filters before it is released to the atmosphere. The tubes are cleaned periodically by a large machine resembling a vacuum cleaner and the collected dust is packed in paper bags. An estimated 99.5 percent of the dust from the refinery's copper-smelting operation is cleaned from the smoke. The collected dust is taken to England and sold for the highly valuable raw metal and chemicals it contains. The company is reluctant to say whether or not the baghouse is paying for itself, but the National Academy of Sciences reports that such an operation, rather than causing an extra burden of cost by air pollution abatement, may indeed *show a profit.*

Not far away, at Portland, Pennsylvania, the Monsanto Company joined forces with two utility companies to conduct a promising experiment to remove sulfur dioxide from coal-fired stack gases and convert it to sulfuric acid at a profit. Sulfur dioxide, as has been shown, is the primary culprit in critical smog situations such as those which occurred in London and Donora, Pennsylvania. (In New York City the average sulfur dioxide level is .24 of a part per million of air, and levels up to 3.4 ppm have been recorded. A level of

5 ppm sustained for an eight-hour period may be fatal in certain circumstances.) At Portland, the Metropolitan Edison Co., Pennsylvania Electric Co. and Monsanto conducted ten years of research on the problem of removing sulfur dioxide from the smoke emitted by large-scale coal-burning for electric power generation. "We're interested in keeping our own air clean," a Pennsylvania official commented, "but we're also in a coal-mining region and we want to make it possible for utilities in cities to keep using coal without emitting sulfur dioxide. Our future depends on the growth of this area."

The smoke from power plant boilers at Portland first is filtered so that 99.5 percent of the fly ash and soot is removed. Then the gases are passed through a vanadium pentoxide converter, which oxidizes the gas and mixes it with water vapor to form the acid. The installations began by handling only 5 percent of the plant's exhaust gases. This produced six tons of acid per day. The sulfuric acid then was readily salable for use in various industrial processes and the manufacture of phosphate fertilizers. Many authorities believe the sulfuric acid process not only will clean up the pollution from utility smokestacks, but also will be profitable in the recovery of valuable resources. It was estimated that Consolidated Edison, blamed for half of the sulfur dioxide in New York City's air, could use this process and add a ten-million-dollar sulfuric acid operation to its business of making electric power.

Obviously, such equipment cannot be installed on all the nation's coal-burning smokestacks overnight, or even in the next five years. Yet it is only through this type of straightforward, visionary research that we can reduce our air contamination. As American ingenuity has demonstrated thousands of times in the past, it may result finally that the conservation of resources will be far more profitable than throwing our coal and chemicals indiscriminately into the sky. Above all, more and more studies demonstrate that whatever methods and techniques are used, they must be drastic enough not only to reduce the air contamination which exists today but also that which will come through the natural growth of population and industry in the future.

One region which has lent itself to fairly simple definitions and thus may become a model for the nation as a whole is PennJerDel, an area including eleven counties on both sides of the Delaware River from Trenton, New Jersey, to Wilmington, Delaware. It contains the metropolitan centers of Trenton, Wilmington, Philadelphia (Pennsylvania) and Camden (New Jersey). The region fits together logically as a "controllable" package because its topography falls largely within the Delaware River watershed; the prevailing wind system carries air pollutants from south-southwest to north-northeast along the axis of the valley; it includes urban, suburban and rural areas, and it has a broadly based industrial sector in which there is a high degree of interdependence among the various firms.

According to the National Academy of Sciences study of the PennJerDel region in 1966, these eleven counties are expected to contain seven million people by 1985 with 80 percent of them living in a ten-mile belt on each side of the Delaware River. In 1960, the population density in this belt was 5500 per square mile, which compares with 6200 in Chicago and 4800 in Detroit. Although the Delaware River Basin Commission, established in 1961, offers the rudiments of regional planning, the eleven counties contain three major metropolitan areas (considering Philadelphia and Camden as one), 377 separate municipalities and more than four thousand civic organizations. Realistic attempts to control water, land and air pollution in this region must cope with the infinitely complex task of welding all these diverse communities, clubs and political units into a semblance of single-purpose motivation.

In order to support the anticipated increase in population during the next 20 years [the Academy of Sciences reported], the industrial sector must expand to provide jobs for about 650,000 additional workers—a one-third increase over the 1960 employment of 1.9 million.

When one looks for factors that may limit the projected growth, the question that confronts the PennJerDel region, as well as the nation, may not be one of space or an adequate labor pool but rather one of the availability of good water or of reasonably clean air.

As an example of PennJerDel's formidable job in just catching up with the contamination that has been allowed to exist, the President's Science Advisory Committee reported that in 1959, Philadelphia's daily dose of air poisons included 830 tons of sulfur dioxide, 300 tons of nitrogen oxide, 1350 tons of hydrocarbons and 470 tons of particulate matter (dust and soot). The city has some degree of temperature inversion two hundred days a year and severe conditions one hundred days a year. Within a fifteen-mile radius of Philadelphia, the Committee wrote, the fallout of particles averages seven thousand tons per month. In southern New Jersey, vegetable and fruit basket for much of the Northeast, thirty-six different species of plants were shown to be injured by pollutants wafting over from the Philadelphia area. "Two points are illustrated," the Advisory Committee said. "First, the rates of pollution are increasing more rapidly than the population. Second, pollution probably can be handled in such areas only by such interstate cooperation as airshed and river-basin compacts."

As one measure of what the PennJerDel area may expect in the future, the Academy of Sciences study extrapolated the air loadings to be expected from the electric power industry. Without controls, the study shows, the sulfur dioxide pollution would jump from 300,000 tons per year at present to more than one million tons in the year 2000. *With* controls, the sulfur dioxide loading would decrease gradually to about 200,000 tons per year in the same period. The cost of control installations, the Academy estimates, would amount to about fifteen million dollars in 1970 and grow to a cumulative total of one billion dollars by the turn of the century. These money figures do not take into account the offsetting revenues, or even profits, which might accrue if truly economic methods are found for trapping and using the stack gases, as is now being demonstrated at Portland, Pennsylvania.

Great Britain, following the London disaster of 1952, recognized that a century of smoke control laws had failed to keep pace with the growth of air pollution and moved immediately into a new surge of action—immediately in the sense of beginning a job which obviously would require years before results would be visible. In July 1953, the Minister of Housing along with the Minister of Fuel and Power and the Secretary of State for Scotland appointed a committee "to examine the nature, causes and effects of air pollution and the efficacy of present preventive measures; to consider what further preventive measures are practicable, and to make recommendations."

The committee, in its interim report six months later, re-stressed what had been painfully obvious for many years: that the primary task was to control pollution arising from the combustion of fuels. This problem, the group pointed out, was particularly acute in the "black" areas of England and Scotland—the major industrial centers of Birmingham, Bristol, Edinburgh, Glasgow, London, Manchester, Newcastle and Sheffield—where heavy concentrations of smoke coincided with frequent days of heavy fog. The committee also found that approximately half of Great Britain's air pollution originated with industry, the other half from some twelve million homes and apartments where coal was burned almost exclusively for heating purposes. The industrial contribution, the committee said, could be greatly ameliorated by greater fuel-burning efficiencies, but the domestic situation imposed an entirely different set of factors. In the first place, virtually all homes were equipped with grates suitable only for burning soft coal, and even if these could be converted without millions of cases of financial hardship, the country did not contain adequate smokeless fuels to stoke them.

In its final report in November 1954, the British Committee on Air Pollution pointed out that more than 172 million tons of solid fuels are burned in the country each year, along with 9 million tons of liquid fuels and 202 billion cubic feet of gas. The resulting pollution was estimated at 2 million tons of smoke, 800,000 tons of grit and dust, and 5.2 million tons of sulfur dioxide. The committee recommended a broad set of changes which included penalties for failing to abate pollution along with incentives for installing equipment which would ease the problem. The committee's work led to action in Parliament and the Clean Air Act of 1956.

Under this code, local authorities are empowered to force reductions in industrial emissions and to establish smoke control areas in which all homes are prohibited from emitting smoke. Failure to comply with the law can bring a fine of £10 ($28) for the first offense and half that amount each day the offense continues. On the other hand, the law is flexible in allowing reasonable periods of time for an industry or homeowner to get in line. It also allows an industry which installs smoke- and dust-arresting equipment, to write off the cost against that year's taxes. In the case of homeowners, the government is willing to pay 70 percent of the cost of converting coal-burning equipment to grates which will accommodate smokeless fuels. The combination of penalties with financial incentives helps to hasten compliance without working a hardship upon either companies or individuals.

In 1958, the Ministry of Housing and Local Government surveyed 555 industrial boilers in the Lancashire area and found that "the installation of economisers and mechanical stokers should raise the efficiency of burning to at least 75 percent of the calorific value of the coal—a figure much higher than that found at most plants." The Ministry estimated that if higher-efficiency equipment were added to all eighteen thousand large boilers in that particular area, it would result in a fuel *savings* of three million tons of coal per year worth £14 million ($39.2 million). "At that rate," the Ministry said, "the initial expenditure [for new equipment] would be recouped by the saving in fuel costs in about a year." The British government also provides a loan plan for fuel-saving equipment in which the borrowed money is interest-free for two years and payable over a twenty-year time span.

In 1959, the Ministry of Housing and Local Government asked the 325 local authorities in the nation's list of "black areas" to decide on the smoke control areas that were needed and how many years it was likely to take to finish the job. By 1962, 188,838 acres of Britain's black areas (approximately 9 percent of the land involved) were included in active smoke control programs. The premises covered (industrial and dwellings) totaled 1,134,091 or 13.8 percent of the total premises in the black areas. A 1966 report indicated that by the end of that year a total of 1,272,656 acres of land and 5,750,997 dwellings would be covered by active smoke control programs.

In 1954, the British Air Pollution committee wrote: "The objective of our recommendations is that by the end of ten to fifteen years the total smoke in all heavily populated areas would be reduced by something of the order of 80 percent. This would mean a degree of freedom from air pollution which many parts of the country have not known for more than a century." It is doubtful that the 80 percent figure had been reached in 1966, but England at last was making solid, persistent progress.

Amidst all the flurry and sweat of belated modern efforts to clean up the atmosphere, Los Angeles, California, still emerges as a shining example of persistent effort and an even more persistent problem with many answers which can serve as guidelines to others.

When the conquistadores worked their way up the North American West Coast centuries ago, they found an Indian encampment where the City of the Angels now abides and a phenomenon so unusual it was worthy of note in the Spanish padres' journals. Between the sea and the mountains, the smoke from Indian campfires rose straight upward in the windless air, then abruptly flattened out in horizontal streaks as though an invisible lid enclosed the coastal basin. A lid it was, the lid of temperature inversion, which in 1966 prompted Morris Neiburger, professor of meteorology at UCLA to comment that Los Angeles and three other cities in the world are built in the "worst possible locations for smog." The others, according to Neiburger, are Casablanca, Morocco;

Cape Town, South Africa; and Santiago, Chile. All four, Nei-burger explained, are located on "subtropical west coasts where often there is not enough wind to carry off air pollution and usually a temperature inversion acts like a lid to hold smog close to the ground." At the same time, Los Angeles is blessed by such a benign climate and beautiful surroundings that city fathers (prodded by Iowans and other mid-Westerners who retired there to live out their years amid winter sunshine and orange groves) were blessedly sensitive to the ugliness as a brown smudge began to smart the eyes and obscure the neighboring mountain peaks from view.

It was in 1943, when the city was busy with World War II, that the first severe smog attack occurred. In late summer a gray-blue cloud settled over the city, burning eyes and causing a dry scratchiness in throats. Officials blamed oil refineries and synthetic rubber factories and advised the haze would go away, as indeed it does during winter rainstorms or when the hot, dry Santa Ana winds blow down from the desert to the northeast. By the late 1940s, however, southern Californians were convinced the smog could not be wished away and set out to do something about it.

Over an eighteen-year span, Los Angeles developed a set of 165 anti-smog regulations and enforced them rigidly against fixed sources of air pollution. Coal burning was banned completely, a step which now is just in the agonizing decision process in most communities. It is a valid argument, of course, that the gentle winter climate eases southern California's fuel problem and virtually all private homes and apartments burn natural gas which is available in good supply. When early controls over industry and refineries did not seem to make an appreciable difference in the Los Angeles atmosphere, all back-yard trash burning was banished. Trash now is collected and buried in sanitary landfill. Finally, oil burning also was banned for six months of the year, between April 15 and November 15. The remainder of the year, as a concession to the needs of electric power generating plants, fuel oil may be burned but only if the supply of natural gas is not sufficient. Oil companies in the region took this regulation to court, charging discrimination, but the city ruling was upheld in 1966.

Concurrently, Los Angeles strongly supported three Texas pipeline companies in their petition before the Federal Power Commission to bring an additional 865 million cubic feet of gas per day into the area. This would permit county authorities to prohibit fuel oil burning all year round. It was pointed out that due to cold air and long hours of darkness, homeowners use an additional one billion cubic feet of gas per day during the Los Angeles winter. Thousands of San Fernando Valley residents complained in January 1966 when the main power generating plant in the region began spewing an unusual amount of visible pollution into the air.

"We must have electrical power," said Louis J. Fuller, L.A.'s Air Pollution Control District director. "Since the Valley plant generates 560 megawatts per hour, it's impossible to shut it down. The main reason for the heavy smoke is the curtailment of the gas supply during the cold spell." Fuller said the single generating plant was burning about 150,000 barrels of oil per day, "which means about seven times more pollution in the air." He said that when industry and power-generating plants in the Los Angeles basin are burning only gas, the pollution amounts to about 238 tons per day. The use of fuel oil adds more than 1000 tons per day.

While the natural gas supply debate was continuing in Washington, David D. Mix, assistant Los Angeles County counsel, startled the commission and southern Californians as well with the statement that "the air may smart the tourist's eyes a little worse in summer, but in the winter it may kill him." He added that fuel oil burned by utilities and industry when gas is not available is "undeniably the major cause of our fall and winter pollution problem."

The oil industry buzzed with indignation. Chamber of Commerce officials, hyperconscious of southern California's tourist trade, tried to convince Mix that he had exaggerated. "You didn't mean literally that Los Angeles air pollution would kill those who stayed in the area for only a short period?" asked FPC Commissioner Carl E. Bagge. "If they were there every winter for a number of years, it probably would," Mix replied. In July 1966 the FPC ruled in favor of the additional gas supply for southern California.

Whether or not the Los Angeles smog can be termed a killer may be debatable. But there is no question that the city is waging a continuous, expensive and vigorous campaign against the air pollution problem.

"The war Los Angeles is waging has already become a modern legend," commented Vernon G. MacKenzie, chief of the U.S. Air Pollution Division. "Only twenty years ago, when eyes first began to smart here, you had to fight alone. Few suspected that the entire nation was entering the age of smog. It harms us in subtly sinister as well as blatantly obvious ways. It contributes to illness and death, destroys property in the city and on the farm, and it imperils air and ground transportation. Smog is an important contributor to the ugliness that diminishes the quality of life for all Americans."

County Pollution Chief Fuller said that since 1957, taxpayers in the Los Angeles area have paid $450 million in smog control and research programs. He referred to a late regulation designed to stop the daily emission of 550 tons of organic solvents from petroleum, paint, furniture, printing, dry cleaning, degreasing and chemical industries and said that more than $130 million has been spent for industrial control equipment, plus $30 million per year for related control activities such as rubbish collection and disposal.

It does not appear that additional expenses can be avoided in the future [Fuller said]. Whatever the price, it must be paid. For all of our expenditures, it is still only the top of the iceberg of the cost of air pollution. There is no way of knowing the full cost of pollution to Los Angeles County over the past twenty years, but we can make an estimate of eleven billion dollars.

That does not include the loss of productivity of smog victims due to distress and the price of pain and suffering, impaired health and loss of well-being. Nor does it take into account the general friction and drag on the entire mechanism of society caused by debate and pulling and hauling over the problem.

In spite of the best air pollution control program in the world, Fuller estimates that 13,730 tons of pollutants still are being emitted into the Los Angeles atmosphere per day. Twenty years of work, he said, have resulted in controlling 6185 tons of the fixed air pollution, with 1310 still being produced by industry, home heating and cooking.

The remainder, 12,420 tons of pollution per day and 90 percent of the entire problem, comes from the exhaust pipes of gasoline-powered engines.

The automobile, with an engine essentially unimproved in fifty years, is responsible for the greatest bulk of all air pollution in Los Angeles and the nation.

The Ego Buggy

*If nine million Americans this year are willing to
buy 250 horses each to transport ten ounces
of cornflakes over miles of solid concrete—well,
who is to say that nine million Americans can
be wrong?*

Peter Blake, Architect and Editor

WHEN HENRY FORD BEGAN MASS-PRODUCING MODEL T'S IN
1908, it is doubtful that he realized what a monster he had
loosed upon the world.

The Tin Lizzie clattered into civilization with the slogan:
"Gets you there, gets you back." Mr. Ford's objective—aside
from the money-making motive—was a fairly noble one. He
visualized a self-propelled vehicle so cheap in price and economical in operation that the average American could afford
one. This would free up a man's spirit to the vistas of the
open road and the glory of far horizons not visible from the

183

horse-drawn buggy or electric streetcar. How well Henry Ford succeeded is apparent each weekday morning when sixty million commuters begin their passionate approach to work and other millions of vacationers move their suburban residence temporarily to the garbage-strewn tent cities of our national parks.

The vista of the open road now extends to the rear bumper of the next car ahead on the freeway. The glory of far horizons is viewed through a brew of gases belching from exhaust pipes.

In 1896, the automobile was such a rarity that the Barnum & Bailey Circus featured one as its main freak of the year. It might well have remained an expensive toy in the United States and Europe but for Ford's major advancements in the art of mass production, which permitted the assembly of a Model T in ninety-three minutes. A car, in the early 1900s, could be bought for $250, and fifty miles to the gallon of gasoline was not exceptional. It was still a man's world until 1911 because women were too frail to operate the hand-starting crank, which was known to kick back and break an arm. That year, however, the electric starter made its appearance on the Cadillac and the woman driver was born.

This threat to the world's emotional and physical welfare was infinitesimal, however, compared with what the automobile has done for—and to—the male of the species. Ownership of a car has become a universal obsession—stronger than any modern religious force—which attacks pre-adolescent boys with an insatiable hunger never fully appeased until death. After attainment of the magic age of sixteen (in some but not enough areas, eighteen) and acquisition of that magic flake of cardboard for his billfold, no young man would consider walking a block to buy a hamburger. Very few men, young or old, consider the car simply as a means of moving from one place to another.

The automobile has become an instrument of aggression second only to the gun which it outnumbers by a factor of thousands in America.

In the first year of the twentieth century, some eight thousand trucks, buses and private motor vehicles existed in the United States. Today the number is above ninety million. In 1900 the average American traveled 200 miles in a year, mostly by train and horse and buggy. Today the average is 9500 miles, more than 90 percent of it by car. During 1965, the 75 million registered passenger cars traveled 700 *billion* miles, while an additional 180 billion miles were traveled by 15 million trucks and buses. The open road, too, has changed. In 1921 the U.S. had 387,000 miles of surfaced highway. Twenty years later, after expenditure of forty billion dollars, there were 1.4 million miles. Today there are some 4 million. Without considering the thousands of miles of highways improved by individual states each year, the National Interstate Highway System, 41,000 miles of it, now is more than half completed. Originally conceived as a ten-year, $40 billion project, it appears the system will cost nearly $50 billion, including 90 percent federal money. Designed to handle the traffic load projected for 1975, the Interstate system will carry *285 billion* vehicle miles, about 25 percent of the estimated *1165 billion* miles which cars, buses and trucks will travel that year. This system will link more than 90 percent of all cities above fifty thousand population and cut cross-country driving time as much as 30 percent. This is about the ultimate in mobility that can be expected from the automobile, at least in its present form.

What have we gained from this marvelous contraption with the internal combustion engine? It is safe to say the automobile has changed the form of society—at least in America—more than any other single device, including the steam engine and television. It confirms the freedom of the individual human being to go where he wants to go, when he wants to go there. Faraway places are within reach, day or night, without dependence upon the schedules and fixed terminal points of trains, streetcars, buses or airplanes. A two-thousand-mile vacation trip, considered a once-in-a-lifetime adventure fifty years ago, today is only an annual jaunt for some families. The car is greatly responsible for the shape and structure of our cities, especially the growth of suburbia. It influences the location of our homes, the kind of houses we build, the schools we attend, the way we earn our living, how we spend our leisure time, the very food that we eat.

The automobile industry itself employs more than one million people, but this is only a small measure of the economic impact. The car absorbs much of the nation's steel production and supports most of the oil industry. More than 800,000 businesses are associated with it and the auto creates jobs for more than eleven million people—one out of seven among all those employed in the United States.

In turn, what is the price we pay for our freedom and mobility?

In 1960, fifteen million Americans each bought a car and borrowed *$18 billion* to pay for them. Motorists spent $300 million to rent vehicles and *$4.5 billion on automobile insurance* alone. In 1965, General Motors produced nearly five million private vehicles, 51 percent of the nation's total, and reported sales of *$20.7 billion*. That year drivers paid *$31 billion* for gasoline, oil, tires, batteries, repairs and other accessories, and another *$12 billion* for highway construction. Conservatively, the average American car owner pays more than $1000 per year—10 to 20 percent of the average family net income—for the privilege of private transportation.

This, unfortunately, is the smallest part of the price. In the twenty-five years following 1940, more than 905,000 people were killed in auto accidents and property damage totaled *$130 billion.*

In 1965, fifty thousand people died, two million were injured and property damage amounted to $8.5 billion.

By comparison, from January 1, 1961 to June 15, 1966, a total of 3883 men were killed and 21,549 wounded in the Vietnam war.

"You and I know," President Johnson said in March 1966, "that the gravest problem before this nation—next to the war in Vietnam—is the death and destruction, the shocking and senseless carnage, that strikes daily on our highways and that takes a higher and more terrible toll each year. It must stop. There is cause for sacrifice in Vietnam. There is no cause for suicide at home."

While residents of the United States were spending $100 billion per year for autos, gasoline, tires, repairs, highways, court costs, fines and policing, others were predicting the growth of the monster. California Governor Edmund (Pat) Brown, addressing the United Auto Workers in San Diego, said: "By the end of the century . . . there will be 240 million cars on the roads and highways, enough to fill 700,000 miles of highway bumper-to-bumper. . . ." Other statisticians expect auto deaths to reach an annual rate of seventy thousand within ten years.

Few if any voices are heard stating the obvious: If any honest approach is taken to ease the harm caused by the automobile, it must include methods for reducing the *number* of automobiles and the *miles* they are driven.

But the cast of the automobile, now and in the future, still is not total until we add the damage from the air pollution it causes. As has already been shown, the filth in our air from industry, generation of electricity, home and other space heating and refuse burning, all added together, is less than that from motor vehicles. Trucks, buses and cars load the atmosphere with 74.8 million tons of pollutants per year, accounting for most of the 65 million tons of carbon monoxide, 15 million tons of hydrocarbons, and 8 million tons of nitrogen oxides. The resulting irritating haze in the sky is not the same as the "black smog" which brought the disasters of illness and death to London and Donora. The black smog results principally from burning coal and oil which produces grit, soot and sulfur dioxide. The "white smog" (certainly a misnomer) fills the sky gradually with a blue, gray and mustard-yellow haze composed of the partially burned residue from gasoline, and the evaporation of the gasoline itself.

Probably the best description of this automotive smog was contained in an article written in 1965 by Philip H. Abelson, editor of *Science* magazine, and placed in the *Congressional*

Record by the special House Subcommittee on Air and Water Pollution.

When motor vehicles burn fuel, they produce a number of products in addition to carbon dioxide and water. Important amounts of carbon monoxide and nitrogen oxides are formed. The fuel is not entirely consumed. Part is exhausted unchanged, part appears as hydrocarbons of smaller molecular weight, including reactive olefins.

At a concentration of slightly more than 1000 parts per million (of air) carbon monoxide kills quickly. Most people experience dizziness, headache and other symptoms at approximately 100 parts per million. Concentrations as high as 72 parts per million have been observed in Los Angeles and values above 100 ppm have been measured in Detroit. In almost every metropolitan area peak concentrations of carbon monoxide approach the 100 ppm level.

In California efforts have been made to decrease the amounts of carbon monoxide emitted by motor vehicles by use of devices such as catalytic afterburners. At the same time there has been a trend toward higher combustion-chamber temperatures. These efforts result in more complete combustion but also contribute to an increase in the production of oxides of nitrogen. Nitrogen dioxide is a poisonous brown gas. The threshold level for toxic effects is not well known, but it appears to be about 5 ppm. On one occasion a concentration of nitrogen oxides of nearly 4 ppm was observed in Los Angeles.

Automobile exhaust products interact to produce physiological and chemical effects which are greater than the sum of the parts. . . . Light hydrocarbons alone are not very toxic, but in the presence of nitrogen dioxide acts as a photoreceptor and is decomposed to ultrogen oxide plus atomic oxygen. This reactive form of oxygen attacks hydrocarbons. The products may react with molecular oxygen to form peroxyl radicals. These in turn react with oxygen to form ozone. The oxidants react further with the original materials as well as with their reaction products. The result is a complex mixture of toxic substances. . . .

The Los Angeles type of smog is indeed a mixture of toxic matter, formed by the interaction between sunlight and substances emitted from auto exhaust pipes and burning of other, more efficient, fuels such as natural gas. No one is yet sure how this mixture affects the human being except to assure us that people breathing smoggy air are likely to be more unhealthy than those living in a clear atmosphere. Throughout the country, research is under way—paralleling that which deals with the dangers of cigarette smoking—to determine what gaseous levels are harmful and how to establish limits for enforcement.

The Stanford Research Institute has found that nitrogen dioxide, a major component of both cigarette smoke and smog, is an important contributor to emphysema. Gustave Freeman, of the SRI Medical Science Department, said experiments show that a person smoking a cigarette is exposed to a higher concentration of nitrogen dioxide than that customarily causing emphysema in laboratory animals. Cigarettes and smog, he said, combine to produce continuous low-level doses which can lead to this crippling and often deadly lung disease characterized by gradual obstruction and destruction of lung tissues. "Man is exposed pretty constantly to low concentrations of nitrogen dioxide in the air he breathes," Freeman said. "This constant exposure, combined with the more intermittent exposure from smoking cigarettes, may contribute to the chronic obstruction breathing diseases so common in modern city dwellers." He did point out, optimistically, that the tendency to emphysema and similar diseases may be reversed by removing the contaminants. In a similar study, Dr. Oscar Balchum, professor of medicine at the University of Southern California, found that people use more energy breathing smoggy air than clean. He told a conference of the American Medical Association in 1966 that patients also use more oxygen when breathing smog than when breathing filtered air; their lungs work harder but to less purpose. The smog he used on his patients contained oxidants, nitrogen dioxide, nitric oxide, carbon monoxide and various aerosols—a mixture similar to the standard Los Angeles smog.

At the same AMA meeting, Dr. Morris Neiburger, meteorologist at the University of California at Los Angeles, described to five hundred doctors the nature of some expected consequences of smog:

The Los Angeles type is characterized by brilliant sunlight that causes the notorious chemical reaction which forms substances that irritate the eyes. Different from the London type, which is cold, damp and dark, this smog typical of sub-tropical west coasts is annoying and undoubtedly bad for human health, but so far it has not been proved to be a killer.

It is said that the kind of air pollution we have here does not kill, but human health, after all, is not just a question of being alive or dead. If smog makes you feel sick, it's a health problem. Even if it only makes you *think* you're sick, it's a health problem.

At present, we do not know whether injection of pollutants into the atmosphere on the world-wide basis exceeds the rate at which they are being removed. But it is clear that as the amount of pollution increases, it is quite possible that this state will be reached.

Unabated increases of air pollution, he said, would mean "excessive concentrations everywhere and all the time with the atmosphere reaching a level of toxicity that will not support life."

The extreme difficulties in determining the exact damage to humans and other animals in automotive air pollution was noted in the 1966 Waste Management and Control Study by the National Academy of Sciences and National Research Council.

Despite the numbers of rather extensive research programs that have been conducted [the report stated], there is still a marked absence of explicit information that may be used in developing a reasonably complete understanding of the effects of airborne chemicals on the mammalian system.

Many difficult problems are encountered in efforts to obtain precise, more than purely circumstantial, information regarding the effects of air pollution on health. . . . A recent survey of lead contamination in blood and urine shows a clear urban-rural differentiation. There is little doubt that the lead contained in urban air is adding significantly to the amounts of this material in the lungs of urban residents.

. . . It is shocking that so much is known about the possible injurious effects of airborne chemicals and so little public concern over the potentialities of damage to health.

In contrast to the lack of definitive evidence regarding men and animals, a great deal is known about smog damage to plants. The Academy, in fact, suggested that the sensitivity of plants to airborne chemicals may make certain varieties useful as pollution indicators. Smog damage to plants was discovered as early as 1956 in the San Joaquin Valley in California. Grape leaves were found to be especially vulnerable and a number of food crops have been harmed in the Fresno area by ozone built up by the photochemical reaction with auto, truck and farm tractor exhaust gases. A number of agricultural research programs are devoted to studies of air contamination, including that of Dr. John C. Middleton, chairman of the Department of Plant Pathology at the University of California in Riverside. Dr. Middleton directs seventy-five researchers and spends $1.5 million per year attempting to solve the airborne chemical problem for farmers operating in the nation's richest agricultural region.

Experiments at Beltsville, Maryland, revealed that certain varieties of growing tobacco are injured by ozone concentrations of not more than eight to ten parts per *hundred million* of air over a four-hour period. Damage to crops has occurred over wide areas in the East. One of the most poisonous substances yet tested is fluorine, to which plants (especially grass) are sensitive in such low concentrations as *one-tenth of a part per billion*. Other virulent poisons include ethylene, peroxyacetylnitrate (PAN) and related compounds. Five parts per billion of PAN may cause measurable effects on plants, but adequate instruments are not yet available to detect such low concentrations in the atmosphere. "The most pressing immediate needs," the Academy of Sciences report stated, "include more information on the effects of PAN and ozonated hydrocarbons, better instruments to monitor these materials, and more information on the phytopathology of many new exotic materials. The additional information to be obtained on these materials is of considerable practical importance. The economic losses through crop damage are considerable; losses to agriculture, considering injury, growth suppression, and quality changes, exceed $325 million annually in this country, not including damage to ornamental plants."

So we now know, within reasonable limits, what the chrome-plated monster costs in damage to clothing, buildings, plants and our other possessions. If it is not yet evident precisely how much it is damaging human health, the experts at least are agreed that the over-all effect is bad. We must do everything within our power to reduce the emissions from automotive fuel tanks and exhausts. It becomes increasingly evident also that we will do well, with present techniques, if we can only prevent atmospheric poisoning from growing worse.

The bellwether in the now-growing crusade was California, and in particular, southern California, the most highly motorized region in the world. Los Angeles sprawls over five counties, absorbing more than seventy other communities, stretching south to meet San Diego, and now creeping north to Santa Barbara. Within twenty to thirty years, it is predicted, the California coast will be solid city from the Mexican border to San Francisco. A similar megalopolitan pattern exists in the East—from Washington, D.C., north through New York City to Boston—but there is a great difference between the two regions. The eastern polyglot of people still is served by a functioning network of intercity and interurban trains, buses, subways and air shuttles. In Los Angeles and its miles of suburbs, 90 percent of all human movement is by private automobile. Probably the same percentage of freight moves by truck. The freeways are clogged with two-hundred-horsepower cars, most of them containing only one person.

In 1966 a traffic survey showed that 614,360 people entered downtown Los Angeles on a typical midweek day. Of these 372,818 traveled by private car, 135,937 traveled in 4674 buses. The remainder were walking or in some other type of vehicle, but the significant facts were that the single vehicle occupants averaged only 1.45 persons per car. One percent of the total vehicles (buses) carried 22 percent of the people.

The reasons why Los Angeles grew the way it did are a mixture of both cause and effect. The fetish for outdoor living in California's pleasant climate—combined with the threat of earthquakes—discouraged high-rise apartment building. The people, for the most part, spread out in single one-story dwellings. World War II convinced millions of veterans they should live here and started a migration from the remainder of the country. That migration still brings thousands of new residents into southern California every month. With a low population density compared with cities which have major apartment centers, Los Angeles suburbia spread earlier and faster than other great municipalities. This diffused population brought uneconomic conditions and cancellation of many bus lines. The traffic problem increased proportionately as more thousands of people drove more miles to and from work. Traffic congestion was eased miraculously by the advent of the freeway, hailed (and still generally worshiped) as the greatest concept in the history of highway engineering. Motorists zipped from home to work and back at sixty miles an hour and thought little of a forty-mile commuting distance morning and evening. Then the sad truth finally became apparent. As suburbia stretched on out to a fifty- and sixty-mile radius and more thousands of people crowded into the area, it turned out that the freeway becomes clogged with traffic, faster than new miles could be built. Now millions of commuters travel at a crawl, stewing in their own smog and breathing concentrations of carbon monoxide high enough to cause drowsiness and auto accidents.

After World War II, when Los Angeles had throttled most of its stationary air pollution and gasoline-rationing was no more, it became quickly apparent that automobiles and trucks were the basis of the trouble. In a city which Hollywood had accustomed to grandiloquent ideas, it was not surprising that grandiose plans would be proposed to waft the smog away. One idea involved drilling tunnels through the mountains to the east and installing fans to blow the smudge up to the Mojave Desert. Another man suggested a city-wide network of electrical grids to heat the air and carry it upward, with its pollutants, through the inversion layer. Other schemes ranged from giant air filters to a continual water spray arching over

193

the freeways to damp down the chemical particles at their source. Seldom a week goes by without receipt of a telephone call or letter at the Los Angeles Air Pollution Control office suggesting a new (or old) panacea for the smog. Some of the ideas may merit a new look in light of modern technology, but more than fifteen years of research, control laws and enforcement have proven there is no easy way.

The two major sources of automotive contamination are the crankcase, where a bluish smoke is visible when the oil filter cap is removed, and the exhaust pipe, which fills the air with carbon monoxide and unburned gasoline. Air pollution officials were faced with millons of smog sources, each one a moving target. It was equally obvious that somehow the pollution must be stopped at its source. Los Angeles has been on that treadmill ever since.

As early as 1953, County Supervisor Kenneth Hahn of the San Fernando Valley, where smog is heavier than most areas in the Los Angeles basin, approached the nation's car manufacturers requesting them to engineer pollution control devices for automobiles. The answers he received were either noncommittal or negative. "Although mindful that automobile engines produce exhaust gases," the Ford Motor Company wrote, "the staff feels these waste vapors are dissipated in the atmosphere quickly and do not present an air pollution problem." J. M. Campbell, administrative director of the General Motors engineering staff, conceded that ". . . studies made by various investigators in Los Angeles have indicated that certain hydrocarbon effluents from auto exhaust gases may be a contributing factor to the smog." It appeared, however, that the manufacturers were paying little attention. All indicated they were devoting research to the problem, but no results were seen until 1961 when California required that all new cars thenceforth sold in the state must be equipped with devices to stop the crankcase emissions. This was done with a relatively simple system which had been used on cars as much as fifty years ago and then discarded. By 1966, more than one million such devices also had been installed on used cars, but the main problem of exhaust emissions still existed.

Hahn continued his campaign with Detroit. He asked, "Why not produce a device which can be attached to auto exhaust manifolds or pipes which would effectively reduce exhaust? When will it be ready?" "As you know," Chrysler answered, "we in the industry are conducting a very substantial co-operative program." Ford said: "Our program has involved many highly qualified technical people and has cost several million dollars." "The fact is," General Motors wrote, "that the solution to this problem has turned out to be much more difficult than was originally supposed by most people."

Hahn and the rest of the Los Angeles County Board of Supervisors were not convinced that the auto industry had been doing its best. In January 1965, they passed a resolution asking the U.S. Attorney General, Nicholas Katzenbach, to investigate "possible conspiracy and unfair competition between manufacturers in the design, production and distribution of auto smog devices." In the same month, Ford said it would cost $500 million to equip each of the cars produced by his firm the following year with pollution control and that this expense would be passed on to car buyers.

Two main systems have been under development for exhaust control. One pumps air into the exhaust manifold to burn gases expelled by the engine. The other involved carburetor and distributor modifications to obtain better combustion. Beginning in 1966, all large new cars sold in California were required to have both the crankcase and exhaust control systems, but no exhaust device had yet been approved for installation on used cars.

In 1966, D. A. Jensen, executive officer of the California Motor Vehicle Pollution Control Board, said the state had approved sixty-five devices for controlling crankcase emissions and ten exhaust control systems for new cars, but none yet for used cars. "There are 3.5 million used cars in Los Angeles alone," Jensen said. "It would take four or five years to get most of them under control under the present system." (This system on crankcase devices requires installation on used cars when they are transferred to a second owner.) "We don't have time to wait for inventors to prove they have something worthwhile," he added, urging the industry to run testing programs around the clock until a satisfactory used-car exhaust control device is made available.

New-car purchasers in the state now are paying for smog devices when they buy their vehicles. When a used-car exhaust device is approved, it is expected to cost each motorist as much as sixty-five dollars to have it installed.

More than four million cars are operated on the roads of southern California, and the American Petroleum Institute in 1966 said the state consumes more gasoline than any other in the union—6.9 *billion* gallons per year. That's an average of almost 1000 gallons per car, statewide. Second is New York, followed by Texas, Illinois and Ohio in that order. California, for another example of motor madness, has 17,545 service stations compared with Alaska's 104. Throughout the United States, *67 billion gallons* of gasoline are sold annually, and *one out of every ten* is wasted to the atmosphere either through inefficient engine operation or evaporation from automobile gas tanks.

Ulric B. Bray, research chemist and consultant to the Los Angeles County Air Pollution Control District, says Los Angeles could have air as clean and fresh as it was twenty-five years ago if gasoline consumption could somehow be cut drastically. He pointed out that Los Angeles drivers burn eight million gallons per day, more than is used in all of France, and more than 640,000 gallons escape into the air unburned.

"Unless something far-reaching is done, we are headed for self-destruction," he said. "We'll never breathe clean air again and we might as well forget the whole thing and rely on tranquilizers."

Governor Brown used air pollution as his main springboard into the 1966 California election fray. "We have reached a crucial juncture in our fight against air pollution," he said. "If we fail, the blessings of mobility which the auto confers on us will become the curse for generations into the future." He called upon the legislature to pass a series of tough new automobile laws. Other politicians accused him of speaking "political hogwash" because the program he proposed would take longer to show results than regulations already in force. The governor said California "has done the nation a service by convincing auto makers to market exhaust and crankcase devices on new cars sold here." Smog, as it turned out, proved to be only a minor campaign issue in the election which saw Brown defeated by Ronald Reagan, but California has been the belwether in achieving exhaust controls on automobiles.

All new American-made autos in the state now do have both devices but foreign cars (generally those with smaller engines) have been given until 1968 to comply. Truck and bus manufacturers have until 1969. This, apparently, is because most smog experts have been convinced that trucks and buses do not contribute to the Los Angeles smog. In New York City, Commissioner Arthur Benline said early in 1966 that "the toxic emissions from buses, which all have diesel engines, are less than one-sixth those of the average auto. They stink and I hate them, and I hope electrical trolley cars come back, but it's just not so. I hate to absolve them, but they are not a major contributor to air pollution. Our problem is the two million automobiles [in New York City]."

A decade of monitoring and persistent control over unmoving smog sources in Los Angeles achieved at least containment of the air contamination. Then in the fall of 1965 there were strong signs the smog was increasing again. The Air Pollution Control District operates under a system of first-, second- and third-stage alerts based upon an hour-by-hour watch of the smog build-up. If the count should reach one part of ozone per million of air, Louis J. Fuller, the pollution director, is empowered to order shutdown of some or all of 350 industries and halt all but essential traffic moving into and out of the basin. This drastic measure has never been necessary, but an ozone count of .9 ppm, the highest in history, was recorded on September 13, 1955.

During the last week of October 1965, Los Angeles sweltered under a heat wave with temperatures above ninety for three consecutive days. The smog count also shot up, swathing the entire region in a choking, eye-watering yellow and gray cloud. The ozone count went to .65 ppm, causing a first-stage alert for three hours and twenty-six minutes, the longest in nine years. There were a total of six alerts during October, alarming city, county and state officials with the prospect of even worse to come.

The pollution was especially severe in the San Fernando Valley to the west of Los Angeles and spread over Orange, Riverside, Ventura, San Diego, San Bernardino and Santa Barbara counties. "By the year 2000, the Valley will be a mammoth gas chamber," complained Clarence Violette of the San Fernando Valley Chamber of Commerce. The Board of Supervisors sent telegrams to Governor Brown and President Johnson. "An alert stage this early in the year would indicate more severe levels of air pollution will be experienced in the coming months, the supervisors said. "Every possible step must be taken to reduce the level of air pollution in the Los Angeles basin."

The several days of intense smog generated almost as much heat and smoke in political name-calling as from automobiles themselves. When a clean breeze finally swept out the city, the influential Los Angeles *Times* was moved to comment editorially:

> Favorable winds have finally eased the smog siege that gripped metropolitan Los Angeles for nearly a week. Relatively clean air has returned and with it a new attack of political hot air. Although there has been progress in air pollution control, last week's smog crisis made it painfully clear how much more needs to be done.
> The long years of research, the virtual elimination of stationary smog sources and the installation of crankcase devices on many cars has helped. Yet at the same time, the number of vehicles in the Los Angeles Basin has increased at so great a rate that the benefits have been largely negated. Had these earlier steps toward pollution control not been taken, the air

above Los Angeles would now be unbearable most of the year.

Yet until vehicle exhaust fumes are substantially reduced, smog will return whenever climatic conditions clamp an inversion layer lid over the basin. The most important single breakthrough in air pollution, therefore, is the equipping of used cars with an effective exhaust control device. Name calling at the various levels of government won't do it.

New York and a couple of other states have belatedly followed California's lead in setting up limits of permissible automobile pollution, but the greatest step was taken at the federal level in October 1965 when an extension of the Clean Air Act of 1963 empowered the Department of Health, Education, and Welfare to establish national standards. The bill, following California's experience and code, prohibits a car from emitting more than 275 parts per million of hydrocarbons and 1.5 percent per volume of carbon monoxide. (The average American automobile spews out 800 ppm of hydrocarbons and 3.5 percent of carbon monoxide, so the controls—if they can be enforced—will at best cut the pollution by a little more than half.) The national law applies to new vehicles, both cars and trucks, beginning with the year 1968. Health, Education, and Welfare Secretary John W. Gardner commented optimistically that "with these standards we will take an important step toward controlling pollution from the nation's greatest source of air pollution."

President Johnson, as he signed the law, called it "another large and forward step toward checking the slow but relentless erosion of our civilization." He said that automobiles in the U.S. discharge enough carbon monoxide to pollute the region covered by Massachusetts, Connecticut and New Jersey. "This has become a health problem that is national in scope," Johnson said.

There is no question that crankcase and exhaust suppression devices are a step in the right direction, but there remains a major factor which state and federal officials seem to have overlooked. They are dealing, not with a few thousand easily enforceable situations, but with ninety-million-plus drivers who own seventy-five-million-plus automobiles, a large majority of the American public and a majority which is fanatic about powerful vehicles and resentful of controls upon them. This was illustrated clearly in California during 1964 and 1965 when used-car owners were informed they must install crankcase devices at eighteen to twenty dollars each. D. A. Jensen of the state pollution control board, speaking before the Society of Automotive Engineers in Detroit in 1966, recalled the "motorists' rebellion" that developed the first time this so-called California public had to reach for its wallet and pay for clean air.

"A pink card explaining the law," Jensen said, "was mailed to ten million motorists and the card evoked almost universal rejection. The challenge of informing the people on a subject as complicated as auto smog control is at least as difficult as the engineering challenges involved." As Ulric Bray, the pollution control consultant, expressed it, "Los Angeles, by virtue of controls over industry, now has less pollution from that source than any other big city in the Western world. But we have millions of small factories running around the streets and freeways, pouring pollution into the atmosphere. Everyone's anxious to do something about it, until it begins to cost money."

It is not surprising that the American public should balk at this cost. First of all, the individual motorist cannot see clearly that his small contribution to air pollution is important. Although he does not stop buying automobiles, he resents the spiraling costs, along with license fees, highway user taxes on his gasoline, prohibitive insurance fees, and taxes to pay highway patrolmen who help prevent men from killing each other in even greater numbers. Adding $85 for crankcase and exhaust controls to each car doesn't seem a great deal, yet if more than ten million cars are sold each year (and new car sales probably will amount to that by 1968), the motorist will be burdened with nearly one billion dollars in new transportation expense annually.

Then, too, no one seems to have considered the policing

problem. Who is to insure that 75 to 80 million vehicles are equipped with the new devices, and more important, that they are kept in good operating condition? The California Highway Patrol started making spot checks in 1966, and motorists pay for this service through an increased registration fee which will average three dollars per year by 1968. Soon there will arise a conflict of jurisdiction between state and federal officials. If anyone thinks that enforcement of pollution control devices can be done by the honor system, he should look at the millions of used cars now traveling our highways, spewing blue smoke from nearly worn-out engines through broken exhaust pipes and mufflers.

It might be argued that the new federal law, given enough time, will automatically solve this problem. By 1968, the annual production of new cars undoubtedly will number ten million per year (it was 9.3 million in 1965). As these are equipped with smog devices through the years, new cars will become used cars and within ten to twelve years almost all cars thus would have controls. Two things are wrong with that. First, the anti-smog devices would not remain in top operating condition any longer than the cars themselves. Second, and more important, smog control by this method could not be achieved until 1980. By then the *total* number of automobiles will have doubled. At best, the federal law can do no more than retain the pollution level where it is today with devices which are only 50 to 60 percent effective. As Ulric Bray says, the cost of smog control "will total ten to fifteen billion dollars over the next fifteen years and the smog will still be here."

The law, before it is in force, already is obsolete.

Someone also must face the fact sooner or later, that the automobile itself, with its internal combustion engine, is obsolete as well.

Freeway Frenzy

You Are Now Entering the Most
Dangerous Area in the World—A HIGHWAY.

Sign over gate leading out of
Tinker Air Force Base, Oklahoma

NEW YORK CITY, BUSINESS AND FINANCIAL NERVE CENTER OF
the nation, suffered a transportation strike in January 1966
which virtually immobilized the city for twelve days.

Subways and buses came to a halt and with them at least
half of the 3.5 million people who commute to work in Manhattan each day from Long Island, Connecticut, New Jersey,
Staten Island and other communities.

Schools were closed. Pennsylvania Station was barricaded
by police because mobs of people who rode commuter
trains into the city had no way to reach their business des-
tinations except on foot. At one time five thousand people
jammed shoulder to shoulder in Grand Central Station.
Bridges and tunnels were filled with automobiles bumper to

bumper as traffic in and out of the city jumped 30 percent above normal. Industry, commerce and banking were crippled by the loss of 500 million man-hours of work per week, and people not paid for their enforced absence lost $25 million per day in wages.

Air pollution control officers watched their gauges carefully under the unprecedented deluge of automobiles, but three factors combined to prevent a disastrous smog build-up: (1) favorable weather prevailed, (2) 5500 buses were absent from the street, and (3) Consolidated Edison Co. cut its electricity production by seven million kilowatt-hours per day, the amount normally required to run the subway system.

When the strike finally ended, the Commerce and Industry Association of New York estimated it had cost the city one billion dollars.

The cost, however, was small compared with the strike's implications, which alarmed civic, state and national officials.

"New York City must find a way to introduce rational planning and co-ordination into its complicated transportation problems before it strangles itself into immobility," the *New York Times* stated editorially.

On an average day, the city's mass transit system carries 7.3 million passengers. Private buses carry 1.2 million, Transit Authority buses another 1.5 million, and the remainder—4.6 million—ride the subway. This does not suggest that subways are necessarily the answer to today's transportation and smog problems but it does substantiate a major point: except for the farsightedness and courage of New York's city fathers *two-thirds of a century ago*, that metropolis would long since have dwindled to mediocrity or smothered in its automotive traffic. No one has really improved upon the underground electric-powered train, for short-haul mass transportation, since 1900.

New York's was not the first subway system in the world. London took note of its civic congestion and opened a coal-burning line in 1863. Glasgow started a subway in 1890, Budapest in 1896, and the Paris Métro system went into operation about 1900. Boston built the first U.S. subway system between 1895 and 1898; Manhattan started its program in 1900 with a line which ran from City Hall to Dyckman Street. The New York Transit Authority now operates the largest underground system in the world—240 miles which cost $1.7 billion to build. Despite its age the subway still carries the majority of people who move about each day in the New York metropolitan complex. Very few devices in modern history have been so capable of withstanding the change and growth of half a century.

New York and Boston, Philadelphia and Chicago perhaps are special cases, metropolitan centers of such size and nature as to justify and support such a transportation network. In other cities, the electric streetcar sufficed for more than a generation, but when it finally yielded to progress, it was to the diesel-driven bus, which has proved almost totally inadequate for the task of moving large numbers of people within a city. At first glance, the bus appeared to offer greater speed and flexibility, but this lasted only until traffic jams began. Then schedules and speed were sacrificed not only to competing auto and truck traffic, but to changes in the weather as well. The pattern of municipal bus lines has become almost universally self-defeating. As buses slowed and failed to meet schedules, fewer people rode them. As bus traffic dwindled, some lines were discontinued, others shortened. This generated more automobile traffic to slow buses still more. As the number of riders declined, fares went up and each fare increase discouraged another group of indignant passengers. In most American cities, private bus lines are being driven out of business and municipally operated systems are resorting to tax-based subsidies.

For more than twenty-five years, city councilmen in hundreds of cities have pondered what to do about the dying bus lines. The only possible course of action, it seemed, was to widen streets and build new ones to improve the flow of the automobile horde. Hopefully, this also would improve the speed of the few remaining buses. A new industry grew up around the design and production of traffic lights but relief afforded by new engineering was often so temporary that traffic jammed the new thoroughfares before they were completed. Foredoomed cities began to die visibly at the heart.

Then the freeway was invented.

Perhaps "evolved" is a better word, because the freeway, or superhighway or autobahn was an outgrowth of engineering efforts to open streets to let the growing flood of automobiles through. Two-lane roads were widened to three, then to four. This speeded traffic, but left an invitation to death at the dividing lines where cars met at a combined speed of 120 miles an hour. Building separations between traffic flow was the next major step, but these changes were gobbled up, faster than they could be made, by the multiplying monster. Four lanes filled with stopped automobiles was no better than two lanes; it only involved more people. The expressway, with its symbolic cloverleaf interchange, eliminated the stoplight, limited the points at which vehicles could leave and enter and infinitely improved Mr. and Mrs. America's mobility.

On the other hand, there are several things gravely wrong with superhighways. First, they are tremendously expensive to build; second, they are gobbling up valuable land; third, the eight- and ten-lane horizontal concrete monuments are ugly. Peter Blake, architect and editor, stated it well in an article published by *Life* magazine:

> Take a look at any modern American city from the air, and you will see that its most imposing structure is . . . the magnificent, self-assured, immensely elegant highway that slashes right through the city.
>
> It may be in the wrong place; it may destroy human and historic values in its path. But it is there, and what is scattered to the left and to the right of it, including some "architecture" is just so much more debris. . . .

It is fitting that Los Angeles, with its fresh air, sunshine and mercurial manners in both ideas and motion, should have had one of the first miles of superhighway in the country. Shortly before World War II the electric railroad system which linked the main city with Santa Monica, Long Beach and

several other suburban communities showed signs of obsolescence. This led planners to the concept that only expressways could solve the transportation problems as southern
California cities melted into one sprawling community. The
first mile of freeway in the region actually was built in Pasadena in 1939. It was the Arroyo Seco Parkway, now an
archaic part of the Pasadena Freeway. World War II brought
sharp restrictions on materials, money and labor, but when it
ended, the planners and traffic engineers set to work proving
that concrete ribbons could take the place of street car rails.
In 1965, twenty-five years and two billion dollars after that
first mile of parkway was built, Los Angeles could boast a
network containing 130 miles of freeway feeding automobiles
and trucks into and out of 6270 miles of streets. The downtown four-level interchange, one of the marvels of the modern
world, handles 333,000 cars and trucks per day, probably
500,000 people.

The freeway fever spread rapidly, once the technique was
perfected for bleeding out funds in the form of gasoline, car
registration and road user taxes. This seemed an equitable
method, requiring the motorist to bear most of the cost in
return for the freedom of his wheels. The Pennsylvania Turnpike, also now almost archaic, pioneered the long-distance
high-speed toll road concept. New York, suburban New Jersey, Boston and Philadelphia found expressways the answer
for allowing large masses of people to move themselves. Chicago, St. Louis and Washington, D.C., opened express arteries
into and around their metropolitan centers. Even ancient, hide-
bound Baltimore, where narrow, cobblestoned streets radiate
out from the waterfront like spokes in half a wheel, earned
new traffic breathing room by construction of a beltway in
the early 1960s. Many states and most smaller cities are just
now reaching the automobile saturation point where the superhighway becomes attractive and necessary; but in others,
where the machinery has been set in motion, freeways beget
more freeways in a sort of perpetual motion. As with the
Reclamation Bureau's dam-building panacea for all water and

power needs, it appears the superhighway has been locked into the American way of life.

Los Angeles, for example, appears to have quite a considerable freeway network now, but it is not nearly finished, according to the grandiose plans written into the future by city, county, regional and state officials and engineers. Orange, Los Angeles and Ventura counties were to have 492 new miles by the end of 1966. The blueprints, drawn out to the year 1980, call for a total of 1542 miles in the Los Angeles region when the system is "complete." The cost to "complete" it is estimated conservatively at $3.5 billion. The plans of other large cities and states probably are just as grandiose.

The ultimate in highways, as has been mentioned before, probably is the national interstate highway system, which will be a grid of expressways both east-to-west and north-to-south over the entire nation. The 41,000 miles, expected to be complete in 1972, first were estimated to cost $40 billion. That prediction now has crept above $46 billion, and it is most likely to exceed $50 billion before it is done. The interstate system is expected to carry more than half of the nation's automotive traffic, and enigneers claim its design will save the lives of eight thousand motorists each year. This may well be true, and the highway's immediate value is not disputed, but in years to come it may also provide the first three-thousand-mile-long parking lot in the world.

The very serious question is: How long will we—the American public which demands better roads and goes into a rage when traffic slows down—be willing to pay the ever higher price for our super roads? Which of us, with two or three cars in the family garage, will give up part of the ten thousand or twenty thousand miles of driving we do each year in order to ease the problem?

In 1939 when the first Pasadena parkway was built, it cost $1 million per mile. To most people, this still seems an exorbitant amount of money to pay for a mile of road, but it was only the beginning. In 1966 a contract was granted for a new freeway stretching northwest out of the San Fernando

Valley. The winning bid was *$14.4 million* for the first mile. Another freeway is planned, for some reason, to cut through the heart of exclusive Beverly Hills. The cost of that one is estimated at $23 million per mile.

Certainly the cost of machinery, labor and materials has skyrocketed during the past twenty-five years, but far more than half of the freeway bill is represented by land acquisition. We are paying fortunes in taxes each year to buy land which will be covered with asphalt and concrete to keep the rubber tires rolling. When the miles are located in rural areas where land values are low, a highway still can be built for less than two million dollars per mile, but in cities and suburbia, *where most superhighway miles are and will be located*, the price is fantastic.

And what about the land? Each mile of urban expressway chews up forty acres. An interchange may require twice as much. As the thousands of new miles stretch out, more and more of our land will be graded, bulldozed, and paved into ugliness only partially obscured from view by the haze of smog above it.

It seems only normal to lay out a $213 million, twenty-eight-mile, eight-lane freeway from the San Fernando Valley, ripping through the beautiful hills of Malibu Canyon to carry surfers to the Pacific beach. Who is staggered at spending $230 million to build ten miles of road through Beverly Hills? Many planners, detecting a partial answer to prohibitive right-of-way costs, are considering double- and triple-deck highways; some now exist in San Francisco and elsewhere. In New York City and Washington, D.C., the "new" plan is called a "tunnel in the sky." This fertile idea was hatched in the brain of Peter Krajcinovic, a sixty-six-year-old Yugoslav who came to the U.S. in 1965 from Africa. Recognizing the expense and difficulty involved in major excavation beneath a metropolitan area with large and heavy buildings, he proposed turning it upside down and building a four-deck, 107-foot-high glass-enclosed road structure. One deck would serve for subway or express buses. The second and third decks would carry automobiles one way each. The fourth, Krajcinovic suggested, could be landscaped with shrubs and trees as a long, continuous park, or utilized as a parking lot. Elevators would give access to the street. The price—$13 million per mile—seemed reasonable when compared with the alternative, a ten-lane horizontal freeway which would cost $20 million per mile. Incidental inconveniences would include tearing down homes (possibly a good urban renewal measure) and relocation of several thousand residents.

As the concrete juggernaut moves on, the voice of dissenters seems to be lost in the clatter and roar of road-building machinery, but there are a few signs that a revolt is in the making. In Washington, D.C., a private consulting firm recommended that construction of a $600 million freeway be halted while planners took another look. In New Orleans, civic groups balked at a multilane elevated express route which would blight the charm of the old French Quarter. In Washington, Arthur D. Little, Inc., one of the nation's outstanding management and engineering firms, said that the Federal Bureau of Public Roads standards for urban superhighways are incorrect and should be restudied. The firm said standards are needed which give weight to "aesthetic and social values." More attention should be given to relocating low-income families whose dwellings stand in the way of freeway projects. "When a city is unable to relocate them," Little said, "then the scale and character of the highway facilities must change."

In the Los Angeles area, residents of La Canada in 1966 rose in sharp protest against the state highway department's plan to bulldoze the eighty-six-mile, $336 million Foothill Freeway through their quiet and relatively secluded valley. With its designs already frozen, and fearful of losing $258 million in federal funds, the state held stubbornly to its course. On April 15, E. T. Telford, district engineer for the State Division of Highways, said loftily that routing of the road through La Canada Valley "was a closed matter and no new studies are planned. We have no authority to build the freeway anywhere else."

County Supervisor Warren M. Dorn, with a fair showing of constituents behind him, declared war: "You are not going to make me and this board [of supervisors] knuckle down to put a freeway through La Canada and Flintridge," he said. "Any argument that this freeway will serve the people in this area is pure hogwash. I will fight anyone, including the State Highway Commission. If you want to have a fight, fine, but you are not going to push this freeway through as long as I'm here."

On April 19, the state agreed to restudy the situation, but "this is not," Telford said, "to be interpreted as a commitment by the state to consider other routes as an alternate to the adopted routing. This study is just to give La Canada citizens a better understanding of the entire problem."

At almost the same time, San Franciscans who love their beautiful city revolted against completion of the Golden Gate and Panhandle freeways, which had been so-designed as to wipe out the city's scenic waterfront. The protest began over the Embarcadero Freeway, which still hangs uncompleted in mid-air. It was intended to link the ends of the Golden Gate and Oakland Bay Bridge. Peter Tamaras, chairman of the Board of Supervisors, warned of the loss of $235 million in federal funds. "San Francisco has a major transportation problem," he said. "Delay is damaging to the city. Traffic is increasing 5 percent per year and it won't go away by doing nothing." Despite his admonition, the Board rejected the freeway plans and apparently the $235 million with it. This action threw the whole state into a snit because of the formula by which federal highway funds are doled out. Total funds are divided between the northern and southern portions of the state. San Francisco's action removed $99 million from the southern California allotment and forced reprograming of work on eight routes in the south.

The political clamor which this aroused poses the question of how many superhighway miles are built without other justification than that federal funds are available. All states in the Union, while crying states' rights and laissez faire, leap like puppets in haste to spend their expressway money before it is taken away. This, of course, is a symptom of universal political maneuvering as officials greedily enjoy the increasing size of budgets they control under the encouragement of cement makers, road builders and land manipulators who benefit most from the freeway frenzy.

Unfortunately, the primary targets for the public uprising are the traffic engineers and planners who are only trying to do a job. As Peter G. Koltnow of Los Alamitos wrote to the Los Angeles *Times:* "What really bothers people about traffic engineers is that they have not as a group joined the presently popular war on the automobile. Most of the engineers assume their responsibility includes helping man and the auto survive together as long as people choose to use automobiles as the main form of transportation."

"Our engineers build tough, hard-boiled freeways," commented Nathaniel Owings of San Francisco, "but they do not understand scenic values." Neither side in the controversy between planners and the public ever seems to consider the end to superhighway building, because this comes back finally to the ultimate question: When and where will Mr. and Mrs. Motoring America decide that a little beauty, a little less noise, and somewhat cleaner air is more valuable than the privilege of employing "two hundred horses to carry a package of Cornflakes over miles of concrete"?

Some strange contradictions and outright hypocrisies have arisen since Lady Bird Johnson set off her "more beautiful America" campaign. Stacked on top of multibillion-dollar road-building programs, the federal government is spending $300 million over a two-year period for highway beautification. Telford, of the California Division of Highways, says that "in many parts of the downtown [Los Angeles] area, the landscaped freeway furnishes the only green open space in sight. The freeway precludes the emergence of what urban planners sometimes call the concrete jungle." Because the new beautification law penalizes states which do not beautify their roads by withdrawing some of the candy of federal funds, Governor Brown was urged early in 1966 to call a special session of the California legislature. This meeting of lawmakers was considered necessary to beef up the state's highway beautification program, thereby preventing loss of seventy million dollars in federal money. "The beauty of our state highways will be materially improved and perpetuated," said Robert B. Bradford, administrator of the State Transportation Agency. "Through control of outdoor advertising and junk yards and acquisition of land adjacent to highways for scenic values, California will more closely conform with federal requirements." In the final analysis, slashing through hills, valleys, woods and homes to build a beautiful highway is no easier than building a beautiful cement truck. Both, at best, are ugly beasts.

While some were urging the erection of false fronts to protect the eyes of sensitive motorists from the sight of automobile junk yards, others throughout the nation were learning with ever greater unease that superhighways, where they run into metropolitan centers, are just as prone to traffic jams as the narrow streets which preceded them. New York had learned even before the bus and subway strike. In Los Angeles, which has lived with expressways for the longest time and probably is building new ones faster than any other city, cartoonists refer to the rush-hour freeways as the world's largest parking lot. The only difference from standard parking is that motorists sit in their cars with motors running, endangering their health with their own gases. Despite the nation's most progressive building program, the Los Angeles metropolitan area is rapidly approaching motorized chaos. Computerized extrapolations to the year 1980 show all freeways (old and new) choked beyond capacity as autos become more and more the backbone of a lopsided transportation system. It may become necessary to seal off the downtown area to all vehicular traffic or impose drastically staggered work hours to reduce the freeway rush-hour volume. The parking problem, another gadfly on the rump of the horse, also is getting increasingly out of hand. City officials say downtown Los Angeles will need 133,600 new parking spaces by 1980 unless something brings a drastic change in the transportation pattern.

"No matter how many freeways we build, there never will be enough to handle peak traffic," was the sober summation by State Senator Randolph Collier of Yreka, chairman of the Senate Transportation Committee.

"To avoid gas rationing by 1970," commented pollution control consultant Ulric Bray, "the government should force a return to lighter and smaller cars by taxing according to weight and size. Car pooling should be required and a rapid transit system built.

"Freeways have only made matters worse. Once we thought these would reduce smog by cutting the number of stops and starts, but this has not been true."

Howard Allen, director of the Southern California Rapid Transit District, said: "Bus riding is declining because the total public transportation system is inadequate. Traffic-clogged streets result in long, slow trips and bad schedules during the time of greatest travel demands. So people who can, seek other methods of transportation—usually a private car."

In 1966 it was estimated that five million autos and trucks would travel *ten billion* miles on freeways in the three-county area (Orange, Los Angeles and Ventura), much of it "halting bumper-to-bumper peak-hour driving through auto- and truck-produced smog." The drivers are not the only ones who suffer from the highest concentrations of carbon monoxide and other contamination. Prof. A. F. Bush of the University of California at Los Angeles said that people who live near freeways breathe air only half as pure as it should be.

"That air has fewer than 1000 parts of fresh air to 1 of auto smog," he said. "For a sound healthful environment, the proportion should be at least 2000 to 1." Professor Bush advocated that parks and belts of open grass, dotted with lakes and trees, should be built, at least a half-mile wide, on both sides of every city freeway. These would help to dilute the clouds of smog, and the plants would remove air pollutants and restore oxygen. Dr. Bush said that smog control devices on cars are necessary but "they won't do the job by themselves." Senator Collier and the Los Angeles *Times*, speaking editorially, both pleaded for state help in financing studies which might lead to a true rapid transit system.

"... the best testimony for rapid transit," the *Times* wrote, "would come from millions of harassed motorists in this metropolis. The evidence lies in the endless miles of freeway that cannot now or ever cope with peak traffic demands. Vehicles have increased 11 percent in one year, but there is a limit to the number of residential areas and scenic resources that any community can allow to be paved."

State Representative Thomas Reese of Beverly Hills said: "Los Angeles is the prime example of an urban area facing a complete transportation breakdown unless rapid transit is developed now."

A dissenting voice, one of the few among the rising chorus of freeway haters, is that of Karl Moskowitz, assistant traffic engineer for the State Division of Highways.

"A lot of people have noticed the advantages of living in Los Angeles," he said. "Its ten-year growth alone was more than the total population of all but four of the other urban areas in the United States. This does not sound like an ailing community. It sounds instead like a thriving community and I think it is because of, not in spite of, the automobile."

No one really questioned his opinion about the past, but Los Angeles is only one among many cities which recognize that the transportation pattern must change, drastically and soon.

Fortunately, Americans have not lost the happy ability to laugh now and then at even their gravest problems. A considerable body of comic lore has accumulated about the freeways, not the least of which was a set of axioms written by Prof. Graham Kracker, who visited Los Angeles on leave from an eastern university.

> Freeways [he said] are built under traffic jams. They enable everyone to arrive late for work at the same time. Freeway helicopters broadcast "sigalerts" which advise the commuter he is moving slowly.
> Many drivers take whatever freeway is the least traveled, even

though it may not go where they want to. These same people prefer to drive in heavy fog, because they can go so far without seeing another car.

One source of freeway congestion is the out-of-state drivers who cannot find their way off and are still on it.

Luxurious landscaping covers the banks of freeways, but it only can be enjoyed by motorists who exit at points other than off-ramps.

Old auto parts—everything from bumpers to mufflers—which litter the freeway are purposely not removed so that in the event the motorist has a breakdown, he may be near the very part he needs.

If we're in a hurry to travel someplace, the freeway seems one of the great boons to mankind; if we are stranded in a house beside such a road, it seems a hideous blight on the land. The sad thing is that we have permitted the freeway and automobile to become so locked into our way of life that we cannot consider alternative ways of movement.

It is certain that Americans will not give up their freedom and mobility, and other nations of the world are just entering the era where the automobile is god. We appear to be frozen into our pattern of building and driving more and more automobiles over more miles of superhighway each year. It will not be easy to break the grip of the monster, nor can it be done quickly, because of the multitude of private and political interests involved in it, but a change must come.

Clearing our atmosphere of smog demands that fewer, not more, gallons of gasoline be burned, particularly in the twenty-five major cities which contain more than half of the nation's people.

The only way a man can be weaned away from his automobile is to offer him a means of transportation which will get him *where* he wants to go, *when* he wants to go, *cheaper* than the ten or more cents a mile he's paying now.

Transport Revolution

*We have airplanes which fly three times faster
than sound. We have TV cameras orbiting Mars. But
we have the same tired, inadequate mass
transportation between our towns and cities that
we had thirty years ago.*

President Lyndon B. Johnson, October 1965

IN SEPTEMBER 1965, NORTH AMERICAN AVIATION, INC., ONE
of the nation's leading companies in the exploration of outer
space, came down to earth and delivered to Governor Edmund (Pat) Brown results of a study of California's present
and future transportation needs.

The findings were both startling and disturbing. Among
other things, the evidence indicated that within fifty years the
demands in California for transportation of people—and the
commodities they use—will increase 700 percent. At the same
time, California's land may be 70 percent occupied, leaving
little room to build new freeways or other surface transport.

The study, however, also suggested *new* transportation systems which could solve California's problems as well as those in other heavily populated areas of the United States and the world. According to Jack Jones, who headed the North American Aviation research team, the following things *could* be commonplace in the year 2015:

• Trains gliding through subterranean tubes at the speeds of today's jetliners.

• Aircraft that rise vertically from small urban pads, woodland clearings and mountain meadows, and then move forward at four hundred miles per hour for hundreds of miles.

• Ships that "fly" a few feet over the waves at several hundred miles per hour, only to nestle gently to a dock where they will exchange containerized cargo in short times comparable to today's airplanes.

• Trucks or buses that ride on a cushion of air on guideways, moving between cities at several times today's cruising speeds, and within cities on wheels at slow speed.

• Other vehicles—public and private, passenger and cargo—which can traverse water and virtually unprepared land with equal ease.

• Overland pipelines which can deliver produce from farm to distant markets in a matter of hours.

• Virtually accident-free electronic freeways, automatically guiding and spacing individual vehicles which *do not emit noxious gases*.

• Urban transit systems offering door-to-door convenience, or subsurface transit systems with average speeds between stations far above those of the most modern systems today.

• Tunneling methods which, by 1985, will lend economic justification to underground installation of transportation networks, parking and transfer sites, particularly in urban areas where surface acreage now is at a premium.

These suggestions, *all within the capabilities of the nation's technology*, sounded to some people like science-fiction dreams. To others, the study was a clear signal that cities, states and the nation already have waited much too long to design and pay for radically new transportation.

This study emphasizes [Governor Brown said] that even while we continue to plan for conventional means of transportation far into the future, it is already obvious that these conventional means will not do the job. Freeways are not going to be the answer to California's transportation problems.

It must be equally obvious that we are not doing enough, even though we are spending $800 million a year [in California] on highways and other roads. People must plan for the future. They have to realize that their grandchildren and even their children are going to face conditions as calamitous as those from some natural disaster, unless something is done now.

These problems of growth are like a slow, insidious disease. It's hard to get people to face up to them. They want the problems to go away, but they aren't going away.

The North American Aviation transportation study was one of three which Governor Brown ordered in 1965. The other two dealt with crime and waste management. All were conducted at a total cost of less than one million dollars, utilizing the systems management technique developed by the nation's industry to cope with major defense and space flight hardware developments. With political acumen, the studies were ordered at a time when the California aerospace industry was in a periodic recession. The publicity which Governor Brown gained apparently did neither good nor harm in relation to the 1966 election which he lost, but his action and the results are among the most advanced in the nation to date.

If the transportation recommendations were carried through, California might well score a humanistic and economic breakthrough at least comparable to the invention of the freeway. At the end of their few hundred thousand dollars' worth of work, North American Aviation scientists pointed out that eight million dollars more should be spent on detailed study and building of models to break the scheme down to practical proportions.

Unfortunately, nearly two years after the study was completed, it still lay on the statehouse shelf with nothing done, gathering dust except for an occasional copy ordered by an out-of-state scientist or engineer.

The California study is not an exceptional case. Sad to say, it is typical of a generation of political leaders, from the city council level on up, who spend millions of dollars each year on "expert independent studies." The completed sheaves of paper in far too many instances are treated as end results when in actuality nothing at all is accomplished. Some cities, such as Los Angeles, can "point with pride" to forty years of successive mass transit studies which led nowhere. Meanwhile, the municipal buses die one by one in the crush of traffic, and railroad operators discourage unwanted riders by jolting them over uneven roadbeds in passenger cars which were new when Theodore Roosevelt was president.

The situation has been summed up succinctly by Dr. Sripati Chandrasekhar, director of India's Institute for Population Studies, and Member of Parliament. While a visiting professor at the University of California in Riverside, he told the American Association for the Advancement of Science:

> Southern California is fast becoming the world's most awesome wasteland—its hills leveled by real estate promoters, its smog-covered highways over-run by unnecessary cars, its population rising incontrollably and its water supplies vanishing in a vain effort to slake the thirst of eleven booming counties.
>
> Southern Californians must ration their cars, ration their output of children, and reclaim every inch of their deserts. If not, the next quarter-century will see the region become the most overcrowded, blighted area in the history of man's settlement on earth.
>
> Man's convenience of the 20th century—the automobile—will become his greatest curse. This means efficient mass rapid transit —*and it may well have to be imposed.*

One city which has grown from the infancy of study to the maturity of action is San Francisco.

That city, combined with its neighbors in the Bay Area Rapid Transit District (BARTD), is installing the first rapid transit system built from scratch since Philadelphia's commuter railroad opened in 1907. Years of political seesawing and public education went by before a beginning could be made.

"As more and more people moved into the Bay area, it

became apparent we were heading for trouble," commented B. R. Stokes, BARTD's general manager. "It was a situation of unbearable traffic congestion, air pollution, central city stagnation, and frantic construction of more parking lots and highways, including a double-decked freeway, in a futile effort to satisfy the automobile's insatiable appetite for valuable urban land."

The figures for the future were frightening. They showed the Bay Area population—in San Francisco, Alameda and Contra Costa counties—jumping from 4 million to 7.4 million by 1985, with a doubling of automobiles to 3.6 million by 1980. This amounted to an anticipated addition of 415 new residents and 240 private vehicles *every day* for twenty years. San Francisco, serving as the working heart for the bedroom communities of Oakland, Alameda, Berkeley, Richmond and cities down the peninsula, found that peak-hour freeway traffic had risen 44 percent in five years. Buses which once shuttled to and fro across the Bay Bridge along with interurban trains had failed to keep pace with the growth of the metropolitan complex. The average commuter required an hour or more to drive from home to his place of work in the city.

Through enlightened civic leadership, San Francisco reached out to its neighboring counties in search of a unified regional approach to the mass transit problem. At the same time, some of the nation's leading industries were invited to apply the latest in space age techniques and materials to the design of a rail system which would move commuters more comfortably, more swiftly, and more cheaply than they could travel by auto. Among these are General Electric, the General Railway Signal Co., Westinghouse Air Brake Co., and Westinghouse Electric.

Engineers committed to paper a seventy-five-mile system which would combine subway, surface and elevated trackage with an earthquake-proof tunnel resting on the Bay floor to link Oakland and San Francisco. The network will reach out to Richmond on the north, Concord beyond Walnut Creek

221

on the northeast, and from Fremont through Hayward and San Leandro on the south. These three lines will feed into downtown Oakland, and for those going beyond, through the Bay tube into San Francisco. The fourth radial prong will extend through San Francisco to the southwest. The system is so-engineered that it can be extended in all directions at a later date if it becomes necessary.

In 1962, San Francisco took the billion-dollar gamble. The Bay Area Rapid Transit District placed a $792 million bond issue, to be paid off over thirty-seven years, before the voting public in the three counties. Homeowners were told the transit system would increase their taxes by about $3.50 each the first year of construction, then up to $27.00 per year until 1972 when the network would be complete. The bond election passed. Beyond the $792 million earmarked for the major construction, another $133 million was set aside from Bay Bridge tolls to build the underwater tunnel. Rolling stock would be purchased with $71 million more from future revenues collected on the new trains.

What the taxpayers are getting for their money will be the world's most modern urban transit system. Comfortable, wide-seated, air-conditioned and lightweight electric trains will speed along up to 80 miles per hour with an *average* speed of 50 mph including twenty-second station stops. The trains, varying in length from two to ten cars depending upon the pressure of traffic, will run every ninety seconds during rush hours and not less than every fifteen minutes the remainder of the day and night. Control will be completely automatic, operated from a central station, although an "attendant" will be aboard each train in case manual control should become necessary. Safe separation between trains also will be automatic, possibly achieved by means of a radar beam along the tracks.

When the first passengers start riding in 1969, some two-hour commutations will be cut to as little as thirty minutes. It will take only eight minutes to travel from downtown Oakland under the Bay to downtown San Francisco. Automobile commuters now spend an average of $6.00 per day, including a parking space. A twenty-five-mile round-trip fare on the new trains will cost only $1.40.

"The Bay area turned to rapid transit because automobiles were literally choking us," said Adrien Falk, president of the transit district. All people concerned realize they are running a race with the growth of private vehicles. Counties around the Bay now have 48 highway lanes with 32 more planned, but with auto traffic expected to increase 60 percent by 1975, another 40 lanes would be needed to keep peak-hour traffic moving, not to mention a requirement for 36,000 more parking spaces.

"We can compete with the cars if our trains average 50 mph," said J. A. Coil, chief development engineer for BARTD, "and if they are no more than ninety seconds apart at rush hours, and if we can move thirty thousand seated passengers an hour in each direction." The ifs were engineering conservatism speaking. Tremendous problems have been involved, some solved, some not yet. Construction started in 1965, and ten years from the beginning—in 1975—planners anticipate that the fast trains will be carrying 250,000 passengers per day. One out of four car owners are expected to use the train all the time, and 61 percent of all passengers, mostly job commuters, will be those people wooed away from driving to and from work each day. If 250,000 passengers ride an average of twenty miles each day, that will mean five million miles *not* traveled by automobile and some 300,000 gallons of gasoline *not* burned to throw chemical garbage into the air.

Philadelphia, Cleveland and a number of other American cities are watching San Francisco's experience with deep interest as BARTD breaks ground in a completely new transportation venture. Under scrutiny, too, are the financial woes which have beset the project in the past two years. Building costs are inflating at 8 percent per year so that the one-billion-dollars-plus earmarked for the total system is being nibbled away uncomfortably. For example, in 1966 only two bids

223

were received for building the Oakland subway section and both were above engineering estimates. Extras totaling $73 million have been approved without a clear view of where the money will come from. California is eligible for $47 million authorized by Congress under the Urban Mass Transportation Act of 1964, but current estimates indicate the seventy-five-mile system will cost $187 million more than was originally thought. Money problems always breed political squabbling, and Berkeley Mayor Wallace Johnson in 1966 called the project "a billion dollar potential fiasco." On the other hand, when the transit board began to waver with thoughts of cutting back, San Francisco's Mayor John F. Shelley wrote: "You can be sure that future generations will curse your shortsightedness if the system is not built." Falk, BARTD president, summed it up: "If you believe in something as we do in this, you work for it. We refuse to let temporary setbacks discourage or dismay us."

It is certain, also, that officials have considered the tremendous savings which the rail system will bring in reducing new freeway construction during the next ten years. That saving alone would more than pay for the rail system, but freeway money is locked into the gasoline and highway user tax structure, and therefore entrenched in state and federal political machinery which can be changed only by the most persistent and intense public education and pressure.

At least now many economists, scientists, engineers and even some politicians are seeing the necessity for following in San Francisco's footsteps. J. F. Due, chairman of the University of Illinois Department of Economics, commented: "Some people fail to distinguish between the interurban railways of early decades and modern rapid transit systems. Many experts are convinced that, with continued rapid growth of metropolitan areas, rail rapid transit is the only effective solution, and that the experience with BARTD will demonstrate to Los Angeles the merits of such a system."

That southland metropolis has been fiddling with rapid transit for decades while the city burned under the mass of slowing traffic and poisoned atmosphere. What makes the sloth and indecision even more ridiculous is that Los Angeles has twice the automobiles and traffic problems that San Francisco has. In the south, however, rapid transit has failed to progress beyond the conference room because of a lack of leadership and clear-cut financing, complicated by the argument (used principally to justify failure to act) that the metropolis is so decentralized that rapid transit would be ineffective.

In 1925, more than forty years ago, the city spent several thousand dollars for advice on how to improve transport and traffic facilities. The advice included proposals for rapid transit lines down the center of major divided streets and a subway under Broadway. "To be a big city," one official said at the time, "Los Angeles must prepare to spend big money." Nothing happened. Since then more than enough has been spent on freeways to have built a magnificent mass transit system. Since 1925, the city financed no less than fifty separate studies and reports. In 1933 a $323 million rail system was proposed. Nothing happened. In 1948 the Chamber of Commerce recommended rapid rail facilities which would have cost $309 million. Again nothing happened. In 1954, the Metropolitan Transit Authority aroused some excitement over a monorail system which would carry people at 60 mph from the San Fernando Valley to Long Beach, using the cement-ditched Los Angeles River as right-of-way. Again the only result was a volume of vocal hot air adding to the city's already serious smog.

In 1965, Harry A. Faull, president of the Southern California Rapid Transit District, said that "we're still where we were a year ago and furthermore we will not have rapid transit until and unless the financial means are provided to accomplish the work before us." The City Planning Department blamed "lack of inter-city and inter-group co-operation, special interests and political activity" for the Los Angeles dilemma. Everybody, it seemed, wanted rapid transit but only if somebody else paid for it.

At the end of 1965, however, Los Angeles *had* completed two million dollars' worth of engineering for an initial sixty-four-mile system of four fast train routes from Long Beach to San Fernando and El Monte to West Los Angeles. "This was paid for," Faull said bitterly, "not by taxes but by bus riders out of the quarters they put in the farebox. But we have run out of quarters for rapid transit."

Faull's bitterness was caused by foot-dragging in the state legislature, which had been asked to enact a law enabling the Southern California Rapid Transit District (SCRTD) to levy a mixture of taxes totaling $3.9 million to complete its engineering. It was not until spring of 1966 that this roadblock was passed after months of political maneuvers and name-calling. One of the taxes Los Angeles was authorized to use was the levy on gasoline, and therein emerged a clue to the long years of stalling and delay. During debate on the bill, State Senator John Schmitz, Orange County, argued: "This legislation sets a bad precedent where we tax one industry—the automobile industry—to finance a competitor, rapid transit." His shortsightedness was typical of (and perhaps prompted by) an industry which somehow cannot see that if traffic congestion and smog are not eased, the auto makers could eventually destroy their own market. "In view of the need for a proper mix in support taxes," Senator Randolph Collier of Yreka countered, "might it not be reasonable to spend a fraction of the gas taxes to help make the freeways more effective by building facilities that will lessen the traffic load?"

SCRTD probably will come to its showdown in 1968 when southern California voters will be asked to approve $800 million in bonds to build the sixty-four-mile skeleton system, the master plan for which is later expansion to 120 miles. The total program is expected to cost two billion dollars. As with the San Francisco project, Los Angeles probably will install automatic high-speed electric trains, moving on a mix of subway, surface and elevated trackage and using existing rail lines for right-of-way wherever possible. According to plans and surveys, rapid transit, when and if it comes, would move 146,000 passengers per day on *two lines alone* and 79,000 of these would leave their cars at home.

"Passengers would board trains at stations providing free all-day parking," said Norman Brown, a representative for SCRTD. "Express feeder buses would take people from remote areas to boarding stations, each of which would become the hub of a complete shopping area." Riders would use credit cards to facilitate ticket handling, and each would be billed for his transit use once a month. "These lines," Brown said, "are not meant to benefit the central business district as many people think. They're meant to unsnarl the entire Los Angeles traffic problem." And if the traffic problem is unsnarled, sunshine will be visible once again, unfiltered through a perpetual cloud of smog.

In Montreal, the New York of Canada, the first train of a new subway system made its first run, on pneumatic tires, in August 1965. It was a test of the first section in a sixteen-mile underground $214 million mass transit system which will have the capacity to carry sixty thousand passengers an hour when it is completed. Crossing north-south, east-west lines will carry 1500 passengers in each train running at ninety-second intervals at fifty miles an hour. Montreal's Le Métro will use 369 modern cars, rubber-shod for quietness, built by Canadian Vickers. The entire system, including a third line under the St. Lawrence River, was scheduled for completion in 1967.

Among other cities, Toronto has a new subway system which carries up to 35,000 passengers per hour. In Washington, D.C., Congress has appropriated $431 million for a new thirty-mile rapid transit system. Smokers, through a special cigarette tax, will pay most of the $225 million which Boston plans to spend modernizing and extending its mass transportation. Philadelphia has passed an $87.3 million bond issue to extend its subways. Atlanta voters recently approved a four-county authority to develop high-speed metropolitan travel. Cleveland recently received a seven-million-dollar federal grant to match a seven-million-dollar bond issue, funds to extend the city's rapid transit to an international airport. New York is subsidizing its bus and subway system to the tune of $100 million a year while the city planning commission sets up a ten-year $2.6 billion program for renovating transit and highways. All across the nation, large cities are stirring out of the transportation lethargy, state governments are taking a fresh look at the habitual methods they use to allocate road building funds, and the federal government is searching for ways to improve transportation, while reducing its ugliness and waste generation, throughout the country.

In October 1965, as he signed the high-speed Ground Transportation Act passed by Congress, President Johnson said: "We will be investigating all the new and promising concepts of high-speed ground travel. We may find that meeting the transportation needs of the coming decades requires radical new techniques as yet unknown." He said that in the past fifteen years, travel between cities had doubled and by 1985 "75 million more Americans will be doing more traveling."

A major first target is the 450-mile megalopolitan corridor extending northeastward from Washington to Boston where the Pennsylvania Railroad now rattles its passengers at a pace which hasn't improved in thirty years. In 1966, the Pennsy began experimenting with new rolling stock which would run up to 125 miles an hour and individual motored coaches which would offer quiet, beauty and cleanliness, as well as improved speed. The Transportation Act authorized expenditure of ninety million dollars over three years for intensive programs of research and development.

In January 1966, despite the terrible distractions of the Vietnam war, President Johnson made another urgent appeal for attention to the nation's transportation problems. "The life of every citizen," he said, "is influenced by transportation services. This vast economic activity not only absorbs one out of every five dollars in the Gross National Product, it shapes the environment in which we live and work. I believe the power of science and technology, demonstrated so well in the evolution of air and highway travel, can be utilized in the solution of other problems, especially rail transportation." A number of research contracts were let to universities, including one at the Massachusetts Institute of Technology. William Seifert, dean of engineering at M.I.T., told a Congressional committee that ground travel at speeds above 200 mph is technically feasible but "would differ radically from passenger trains and railways as we know them today."

Late in 1966, in response to Johnson's appeal, the Congress passed a law establishing a new cabinet level Department of Transportation. In October the President signed the bill which included authority to spend some $5.5 billion per year. The Department will consider such things as new safety standards for cars and trucks, development of advanced aircraft, establishing special expressway lanes for trucks and buses to help eliminate traffic jams in cities, automatic traffic control on freeways, and above all, new forms of ground travel. Our country today, Johnson said, has "sleek and efficient jet aircraft and yet cannot move passengers to and from airports in the time it takes those aircraft to fly hundreds of miles."

American industry was ready and willing to respond to the President's appeals, but the country's railroads, in their fifty years of creeping obsolescence, had shown little interest in improving their trackage or rolling stock since introduction of the diesel locomotive. This was a matter of economics, which showed that about the only hope for profit lay in hauling of freight, not passengers. Thus, except for a few major lines, the rails were actually trying to discourage human riders. Declining service in both speed and comfort proved excellent tools for this purpose. The railroads did not want, or could not afford, the wealth of fine new equipment which industry had been developing through use of space-age metals, materials, techniques and controls. Now, with the President's prodding, it appeared a transport revolution might be in the making.

Experts attending the first International Urban Transportation Conference in Pittsburgh in 1966 agreed that urban transit is on the brink of a massive technical and spending breakthrough. They predicted a multibillion-dollar nationwide effort that would revolutionize urban living by providing transport which is rapid, frequent, silent, handsome—and perhaps without a charge for fare. Richard K. Mellon, of the Mellon banking family, announced he was giving $300,000 to set up a Transportation Research Center at the Carnegie Institute of Technology. Alan S. Boyd, then Undersecretary of Commerce and later named to head the new Department of Transportation, sounded the first strong hint of one of the major levers which may be used in bringing the transport revolution to pass. "Political considerations," he said, "are tending to end federal support for building concrete highway jungles in the middle of cities. There will be a lot of agony in revisions of policy, but I expect federal highway funds to be switched to off-highway transit systems." Thus, despite the powerful lobbying of automobile, petroleum, cement and rubber industries, political leaders may be forced to genuine planning and building of modern transit systems if they wish to continue devouring money from Uncle Sam's big public trough. As I. W. Abel, president of the United Steelworkers Union, commented: "A country that can spend $40 billion to put a man on the moon and $48 billion on interstate highways can spend $10 billion for rapid transit."

Ten billion dollars is enough for only a fraction of the work which needs to be done, but that much would pay for the advanced development and testing of new equipment which industry already has designed with its own money. Representative Henry S. Reuss of Wisconsin said that "more space age thinking" is needed to help solve such down-to-earth problems as transportation.

> The space program has taught us how far we can go when we really harness the nation's research and development genius to a national goal [Reuss said]. In melding the talents and resources of scientists, engineers, industry and the government in the space program we have perfected new ways of thinking and organizing. Management has come of age along with space technology.
> This is the kind of effort our domestic programs have NOT had. I urge you [the aerospace industry] then to help with the effort to firm up research and development programs in these

areas of domestic need. . . . When the government talks about new concepts of travel, it usually means minor improvements in essentially the fixed rail systems developed originally to serve the high density cities of the 19th century.

Some of the guidelines already have been established in other nations. Japan is running a 150-mile-per-hour train which covers the 322 miles between Tokyo and Osaka in three hours, less time than that required to get to and from the airports at both cities. The Hikari Flash runs smoothly and quietly on long jointless rails. Italy's Martian covers the six-hundred-mile Milan-Rome-Naples run at above 100 mph. In France, the Mistral averages 80 mph on the Paris-Riviera run. The Talgo, in Spain, averages 50 mph on the four-hundred-mile trip from Irún on the French border to Madrid.

Russia has announced plans to build railroad systems permitting passenger operations up to 150 mph. Pyotr G. Muratov, Deputy Minister of Railroads, said experimental runs are under way with electric engines built in Czechoslovakia. The test train, he said, has reached 130 mph on the Moscow to Leningrad run. In 1964, trucks carried only 5 percent of the Russian freight load.

In America the railroads gave up the fight when trucks stole away the bulk of freight and people turned to automobiles and airplanes for transportation. However, sparkling modern equipment is ready for a new generation of underground tubes and surface rails—whenever the tubes and rails are ready.

The Budd Company has proposed to San Francisco and Philadelphia its new 160 mph train which would operate either with turbine or electric power. Philip W. Scott, Budd's president, said the trains can be delivered as soon as adequate tracks and equipment are available. The trains feature reclining seats in spacious lounge cars which use aircraft methods for heating, ventilating and cooling. Hostesses or stewards would serve meals from galleys. The train is almost noiseless and vibrationless. During 1966, the commuter version of the Budd train was tested on a twenty-mile nonstop stretch of track belonging to the Long Island Railroad. Harry H. Wetzel of Garrett Corporation, which makes the engines and air conditioning, said: "Since weight will be a very important factor in efficient operation of this car, aerospace technology, which puts a premium on size, weight and reliability, has been used to develop these small gas-turbine engines. The passenger will feel a quiet surge of power as the trains accelerates. There will be no pulsating or jerking of cars." The Budd Company also is building four high-speed electric-powered cars for the Department of Commerce. These are being tested on the Pennsylvania Railroad between New York and Washington.

The U.S. Steel Corporation has demonstrated new transit ideas including steel cars, aerial structures, passenger stations, and three types of steel tunnels. A seventy-five-foot car would carry three hundred passengers on a duorail, as a bus, or on a monorail. United Aircraft Corporation has built a jet-propelled aluminum train capable of speeds up to 160 mph on existing tracks. It would cut one hour off the current train time of three and one-half hours between Washington and New York City.

At Cleveland a jet-powered train, nicknamed the Black Beetle, has been test-run above 100 miles an hour on tracks which are magnetized to help keep the wheels on the rails. In Detroit a group has developed a system in which trains would be propelled by electromagnetic pulses as they move along. In France two inventors are testing the Aerotrain, a high-speed car powered by airplane propellers and traveling on a cushion of air a fraction of an inch thick. A full-scale train, carrying eighty to one hundred passengers, would travel at 250 miles an hour.

For medium-sized cities, which cannot afford the intricate transit systems of New York, Los Angeles, Chicago or Philadelphia, the Westinghouse Electric Corporation has developed a low-cost, lightweight, high-speed rail system in which the aluminum cars ride on pneumatic tires. This system has been under actual test with passengers since 1964 on a 9340-foot stretch of elevated track in South Park in Pittsburgh, Pennsylvania. Operating in trains of one to ten cars, depending upon the traffic loads, the Westinghouse equipment is electrically driven at 50 mph and higher. Computerized operation and control are automatic under the watchful eyes of controllers at each station stop. Westinghouse designed its low-cost train system so that it could serve as the total transit network for cities of small to medium size, or as a feeder network to the main transit lines in major metropolitan areas.

The most advanced and visionary of all the new transportation schemes is a super-subway which would travel up to *five-hundred miles an hour* through vacuum tubes tunneled deep under the crust of the earth. The idea was first advanced in 1963 by L. K. Edwards, then an employee of the Lockheed Missiles and Space Company at Sunnyvale, California. In 1965 he took extended leave from Lockheed to form his own company, Tube Transit, Inc., and devote all his energies to the project. The tube transit system would operate on the same principle as the pneumatic tube change-makers once common in large department stores. Tunnels would be drilled in the ground, as much as four thousand feet deep, in the plan devised for the northeast corridor between Washington and Boston. The tubes would curve upward at each end at intermediate and terminal station stops. Trains would roll on steel rails welded to the bottom of the tunnels. Power would be provided by a unique combination of vacuum, air pressure and gravity.

As a train departed from a station, such as Washington, the air would be evacuated out of the tube ahead of it, and air pressure pumped up behind it. The cars would accelerate smoothly, reaching high speed within a few minutes. As the tube curved downward, like a swinging pendulum, gravity would add to the acceleration. At the midpoint, gravity and increasing air pressure ahead of the train would decelerate it in the same fashion. The tube transit—quiet, air-conditioned and with almost no sensation of motion except for the initial starts and final stops—could cover the 450-mile Washington-Boston run in less time than a jet aircraft, including stops. In addition, it would deposit passengers in the center of a city, not at an outlying airport; travel between the airport and the center of a city eats up additional hours. The tube system is calculated to handle nine thousand passengers an hour and could be operated on a small fraction of the power required for electric or turbine-driven trains. Initial tunneling expense would be high, but once this had been accomplished, the deep tube train would take millions of automobiles off the road for a half century to come.

Although his original design was aimed at high-density intercity travel, Edwards has also adapted it to urban transit needs. A system laid out for the New York City complex calls for lines radiating outward from midtown Manhattan to Babylon and Huntington on Long Island; White Plains, New York; and Paterson and Union, New Jersey. Other lines would run to Staten Island and Kennedy International Airport.

One complaint still inherent in all urban transit systems is that the passenger still must travel to a station at his origin, and from another downtown station to the point of his destination. This is where the new electric automobile must make its entrance on the stage of transportation history.

The electric car preceded the noisy and noisome gasoline-powered vehicle by a good many years. The first working model in the United States was built in 1836 by Thomas Davenport, and by the year 1900 this type of automobile was most widely used on the nation's roads. The electric car was silent and gave off no poisonous fumes, but it was limited in both speed and endurance. The two- to five-horsepower motors were driven by current from lead-acid batteries; the vehicles could travel at twenty miles an hour for a distance of fifty miles before the batteries required recharging. In 1900, three hundred of these quiet little conveyances were serving as taxicabs in New York City; 35,000 were built in the U.S. between 1896 and 1915. The last one was built in 1928, though a few could be seen on streets and highways as late as 1940.

After World War II, the nation's suppressed hunger for private transportation expressed itself in a demand for larger and more powerful automobiles, a trend which has continued ever since. The power and speed obsession of the American male could be satisfied only by the internal combustion engine, and with this the auto industry has continued to reap its multi-billion-dollar annual bonanza. Although that industry also spends billions of dollars on research, the results have generally been visible only in body styling, chrome plating, and niggling improvements in engine efficiency. Genuine advancements, such as Chrysler's experiments with the gas turbine engine, are not attractive to the auto (or the oil) industry as long as the gullible car buyer is content to pay three thousand to five thousand dollars for a new copy of the same car he bought three years ago.

However, the electric automobile is ready to make its comeback, and many experts, such as Dr. Morris Neiburger, UCLA meteorologist, see it as the only ultimate answer to smoggy municipal skies. "Fully smog-free transportation can be attained," Dr. Neiburger said, "only if a substitute for the internal combustion engine as a means of propelling vehicles is developed. The most likely prospect at present appears to be the electric automobile." Representative Chet Holifield of California told the Los Angeles Chamber of Commerce that "these cars may sound far-fetched, but hardheaded businessmen are spending corporate funds to develop just such devices."

A two-seater electric car with operating costs about one-fourth that of a small, gasoline auto has been invented in England. Fumeless and quiet, it is called the Scamp. It is seven feet long and four wide. The electric batteries weigh eight hundred pounds and the electrobile has a range of about twenty miles. M. G. Smith, vice president of the Electric Storage Battery Company of Philadelphia, said in 1965 that forty thousand electric-powered vehicles then were operating on the roads in England.

"We have the technology for the same thing here right now," he said. "We could develop a cheaper and better DC motor, then let Detroit put their know-how to work and engineer the car from the ground up. Don't let them try putting batteries in existing designs." Smith said that cars powered by "space age" batteries could handle 90 percent of the driving needs of the American public. His company has devolped electric delivery trucks which "out-perform, even out-speed on pickup" combustion engine vehicles. More than 240 delivery firms already have contracted for Smith's Exide meter plan, which provides truck batteries without down payment or capital investment. Payment is made on a metered rate according to kilowatt hours of electricity used.

Lear Siegler Inc. of Cleveland in 1966 unveiled an experimental army truck powered by an electric drive system utilizing alternating-current induction motors for driving individual wheels. The truck has no transmission, driveshaft or axles, and thus has lower maintenance cost and involves less maintenance time than ordinary trucks.

Ivan L. Bateman, an engineer with the Los Angeles Department of Water and Power, sees the day coming when a motorist can pull up to parking meters or lots and have their car batteries recharged while they shop. The electricity would be fed directly from the municipal power system.

It was not until late in 1966 that the big American auto producers revealed that they have been actively researching the electric car problems and indeed are near the point of producing working models.

The Ford Motor Company's President Arjay Miller said his firm has developed a sodium-sulphur battery which may overcome the past major disadvantages of the electric auto—low power, short range and slow speed. Miller said this battery could power small cars within five to ten years, as soon as experimental models are scaled up to working size. Ford anticipates that batteries weighing fifty to 100 pounds will provide five to ten kilowatts of power, enough to drive an 1100-pound automobile carrying four people. Prototypes were being built in England with tests designed to start in 1967.

Dr. Manfred Altman, director of Pennsylvania University's Institute for Direct Energy Conversion, predicted in 1967 that a family of electric automobiles, ranging from tiny city runabouts to high-powered family vehicles could be available within ten years. He pointed out there is "a dire need" for such a logical evolution to help relieve noise, air pollution and congestion in cities. Technology is moving so fast, Dr. Altman said, that within two or three years suburbanites will become interested in buying electric vehicles as "town cars," and while this is going on, "people will be working on long-range vehicles to replace today's gasoline-powered cars."

Great advantages in the electric car are the absence of smog and noise. Beyond batteries is the fuel cell. This marvelous device was developed to power the Gemini and Apollo spacecraft in the nation's manned space flight programs. The theory is 150 years old, but just now reaching practical reality. It uses the principle of reverse electrolysis, in which tanks of hydrogen and oxygen are combined to produce electricity with water as a by-product. Fuel cells now in existence are small enough to fit under the hood of an average automobile and develop electricity equal to twenty-five to thirty horsepower.

"It's certainly conceivable that fuel cells someday could be used to power autos," said Paul Schratter, manager of business planning for General Electric. "They operate with extraordinary efficiency and there are no exhaust fumes." The Gemini fuel cells operate on liquid oxygen and hydrogen, but this would not be necessary in the automobile. Schratter said the necessary oxygen could be drawn from the atmosphere, as the auto runs, and hydrogen could be manufactured by a device attached to the fuel cell.

In January 1967 it was revealed that the fuel cell approach to electric automobiles also is under active research and development by General Motors. Although vehicle weight and costs are still prohibitive for mass sales to the public, a prototype has been built and is in experimental operation.

Dr. Clifford C. Furnas, president of the State University of New York, goes farther—he predicts flatly that autos will be powered universally by fuel cells within seventy years. "There will be no noxious fumes or other undesirable products," he said. "They will be silent in operation and will produce electrical energy at high efficiency." The fuel cell and its elimination of atmospheric contamination from the internal-combustion engine might well, in years to come, justify all of the billions of dollars spent by this nation on its space programs.

There is no doubt that a practical electric automobile could be available in five to ten years. However, considering the stubbornness of the motoring public and the retardation pressures built into the automotive and relative industries, it probably will require a generation to convert gasoline pumps at a million service stations to replace them with electric plug-ins.

The electric car, however, is ideally suited immediately as a mate to the new rapid transit systems. As it should work in practice, a city would build a new transit system which would move passengers into and out of the downtown district twice as fast as the auto travels. The fare, ideally, would be *nothing*. The entire operating expense of the transit system would come from increased gasoline taxes, thereby forcing auto drivers to pay for a system which will eliminate their dirt. A fleet of electric cars would be located at all stations and the cars could be checked out automatically by mechanical ticket dispensers. The businessman or shopper would use the electric car to reach his precise destination and pay in return for the mileage and electricity he has used. Commuters, in larger numbers and headed for more centralized locations, would ride feeder buses. Upon return, the passenger could drive his own car home from the station.

Such systems in years to come will save billions of dollars and billions of miles of auto travel. People will be able to travel in their metropolitan districts faster and cheaper than the ten cents and more a mile they are now paying to operate a car, and the nation's smog will disappear, just as manure disappeared from city streets when the automobile replaced the horse.

It is interesting to note that modern mass transit systems could be built in *all* of the twenty-five largest American cities which contain half of the nation's population, with the $67 billion which would result from a ten cent tax on each gallon of gasoline used over a ten-year period.

It would be a small price to pay for a better America.

Pesticides and Particles

Can anyone imagine anything so cheerless
and dreary as a springtime without a robin's song?

Rachel Carson, Silent Spring

TWO SOURCES OF ENVIRONMENTAL CONTAMINATION—CHEMICAL
pesticides and nuclear radiation—are considered here together
for several reasons. First, they affect the purity of all three of
the world's major elements, land, air and water. Second, the
danger from both at the present time appears to be potential
rather than actual. Third, both have been and will continue
to be of tremendous benefit to man. Fourth, the layman is
generally unable to detect their presence in the soil, foodstuffs,
and the atmosphere.

It has been the nature of the human animal, since he first
peered into the darkness beyond his cave door, to fear the
unknown, the dangers—real or imagined—which could not be
identified by his senses. By such fears, women were killed as
witches, and children still dream atavistically of monsters in

the dark. Men are frightened, then, both rationally and irrationally, by the threat of accumulating insect poisons and the infinitesimal particles of radiation born by the frightful fireball over Hiroshima, and their successors. But all of man's great tools—the steam engine, electricity, gasoline, even the lever—are dangerous when improperly used, and the danger side of the coin is almost always proportionate to the beneficial power within the tool. This is especially true with pesticides and nuclear power. The essential thing regarding both is to regulate their use and control their harmful by-products *before* the problem becomes acute rather than waiting until it has grown out of control, as is the case with other forms of air, water and land pollution.

Pesticides

The late Rachel Carson wrote a magnificent book in 1962, titled *Silent Spring*, which chronicled in vivid detail the dangers introduced to the world by modern insecticides and weed killers. The book has since become a bible for conservationists and others who fear that indiscriminate and uncontrolled use of long-lived chemical poisons is seriously upsetting the ecological balance on earth by killing innocent insect, animal and aquatic life as well as pests. Miss Carson also warned that pesticides, building up in the air, water and soil, are a direct threat to human life.

> For the first time in the history of the world [Miss Carson wrote] every human being is now subjected to contact with dangerous chemicals, from the moment of conception until death. In the less than two decades of their use, the synthetic pesticides have been so thoroughly distributed throughout the animate and inanimate world that they occur virtually everywhere.
>
> They have been recovered from most of the major river systems and even from streams of groundwater flowing unseen through the earth. Residues of these chemicals linger in soil to which they may have been applied a dozen years before. They have entered and lodged in the bodies of fish, birds, rep-

tiles, and domestic and wild animals so universally that scientists carrying on animal experiments find it almost impossible to locate subjects free from such contamination.

They have been found in fish in remote mountain lakes. They have been found in soil, in the eggs of birds—and in man himself. For these chemicals are now stored in the bodies of the vast majority of human beings, regardless of age. They occur in the mother's milk, and probably in the tissues of unborn children.

With numerous cases of documentation, Miss Carson told of birds and bees, animals and fish dying or threatened with death because of man's efforts to control the insect and weed life around him. Three years later, in 1965, Wheeler McMillen wrote another book, *Bugs or People*, setting forth the opposite side of the story. He quoted Dr. Wayland J. Hayes, chief of the U.S. Public Health Service Toxicology Center, as saying that "during years of investigation it has been impossible to confirm the allegation that insecticides, when properly used, are the causes of any diseases either of men or animals. When misused, however, they may produce poisoning." Dr. Edward F. Knipling, U.S. Department of Agriculture leader in the development of nonchemical insect control, added:

> To my knowledge not one death (excluding accidents) or serious illness has been caused among the people exposed to the insecticide DDT in connection with the control of insects. On the other hand, I estimate that no less than five million lives have been saved; no less than one hundred million serious illnesses have been prevented through the use of DDT for controlling malaria, typhus, dysentery and many other diseases.

Somewhere between the death of Miss Carson's robins and the worldwide saving of human life there lies a middle ground wherein a certain percentage of mistakes have been made in the handling of these deadly poisons which not only have helped eradicate disease but also have greatly increased the world's food supply.

In the United States it is estimated that insects and other pests cause damage amounting to $17 billion per year. This includes $4 billion in crop losses from bugs; $3 billion from fungus; $5 billion from weeds; $1 billion from nematodes, and $2 billion from rats, mice and other rodents. Conversely, these figures are no excuse for blanketing a city or farm region with a broad-spectrum, long-lasting insecticide capable of killing birds and animals as well as its intended target.

Of all pesticides presently used in agriculture, a class of chemicals known as *chlorinated hydrocarbons* pose the greatest dangers. Not only are they highly toxic if contacted by animals or humans, but they are slow in breaking down and tend to accumulate in soils and water. The most persistent of these that have been widely used in agriculture are aldrin, dieldrin, heptachlor, endrin, DDT, and chlordane. When DDT was first introduced in 1942, with the promise that it would rid the world of flies and other insect pests, the long residual effect was considered a virtue because it controlled insects for extended periods after application. For some uses, persistence still is a virtue, but the quantities which have been used over the years have caused long-term accumulations of alarming magnitude. In addition, recent years have shown that these chemicals have spread into watercourses around the world, including the oceans.

In 1966, researchers found that of four hundred samples of ocean fish, shellfish and other invertebrates collected in the Pacific off the West Coast, only four were free of some residue from insecticides. DDT was found in thirty-three species collected from Seattle to the Galapagos and from San Francisco to Hawaii. "We cannot assess the hazard to the use of the oceans as human food sources," said Dr. Daniel B. Menzel of the University of California at Davis, "but it gives us great concern to have found in certain species a tissue distribution indicating that as much as ten times the tissue level of DDT may be concentrated in the ovaries." The levels of poison found in the fish was nowhere near that required to harm human beings, but Dr. Menzel stressed that every nation in the world has a grave responsibility for controlling indiscriminate use of pesticides.

Poisons such as copper and arsenic have been used by

farmers and orchard growers for at least a century to control pests which spoiled and devoured fruit and vegetable crops, weakened farm animals with disease and reduced the production of dairy cattle. It was not until World War II, however, that the true broad-scale bug and weed killers began to demonstrate large improvements in agricultural yields. DDT and other insecticides have played a major role in the revolution in American farming whereby 7 percent of the nation's workers now feed the rest of us. Worldwide, it still requires the labor of half of the people to feed themselves and the other 50 percent. One example of what could happen if pesticides were *not* used is the aphid. According to Dr. Leland O. Howard, entomologist: "If all aphids lived through a season, the descendants of *two* could outweigh the earth's entire human population."

The great blessing, however, has come in the control of ten thousand kinds of mites, ticks and insects which infect men directly or indirectly with disease. According to A. W. A. Brown, professor of zoology at the University of Western Ontario:

> Between 1945 and 1954, the death rate in underdeveloped countries decreased by 32 percent so that the world death rate fell to 18 per 1000, less than twice that in developed countries; since 1947 the death rate in India has been halved.
>
> Only a small part of this phenomenon is due to improved nutrition, and a little more to improved housing. It is the incidence of insect-borne disease that has fallen so dramatically, and modern insecticides are responsible.
>
> The use of DDT in virtually every part of the world has had no deleterious effects on the occupants of the sprayed houses, and there have been virtually no accidents among the 130,000 spraymen now involved in the World Health Organization campaign.

Such statements tend to remind us how infected and infested we would be if insect control measures did not exist. Yet this also is no blanket permit for us to continue smothering our cities and countrysides with broad-spectrum bug killers without consideration for the ultimate effect upon us all. According to the President's Science Advisory Committee, the sales of organic insecticides, fumigants, rodent killers and soil conditioners amounted to about 400 million pounds per year from 1962 through 1964. During the same years, weed killer and plant hormone sales increased from 95 million pounds in 1962 to 152 million pounds in 1964. Pest extermination with chemicals is a $450 million annual business in the United States and is presently growing at a rate of 13 percent per year. It is interesting to note that one-fifth of all pesticides used in the nation are applied to farms in California, which points up the additional fact that only about 5 percent of the land nationwide is subjected to such treatment.

There are several classes of hazard in the use of chemical bug and weed killers. First is accidental harm to people working with these materials, and to people and animals living where the killer has been improperly used. Second is the long-term accumulative effect upon insects, wildlife and fish not intended as targets. Third is the long-term accumulative effect upon humans.

Almost all instances of acute illness and death from pesticides have occurred through accident and malpractice. In 1966, for example, ninety Hereford cattle died in West Virginia after they were accidentally sprayed with parathion aimed at insects in an adjoining field. Agricultural workers in California, according to Dr. Lester Breslow, State Health Director, have the highest rate of occupational disease of any laborers in the state because of farm chemicals. He said the rate of such illness was 12.4 cases per 1000 in 1963. Of all cases of poisoning, 288 involved chemicals and half of the respiratory disease cases also implicated these materials.

Dr. M. M. Hargraves of the Mayo Clinic believes that insecticides may be a contributing cause of lethal blood diseases such as leukemia and aplastic anemia. Addressing an environmental health conference in 1966, he said people so stricken may number as many as fifty thousand per year. Repeated exposure in homes and on farms may lead to chronic and possibly fatal illness. He singled out lindane vapor as one such apparent villain. One woman with aplastic anemia, a disease which destroys blood cells, was found to have a lindane vaporizer in her music room. When it was removed, her illness improved and she is now completely recovered. In another case, Dr. Hargraves told of a camper who sprayed his tent with lindane every night while on a mountain trip. Several months later the man developed anemia and died of leukemia. The doctor emphasized that people so affected by pesticides probably are in a small minority of the population, but the number of such "sensitives" is large enough to cause concern.

DDT, since it has been around the longest, is the first to appear in measurable concentrations in fish, birds, animals, milk and humans. Dr. Robert L. Metcalf, professor of entomology at the University of California in Riverside, says that DDT now appears to be present, in small amounts, in almost all creatures. Concentrations have been found to run as high as 118 parts per million in the breast muscles of bald eagles, 7.5 ppm in human infants, and 150 parts per *billion* in penguins caught in Antarctica. Dr. Metcalf said, "Surveys have shown that U.S. inhabitants have an average fatty-tissue concentration of 4 to 7 ppm of DDT which, while apparently harmless, is clearly undesirable." (By comparison, a completely healthy worker in a DDT factory was found to have 648 parts per million of the chemical in his fat.)

These figures demonstrate there is little cause for immediate alarm about widespread lethal fallout from insecticides, but long-term accumulations, if not controlled, eventually could cause considerable danger. One reason why the quantities of chemical residue continue to increase is that DDT and the other persistent pesticides have not lived up to their original promise as a panacea. Many insects have developed immunity through thousands of generations of selective breeding so that it has become necessary to use larger quantities of more powerful chemicals as the years go by.

A number of methods are available, some already in practice, which can bring the pesticide threat under control in a much more simple measure than control of other land, air and water pollution. Since *Silent Spring* alarmed the nation, the chemical industry has been working to produce specific insecticides which will kill particular pests without harming other life. In addition, the new pesticides break down and lose their lethal powers in a short time, thus forestalling any major accumulation in soil, water or the atmosphere. Another method, which has been used with considerable success, involves the importation and breeding of natural enemies of the particular pest. Still another promising technique is the sterilization of large numbers of male or female insects so that their failure to breed in an infested area will eventually cause the species to die out. The most important thing which needs to be done, however, is the establishment of standards at the federal level followed by reasonable enforcement. Realistic standards in turn require modern instruments capable of detecting the infinitesimal quantities of poison building up in the environment. Such instruments have not been available until most recent years.

In April 1966, the Food and Drug Administration announced that it had established maximum human daily intake for 140 pesticides, but more than 300 chemicals already had been cleared for use on crops to kill insects and weeds. All manufacturers since have been ordered to resubmit their chemicals for FDA testing. Pesticides which fail to meet new safety standards will be barred from the market starting in 1968.

A two-year pesticide study by the Senate Subcommittee on Executive Reorganization ended in July 1966 with a written record running to four thousand pages of testimony. According to Senator Abraham A. Ribicoff, chairman, the evidence showed no significant human health hazard from pesticides today, but "this does not constitute adequate proof that hazards will not be encountered in the future." The subcommittee recommended stricter control over the pesticide industry, reduction of aerial spraying over populated areas, safer insecticides, non-chemical means of pest control, increasing public education and most significantly, "continuing study of man's total impact on his environment."

Society is continually faced with the task of balancing benefits against risks [the report stated]. Pesticides that have produced immeasurable benefits for mankind—despite their potential for harm—have not upset that balance.

Despite this reassuring finding, the committee was also impressed by the fact that, although our store of knowledge regarding the risk of chemical pesticides is large, it will have to be broadened and refined. . . .

The quantity and quality of scientific information on pesticide effects proved to be much greater than had generally been recognized. Thus many sweeping generalizations of impending disaster aroused great anxiety, not because there was insufficient evidence to challenge these prophecies, but because the public was simply not sufficiently aware of the existence of this information.

As a result of the study, the Public Health Service announced in August 1966 that it was forming a nationwide network of monitoring stations to determine how, and how much, harmful pesticides accumulate in human tissues. Scientists will work with hospitals to obtain samples of human tissue—fat, liver, kidney and brain—as well as blood and urine. Studies throughout the country will determine how long and in what way individuals have been exposed to insect poisons, and also how various kinds of chemicals are expelled by the body after they are injected. The interagency effort will include Department of Agriculture studies of pesticide residues in soil, Food and Drug Administration watch over food, and Interior Department examination of chemical residues in fish and wildlife.

These many actions, which now promise to bring pesticides under control before their environmental threat becomes a real hazard, are a prime example of how an informed public (even if that original information posed an exaggerated danger) can move to protect itself. When the public becomes sufficiently informed, and alarmed, about smog, garbage and bad water, the same self-policing action will take place.

Nuclear Radiation

People throughout the world have been frightened out of their wits by the threat of nuclear radiation.

Before 1945, no one thought much about it despite the fact that every human being who ever lived, every minute of his life, has been bombarded with radiation particles, either from radium, uranium and other minerals in the ground or from cosmic ray particles which dart in from outer space and penetrate deep into the earth. Since 1945, when atom bombs fell on Hiroshima and Nagasaki, every adult has been haunted by fears more debilitating, and in many ways more irrational, than any dread suffered by the witch hunters of Salem. The reasons for this are valid enough. Out of those two atom bomb explosions, which killed thousands of people immediately and directly, scientists of the world obtained enough gory data about nuclear radiation effects to write horror stories for a generation. Again, if a man can see and identify his enemy his fear is reduced, but it is terribly frightening to consider millions of tiny bullets which cannot be seen and do not hurt, but which tear through the flesh destroying some cells and altering others. It is especially frightening to be told that such radiation can strike at the very root of a man, his reproductive organs, and cause sterility, or worse, mutations in his offspring.

America's Manhattan Project and the atom bombs which ended World War II were produced in an emergency program under secrecy so tight that no one had the time or opportunity to investigate human, plant or animal tolerance to radiation. Scientists then leaped to the conclusion—drawn in almost absolute ignorance—that any radiation level above that which exists naturally all around us, must be considered harmful. This alarm, which spread with the speed of lightning, was enhanced by a certain group of physicists who felt a deep sense of guilt about the monster they had created in the atom and hydrogen bombs and tried to stop the opposing nations of the world from building more nuclear bombs. The main tool used in all sincerity by these guilt-ridden ones was the threat of radiation, the threat of invisible nuclear dust falling from the skies to kill us all. As the United States and Russia, in particular, pushed forward their atmospheric testing of H-bombs, a threat which had been no more than a vague potential became very real. Although it still was not known with great accuracy how the human being might react to small dosages of nuclear radiation suffered over a long period of time, it became obvious that continued atmospheric testing would within a few short years cause actual damage to plants, animals, fish and people.

Two things, however, should be borne strongly in mind at this point in history:

1. Virtually *all* of the artificial radioactive particles which have been added to our air, water and soil came from atmospheric testing of bombs.

2. Except for the two bombs of World War II and a few rare accidents, *not a single human being has been killed or rendered seriously ill by man-made nuclear products* during the quarter century since the first atomic pile started operating in Chicago in December 1942.

These two points are essential because they bear upon the irrational fear which, more than any other single factor, has slowed the utilization of nuclear power for peaceful purposes. At the same time, the world still rests in the uneasy shadow of international conflict. Though atmospheric testing of nuclear bombs has been controlled (except for France, China and other neighbors who may acquire the H-bomb), such testing in the future would throw a new cloud of danger into our environment.

According to the National Academy of Sciences, nuclear explosions so far have equaled a worldwide total of 160 million tons of TNT and "put a sizable quantity of radioactive debris into the atmosphere."

As a result of nuclear testing [the Academy wrote in 1966], there is today no place in the atmosphere or on the surface of the world's land or oceans without traces of this radioactivity. To the fission products, tritium and carbon-14 have been added. Presently, the tritium content is 100 to 1000 times greater than before nuclear testing, and carbon-14 has been doubled over that produced naturally by cosmic rays.

When testing [by Russia] was resumed in 1961, the amount

of radioactivity added to the atmosphere was about equal to all that produced in all the years prior to 1958. If testing were ever to be started again, we could anticipate a similar increase.

As the President's Science Advisory Committee pointed out in its 1965 report on environmental pollution, one of the primary concerns with radioactive fallout is the eventual incorporation of some radionuclides in food. About two hundred isotopes of thirty-five elements have been identified from nuclear explosions and fallout. "Many of these are not important as internal radiation hazards to man," the Committee wrote, "because (1) small amounts are involved; (2) half-lives are extremely short, or (3) they are not incorporated into the food chain."

The most important radioactive elements in fallout are strontium 89 (half-life 53 days); strontium 90 (half-life 28 years); barium 140 (half-life 13 days); cesium 137 (half-life 27 years); iodine 131 (half-life 8 days); and iodine 133 (half-life 22 hours). "Half-life," in reference to radioactive elements, means that half of the radiation power is dissipated in that period of time. For example, iodine 133, with a half-life of twenty-two hours, would lose half of its damaging power in twenty-two hours. After the next twenty-two hours, only one-fourth would remain, and in twenty-two hours more, only one-eighth of the original quantity. From this it can be seen that strontium 89, barium 140, iodine 131 and iodine 133 would, in a matter of months, dissipate their energy to the point where the resultant radiation no longer poses a danger. However, the elements with half-lives of many years are a different proposition. Because of its long half-life, as well as its occurrence in milk and deposition in bone tissue, strontium 90 has received more attention than other fallout nuclides. The U.S. Department of Agriculture and the Atomic Energy Commission have conducted a soil-monitoring program to determine world-wide distribution and total strontium 90 deposition from nuclear testing. The two most important factors that affect distribution are latitude and rainfall. Generally, the higher the rainfall in a given area, the greater the strontium 90 deposits. Because most of the bomb testing has been conducted in the Northern Hemisphere, most of the strontium 90 is confined in that half of the world.

One encouraging point discovered in the government study is that strontium 90 is relatively immobile in soils; that is, the amount of this element deposited by atmospheric fallout remains in the upper few inches of the soil and does not leach out into the world's watercourses. "Strontium 90 has been in the upper soil layers for many years," the Science Advisory Committee reported, "and many more years would be required for it to reach ground water. During this time, the concentration would be reduced by a factor of one-half each 28 years."

According to a recent report by the U.S. Department of Commerce, radioactive fallout from the atmosphere in 1965 was about half that in 1964. "If atmospheric testing of nuclear weapons is not resumed," the Committee said, "the rate of deposition will continue to decrease; and after 1966 the rate of decay of strontium 90 will exceed deposition so that the *total quantity in the soil will decrease.*" In other words, if fallout continues to decrease as predicted, the total radioactive contamination of our environment in future years will be less than it was in 1964. It should be repeated that the levels which existed then were far below that which would harm human life.

Thus the line between real and unreal fears is clearly drawn. If atmospheric testing is not resumed, the total radioactive contamination will go down. The fear that testing may be resumed, with a new cloud of radionuclides produced in our atmosphere, water and soil, is very real. The unfortunate thing is that unreal fears have spilled over into the area in which controlled nuclear power promises to be the most useful tool ever devised by man. Already in America, nuclear power plants are producing one million kilowatts of electric power. This could increase nearly a thousand times by the year 2000 if irrational human fear can be eliminated.

The illogical fears are twofold: (1) that a nuclear power plant emits radioactive material into the air in the same manner as smoke from a conventional coal- or oil-burning power plant and (2) that nuclear reactors are likely to blow up like a bomb, scattering radiation debris over the countryside. Both fears are false. First of all, virtually *no contamination* is put into the air by a nuclear power plant. Second, the science and engineering of nuclear reactor containers has advanced to the point where there is not a chance in ten billion that one could split open or erupt. Fission material, such as uranium, for power-plant purposes is encased in heavy steel and concrete shells and buried deep in the ground so that not even an earthquake could cause a rupture. Despite these facts, public opinion frequently runs high against any proposal to build a nuclear power plant in or near an inhabited community. Such a running argument has been continuing along California's Malibu coast for more than two years even though the proposed nuclear plant would be hidden away in a canyon and cause neither danger nor an unsightly condition.

"People are going to have to get used to nuclear power plants in their neighborhoods," commented R. P. Hammond, who heads up water desalting research for the AEC's Oak Ridge Laboratories. "The smoke coming from a coal furnace carries ten times as much radioactivity as the fumes from a nuclear power plant stack."

It was perhaps fortunate that the A-bombs and radioactive fallout from nuclear testing threw the fear of God and the devil into scientist and layman alike. From this the Atomic Energy Commission has built a system of controls so strict that not an ounce of fissionable material, or spent elements from a power reactor, can be moved without safeguards which prevent any scattering of radioactive particles. The site of a new reactor is carefully considered, under public debate if necessary, before any utility or industry is allowed to build.

The clouds of fear are dissipating gradually as more and more communities accept nuclear-generated electric power and discover that such plants are clean, sightly, and above all help to diminish the deluge of sulfur dioxide and other airborne substances into our atmosphere. As the fear diminishes, more and more nuclear plants are springing up across the nation and the world. John P. Adams, a Borg-Warner executive, recently predicted that the nuclear reactor will the source of at least half of all electric power generated in the U.S. by the end of this century "and the world outlook is the same." From the one million kilowatt total nuclear generating capacity now, it is expected to increase to 6.5 million kw by 1970, 90 million by 1980 and 700 million by the year 2000.

There is an old myth [columnist Holmes Alexander wrote recently] that the atom is an indiscriminate killer which requires careful national and international control. The fact is that atomic fuel can be entrusted to private corporations. This fuel gives us clean, safe, sightly and neighborly power plants. . . .
There is a myth that uranium pellets are likely to explode or give off poisonous vapor. This is not so. There also is a myth that water taken from a river, circulated through a nuclear plant at higher temperature, will damage the fish population. This fear has been discredited by many studies. . . .
The industrial revolution of our day is not bad for people, not unhealthy, not unsightly, not insidiously destructive. Myths to those effects are put into circulation by intellectual throwbacks who very much resent the unexpected turn of events since 1945. . . . Atomic energy, a war baby, is a good example of a well-developed reality.

There is always danger, of course, as our use of uranium and other fission power sources grows through years to come that increased quantities and familiarity might lead to carelessness and accident. There is no indication that either government or private industrial officials will allow this to happen. They are painfully aware of the acute danger which exists.

Another concern has to do with disposal of the radioactive waste matter from reactors, and such waste obviously will increase in the future. However, spent nuclear fuel will not accumulate around reactor sites, but will be centralized at fuel-processing centers where disposal grounds can be provided and extreme caution exercised at all times. Quantities of waste, in any case, will never approach such proportions as garbage or trash, or ashes from burning coal. The power inherent in a pound of uranium equals that from the burning of three million pounds of coal, so nuclear waste disposal areas can be confined to small quarters in isolated deep-earth areas of the world. "Looking to the future," the Academy of Sciences reported, "it appears that with the present reactor design, barring a catastrophe, the major problem may be limited to nuclear fuel processing installations. Here one deals with large quantities of volatile isotopes, and the actual releases to the atmosphere could become significant."

In the final analysis, adequate controls already are in force to prevent environmental contamination by radioactive material—barring weapons-testing or war. Fear of the peaceful atom is far out of proportion to its present or potential danger which, if examined, is no greater than that of electricity or gasoline. An accidental victim of radiation sickness is an ugly sight. So is the purple swollen corpse of a repairman electrocuted by a high voltage line, or the mangled body of a young girl who suffered an automobile accident.

Radioactive materials are dangerous—there is no question about that—but the level of radiation is beginning to decline over the world now, and the *safe* use of nuclear power in fact offers hope for eliminating much of our other air, water and land pollution.

A Cleaner Land

Man may well have reached that point in history,
that stage in his development where he has not
only been made master of his fate, but where
his technology and his morality have come face to
face, where we now realize we are essentially
all in the same boat. I believe we can be
masters of our fate.

    Glenn T. Seaborg, Chairman, Atomic Energy Commission

"WE BELIEVE THAT ALL CITIZENS HAVE AN INHERENT RIGHT to the enjoyment of pure uncontaminated air and water and soil; that this right should be regarded as belonging to the whole community; and that no one should be allowed to trespass upon it by his carelessness or his avarice or even his ignorance."

Those words were written by George C. Whipple of Massachusetts, an early sanitarian, in 1869. In the century that has almost passed since then it seems that governments, cities and industries have totally ignored or at best paid only lip service to the concept while our land, our water and our atmosphere continued to grow dirtier and uglier. It is not enough, however, to blame city councilmen, governors and Congress, industries, power producers and junk dealers. We must realize—every one of us—that each time we toss away a cigarette butt, drive an automobile or urinate in a river we are trespassing upon our neighbors. As our neighbors become more numerous, and the friction of our passing more disagreeable, we must pay for cleaning up the dirt we create. This lesson has been fairly well learned in England, Germany and other industrialized nations where population density has forced realistic pollution control measures. In America, although the municipal water supplies generally are free of disease, we are only at the beginning of the learning curve.

Nature is a great digester of the dirty animal's refuse but the saturation point is upon us. If you force-feed a goose long enough, the result is a diseased liver and *pâté de foie gras*. If nature is force-fed with our wastes long enough, we will suffer from the equivalent of a diseased liver but nothing pleasant will emerge as a result.

The first step in our learning curve is to realize that we can no longer pollute one acre of land, then pull up stakes and move to another that is cleaner, more beautiful and smells better. In 1966 Gus Vignolle, a retired Los Angeles newsman, wrote a letter home from the paradise he had found in Mazatlán:

> It took me one and a half coronaries to learn that a guy is a sap to risk demolition of his central nervous system on the freeways, pulmonary disintegration from inhaling poisonous gases, and ossification of the eyeballs and cerebral decimation from staring at the idiot tube.
>
> I sit in the plaza under the warm Mexican sun and shell *cacahuates* [peanuts] as Antonio Salcido, 12, shines my shoes. I think of people in Los Angeles rushing around, purple-faced and choking, to make a buck, patting business associates on the back to find a soft spot for the knife. . . .

It is a block and a half to the sea. I walk there slowly—there is no other way to walk here—and watch the indescribable *puesta del sol* [sunset] and I wonder how the folks are in the "wonderful" City of the Angels—but not for long. . . .

If we all, or even a small percentage of us, hied ourselves away to Mr. Vignolle's tempting paradise, or one of the other subtropical areas of the world where life is quieter, cleaner and easier, we would soon make a mess of it—and that is exactly what will happen to all of the world's Edens as our population grows to fill them. Running from our malodorous privy is not sufficient. We must shovel it out.

The hopeful part of the entire pollution picture is that the technological tools already exist for bringing the problem under control. It is the social, political and financial factors which keep us plodding down the same roads of inertia and irresponsibility.

"We Americans are masters of technological and economic change, and our mastery has given us abundance beyond precedent," Henry Ford II said, speaking in Detroit in 1966. "But material abundance is only the means to higher ends. Our task now is to build a society in which technology is harnessed to human fulfillment and the growth of our economy is matched by the growth of harmony and respect among men." This indeed was a noble expression, yet less than two months later the same man criticized planners who "believe the government should plan cities and transportation to reflect their own conception of the ideal city, regardless of what people prefer.

"As far as urban transportation is concerned," Ford said, "what people want is clear. They have voted overwhelmingly in favor of the automobile. Critics would have us believe that the automobile is a monster that has run out of control and taken over our lives. This is not only false, but so is the argument that the city has no more room for cars."

It is not surprising somehow that Mr. Ford discovered that Americans have voted overwhelmingly in favor of the automobile. Probably a candymaker would find children voting overwhelmingly in favor of candy, despite the bellyaches which would result. On the other hand, perhaps in light of our society's lack of maturity, candy and cars *are* the proper expression of technology harnessed to produce "the growth of harmony and respect among men."

Robert M. Hutchins, addressing the British Association for the Advancement of Science, advised the people of the world to consider where blind allegiance to technological "progress" is leading them:

> Technology is the use of knowledge acquired by science. It is a human product. Man can decide whether or not he wants it. In reaching a decision, the most important consideration today is not human welfare, but corporate profits and national power. The headlong race for corporate profits and national power proceeds at such a pace that the political, social and human costs are not examined. . . .
>
> The whole people have to be educated to understand technology. If it is to be placed under humane direction, engineers have to receive a humane education; they cannot be turned loose on the world, illiterate and uncomprehending, as they are after the narrow, technical training they get today. But, since the race for corporate profits and national power is the source of the evil, we shall continue to flirt with suicide until we can find a way of transforming it into a race for human betterment on a global scale.

Dr. Simon Ramo, vice chairman of Thompson Ramo Wooldridge, Inc., symbolic of the brilliant minds which have led us into the computer age, places the socio-technical gap in different perspective:

> The advent of the computer age means that we are going to have brain power, just as in years past the machine gave us greater muscle power. The technology of computers is going to help meet society's pressing needs. The quality of human life will be changed for the better. The important thing to keep in mind is that what we are talking about is a new man-machine partnership, not the replacement of man. . . .
>
> We have the technological capability of greatly improving our urban mass rapid transit systems. But because socially— or politically—we are not mature enough to put that technology to work, we fail to get the benefits. . . .

The law for social breakthrough seems to be that things always have to get worse before there is a readiness to make needed improvements. When and if smog becomes so serious, for example, that everyone is willing to make sacrifices to get the problem solved, then we will be on our way. Right now we seem unwilling to organize ourselves socially to take action. We have the technology to make improvements, but we are not yet socially organized to do so.

Perhaps typical of the mind which will settle for a 50 or 70 percent smog control on an automobile, while autos themselves are increasing in number by 50 to 70 percent, is Dr. Leo Grebler, professor at the University of California in Los Angeles. He believes it is a disservice to "approach tomorrow's world with science fiction ideas.

"If this is a new trend in planning, then it is in danger of diverting talent and energy from the grubby tasks that lie ahead," he said. Referring to plans and suggestions for major pollution controls possible twenty to thirty years from now, he added:

It is as if the turn of a century will produce a magic transformation of technology, governmental institutions and people's preferences. Such far-out ideas have only a thread-like relation to reality. The changes to be visualized realistically will be more gradual, slower and less startling than the growing fiction-type literature suggests.

By the year 2000, half the urban population will still live and work in buildings and neighborhoods already here, just as half of our city dwellers are now living and working in places built before 1930. There is little point in issuing promissory notes to the public that are backed merely by a flight from the next generation's problems into the dim and dubious potentials of the next century.

Dr. Grebler, of course, is correct that there is a great deal of grubby work to be done; but *without* some rather radical future ideas and planning, we can go on doing the same grubby work as we have been for the past thirty years without anything to show for it in this century or the next. People may grumble about grit in their teeth as they walk down Park Avenue, but they will do nothing about it until a sincere

259

and exciting goal is set before them. This facet of human nature has been demonstrated thousands of times through history, most notably by the late President Kennedy when he started America on its forty-billion-dollar journey to the moon. President and Mrs. Johnson have attempted to get the same ball rolling toward a cleaner, more beautiful America, but unfortunately most of the effort has been smothered to date by the Vietnam war.

As the Morgan Guaranty Bank of New York commented in 1966: "Society at large will ultimately have to pay the costs of pollution controls just as it now pays for such other social goals as factory safety. The ultimate cost of stepped-up pollution control programs defies meaningful estimate, but it is certain that many billions of dollars will be involved. Economic costs rivaling those for space exploration, for instance, are easy to visualize." The bank's officers said that business concerns and communities need special incentives to clean up water and air and applauded Ohio and New York for providing tax incentives to those who undertake antipollution measures.

"Many of the debilitating effects of a dirty environment on human beings cannot be assessed, physiologically or psychologically," the Academy of Sciences Waste Management report remarked in 1966. "The hidden costs of people's lost time—and the accompanying expenditure of resources—traveling to work and returning to pleasant or perhaps only bearable homes, or to find open spaces for recreation, are also increasing.

"*The problem is of the utmost urgency because many of the effects of pollution on our environment may be irreversible or, at least, may take generations to correct even if we start right now.*"

It may be argued on the one hand that we *have* started, but on the other there is great evidence, already shown in some instances, that the tools, techniques and expenditures which we now are using against environmental pollution are barely adequate to keep up with *increasing* pollution and certainly allow no margin for the future. This point was stressed in July 1966 in a report of the Research Management Advisory Panel to the House Committee on Science and Astronautics. "Forecasts show that present technology, if applied to the fullest extent, will barely keep up with, and not reduce the pollution load on the environment," the panel stated. "For example, noxious emissions from motor vehicles, even if equipped with presently known devices for suppression, will rise by the end of the century to equal the 1965 rate when no suppression was employed.

"In the long run, improved methods must be found to actually reduce the total pollution load."

As late as January 1967, the same somber message was repeated by John W. Gardner, secretary of Health, Education and Welfare. "The truth is," he told a Washington conference on air pollution, "we are actually losing ground in the fight against air pollution—the smog continues to grow more dense even as we talk about it. We are at a point where we can tip the balance and have clean air, but it will not be easy. And certainly we cannot afford further delay."

Let us re-examine briefly some of the tools—both technical and administrative—now in use, and those available for immediate application if coherent and realistic effort were applied to the problem.

Our solid refuse—garbage, paper, glass and metal—now is tossed into open dumps, burned in incinerators, and in a growing number of communities buried in sanitary landfill. In rare instances garbage is pulverized and composted, reducing the bulk and returning the organic substances rather quickly to usable fertilizer (Houston, Texas, has recently embarked on such a program under a twenty-year contract).

The sanitary landfill method probably is the one most immediately suitable for extension to communities throughout the land. Techniques have been developed which prevent most of the water pollution (which can be an adverse result), and landfill offers a ready-made opportunity to convert wasteland into good land. Gravel pits, strip mines, swamps and desert canyons can be filled with refuse. The resulting level land then can be used for parks and golf courses or sold for industrial and housing developments.

Composting will be applicable to the disposal task of more and more communities in the future because it converts garbage to a salable item while salvage, such as tin, glass and aluminum may also be returned to the nation's economic mainstream at a profit.

Another method proposed by sanitary engineers is to pulverize all garbage, wood, trash, metal and glass and flush it with water out of the city through large pipelines. This device should be especially attractive to coastal cities which could thus dump their refuse into the ocean where, in its pulverized form, the refuse would quickly decompose or settle as sediment to the bottom. This method also would be ideal for building valuable dry land in useless swamps.

Known as the Garchey System, flushing out solid wastes with garbage is used now in a few European countries. Basically, it is a vacuum system with water added as a lubricant. Refuse is put into a tube or duct in the kitchen sink of an apartment and then sucked down into a holding tank in the basement of a building. From there it is pumped into a collection-tank truck for transport to the final disposal site. The Los Angeles County Sanitation District has studied transporting refuse hydraulically in existing sewers. Mixed household refuse is collected by normal methods, taken to a nearby station where it is ground, the metal and glass removed by magnets and gravity (shaking or centrifuging until it settles to the bottom) and the rest discharged into a trunk sewer. This makes more work for the sewage treatment plant, but it also produces more methane gas—a source of energy for the plant, and results in sizable savings in hauling costs.

Some thought has been given to baling refuse under high pressure at transfer stations and disposing of these bales at sea, where they would sink, due to the high density, or in landfills where they would take up less room than non-baled refuse.

It should be kept in mind, however, that virtually all of

these disposal techniques—both old and new—serve only to reduce the bulk of the waste matter. The eventual result, while the land is being cleared of litter, is burdening some other part of our environment.

Cleaning our lakes and rivers has a head start on air and land pollution because the U.S. and other industrialized nations at least have learned how to keep drinking water free of disease-bearing agents. Thus the technology of water purification is relatively advanced. Yet, after centuries of water control, we still talk only in terms of sewage treatment by conventional methods for both municipalities and industries. Even in the Ohio and Delaware river basins, where regional control of water cleanliness has gained a foothold, the emphasis is being placed upon installation of standard sewage treatment plants in communities which don't have them. A 1964 survey by the Conference of State Sanitary Engineers indicated that the backlog of sewage plants needed in the U.S. involved six thousand communities with total population of thirty-five million people. An investment of two billion dollars is needed to bring those communities up to date. Municipal water treatment facilities now represent a capital investment of about fifty billion dollars, according to the National Academy of Sciences, with operating and maintenance costs some 2 to 5 percent of this investment per year. "The total cost of meeting all projected needs will undoubtedly run into tens of billions of dollars," the Academy report said. "For the future, it becomes clear that a major investment will be required to keep the quality of the waters in our streams, lakes and estuaries at reasonable levels."

Some progress is visible. Cities without sewage treatment at all are beginning to get it. Others are providing secondary treatment. A few are thinking of the tertiary stage of purification, which would permit sewage water to flow back into the municipal water system. Some industries are changing their manufacturing processes so that less waste is dumped into lakes and rivers. Others, such as Bethlehem Steel, have discovered that their most virulent waste chemicals can be eliminated by pumping them into deep wells—tubes reaching thousands of feet into the earth to inject the chemicals into sandstone and other rock *below* the water-bearing strata. This technique is being used successfully by the Rocky Mountain Arsenal near Denver, Colorado, an arsenal which for years has housed manufacturing and storage facilities for insecticides and deadly nerve gases. Most industries finally are accepting the expensive fact that they must share responsibility for clarifying the waters, that it is no longer the easiest alternative to dismantle a manufacturing plant and take it south to a cleaner river. Once regional authority has taken root, controlling entire lake and river systems, a realistic change will take place in our foul waters. As in the Ruhr Valley, each industry, each town, each individual must eventually pay in proportion to the waste each dumps into a river.

Here again, however, it would appear that the waste must go somewhere. If it is kept out of the water, then it tends in some manner to contaminate both land and air.

Cleaning the atmosphere is most complex of all, for obvious reasons. Land remains in fixed position and its pollution is thus easily seen and defined. Water also, though we are just learning the concept of the regional watershed, remains in a visible, limited area. It is relatively easy to identify the cities and industries which are the polluters. In the atmosphere we are dealing with a three-dimensional gaseous element which crosses all geographic and governmental lines in a continually shifting pattern. This amorphous mess defies assignment of responsibility for the dirt it contains. Shifting winds and temperature inversions, which make the air pollution control task so difficult, are no more complex than the number of pollution sources which must be controlled. We are dealing with thousands of industrial and power-plant smokestacks, thousands of open-burning city dumps, millions of back-yard trash burners, millions of home furnaces, and tens of millions of automobiles and trucks. Controlling pollution at its source is a popular and valid concept, yet the policing and administrative burden facing municipal, state and federal governments is no less than that of counting grains of sand on a beach.

No governmental unit—including California where the most stringent control laws now exist—has yet made a realistic assessment of what the taxpayer will pay to hire enough highway patrolmen to police smog control devices. Governments are depending upon the automobile industry, prayerfully, to contain the enemy by putting anti-smog devices on all new vehicles.

As Dr. Grebler says, there is a lot of grubby work to be done and some of the implements already are in service here and there. In St. Louis and Los Angeles the requirement that natural gas be used for fuel wherever possible instead of dirtier coal and oil has produced excellent results, but this measure can apply only where gas is available. Pittsburgh and a few other eastern cities demonstrate how industry can be persuaded (sometimes at their own ultimate profit) to control their outpouring of dust, grit and fly ash. Experimental plants are showing how sulfur and other chemicals can be recovered from power-plant stack gases, reducing air pollution and at the same time returning valuable substances for reuse.

Requiring smog control devices on automobiles is certainly better than nothing; but as has been shown, the best that can be hoped from such measures is that our smog will grow no worse than it is today. If we are sincere about improving the condition of our atmosphere, drastic new methods of rapid transportation must be developed. The automobile removed horse manure from our city streets; now something must remove car-manure from our air. True rapid transit will help immeasurably. The electric-powered automobile is technically feasible now, although it will require from ten to thirty years before purchase price and operation cost can match that of the internal-combustion monster as a means of personal transportation. Even this time scale is meaningless unless the public can be educated to the need for reducing air contamination, and shown that such vehicles are as good as, or better than, what we are driving today. The alternative, already suggested in some cities, may be the prohibition of all gasoline- and diesel-powered vehicles from metropolitan areas. No municipal administration has yet found the political courage to try this but it could well become a desperation measure after a city's traffic system has degenerated so badly that no alternative exists.

Little has been said here about the fifteen million trucks which clog our streets and highways justifying their existence by paying high road user taxes *and* providing us goods and services more efficiently than any other transport system in the world. The diesel engine, when operated in top condition, contributes less to our air pollution than does the gasoline engine, but few diesels ever operate that perfectly. Thus the smoke and fumes from trucks and buses add their measure to the over-all problem.

The truck, however, is approaching its day of obsolescence along with the gasoline buggy and the freeway. This is happening, surely and logically, in the same way the truck drove the railroads virtually out of business. During the past ten years, a quiet revolution in air transportation has taken place, a revolution which by 1975 will alter the long-distance travel of both people and freight as drastically as the travel freedom introduced by the automobile itself. The jet transport already has siphoned away a fairly large percentage of long-distance travelers who ten years ago moved by car or train. At the same time, the volume of air freight has grown steadily, especially in the shipment of items which require speedy delivery. The great breakthrough in this area, however—when the giant Boeing 747 and Lockheed 500 jetliners will be in standard service—is less than ten years away. These giant aircraft will carry from 500 to 1000 passengers each, at fares lower than any charged now. More importantly, such jets will move freight at three to four cents per ton-mile—*a cost lower than present trucking fees*. When that cost break occurs, a truck load or rail carload of freight can be moved 500 miles, 1000 miles or 3000 miles in hours compared with days required now, and at lower cost.

From an air pollution point of view, these giant airliners, traveling in ever greater numbers, will take smoke and smog from the surface of the earth, where it disturbs people most, and distribute it through a three-dimensional layer of the atmosphere from sea level up to seventy thousand feet (when the supersonic plane starts flying). This will help remove the stink from our noses immediately but some scientists already are warning us that high-flying jets may be altering the upper layers of our air blanket. Dr. Walter Orr Roberts of the University of Colorado believes jets may be changing our weather pattern. Others suggest that pollution of the upper atmosphere actually could reduce the amount of sunlight reaching the surface of the earth. This could cause our planet's surface to grow cooler, in opposition to the trend previously related in which the build-up of carbon dioxide may be increasing our temperatures.

No matter which way we turn, in trying to clean up our dirt, it seems always that one action leads to an equally bad reaction. If we burn rubbish, it pollutes the air. If we dump it in the ocean, it pollutes the water. If we remove sewage or salt from water, it pollutes the land. These thorny contradictions point up a single essential fact: pollution control cannot be a piecemeal consideration of air, or water, or land. Wherever it exists in our environment, pollution is one problem and must be attacked as such.

The first comprehensive recognition of this fact was contained in the California Waste Management Study conducted during 1965 by the Aerojet-General Corporation. Undertaken at the behest of Governor Brown, the study attempted, with considerable success, to apply the methods of systems management originally developed for solving the immense technical problems posed by the nation's defense needs and the space programs which are taking us to the moon.

The study considers all human waste—liquid, solid and gaseous—as a single entity and suggests integrated programs for tackling all pollution problems as one.

Assuming that present practices are continued [the report stated], the problems of waste and its ultimate disposal are going to get worse. As the population doubles and automobiles more than double in California between now and 1990, air pollution will spread over every major populated area of the state. In the same time span, sewage wastes are expected to increase 2½ times and municipal solid waste nearly fourfold. . . .

As the gap between the finite assimilative capacity of the environment and the amount of waste emission closes, it will take larger expenditures just to maintain the present pollution level. . . .

At present, there are many separate state and local bodies regulating, collecting, and disposing of different wastes. No single organization is charged with the responsibility of studying and managing all aspects of this complex problem to obtain a waste management system that will produce the desired effect at minimum cost.

Although the population patterns might be somewhat different elsewhere, these statements apply to every state and region in the nation, every industrialized nation in the world. "The natural preoccupation of local operations with selection of the cheapest available method of waste disposal," the Aerojet engineers said, "has tended to conflict with those objectives which emphasize health, aesthetic values, and broad and longer range economic considerations." Paraphrased, that statement means that an integrated method of handling all wastes in a region probably will be much more satisfactory, and cheaper in the long run, than the piecemeal approach. For purposes of the study, the industrial engineers and scientists divided the state into regions, then suggested the types of controls that could be used, along with their cost.

Looking to the future, the study recommended that for control of gases all home heating and cooking for the future be electric-powered. Industries would be grouped and their gaseous waste drawn through tubes to a processing and separating plant. Non-noxious waste gas would be released to the atmosphere, the remainder confined and stored. Open burning of agricultural stubble fields would be forbidden. Automobiles would be powered by electrical fuel cells or equipped with effective low-cost smog devices.

Liquid municipal wastes would go through sewers which serve *all* the people, with solids extracted, stabilized and collected. Secondary treatment would permit partial return to the water system, particularly for irrigation. Industrial effluent would be treated by the industries themselves, with part of the treated waste flushed into the sewer system and carried to a master drain. All agricultural liquid waste—such as salt-laden irrigation water—would go to a master drain.

Solid refuse would be ground and flushed down the sewer or dropped into a collector-conveyor system. This would carry it to a central point where vehicular collectors could transport it by rapid transit to automated processing and separating plants. There materials would be salvaged and supplied to industry. Farm refuse would be plowed under or transported to the same separating plant.

Radiological waste matter—principally from nuclear fuel processing plants—would be buried underground and cycled for isotopic use by hospitals and industry, while liquids with low radiation levels would be diluted and pumped into rivers.

Although researching, developing and building adequate systems to carry out the future waste disposal system would cost billions of dollars, the Aerojet study showed that in future years the benefits to society—in measurable dollars and cents—would more than offset the cost. The engineers recommended that the state embark upon a ten-year developmental waste management program, including three years of planning alone.

Frank M. Stead, chief of the State Health Department's Environmental Sanitation Division, described the Aerojet study as "sensible." He proposed that price tags be placed on social and aesthetic values so that the proposed solution to the refuse disposal problems could be shown to be "a profitable venture." He recommended that a pilot program be put to work in a region such as San Francisco Bay. "Southern California learned that a good water supply is worth what it costs," Stead remarked. "It must be shown that a systems approach to disposal doesn't break anybody's back."

The Aerojet study warned that without a systems approach to waste disposal, California could well be smothered, drowned and buried in smog, sewage and rubbish. Life could become intolerable within twenty-five years. On the other hand, if the proposed project were undertaken at once, the state could have a disposal system by 1975 that would keep the state habitable.

Dr. Dwight Culver, who directed the study for Aerojet, predicted that within ten years a significant fraction of the aerospace industry's activities will be devoted to the solution of civic and urban problems. In the past, he said, pressures of population size and density were less extreme and thus did not require that problems be viewed as integrated systems. "This situation," Culver added, "has resulted in a number of separate groups looking at various components of the problems with little or no attention given to the system as a whole. We will not be able to afford this practice very much longer."

The National Academy of Sciences waste management report of 1966 agreed in principle with the Aerojet findings. The committee on pollution, headed by Dr. Athelstan Spilhaus of the University of Minnesota, visualized "ultimately gigantic complexes that would process sewage, burn refuse, generate electricity and purify water for reuse. Energy from the burning of refuse—and possibly from sewer gas—would aid in the heating."

The day is foreseen by many of these scientists and engineers when virtually all of a region's pollution problems—air, land and water—could be solved by a single, gigantic nuclear power plant located perhaps twenty or one hundred miles from densely populated centers, but serving those centers as well as the farming areas around them. Such a plant would:

1. Produce all electric power including that needed for operating and heating factories, homes and other buildings.

2. Provide power for a rapid transit system and "plug-in" recharging for electric automobiles.

3. Distill fresh water from the sea or brackish underground reservoirs.

4. Remove solids from sewage and process the water by distillation so that it would return, absolutely pure, to the water system.

5. "Burn" sewage solids and other refuse at such high temperatures that the constituent materials would be converted back to their original gaseous elements. These gases

then could be utilized as an auxiliary fuel supply or seperated (by diffusion or other methods) and recondensed as pure chemicals. Those could be channeled back into the country's economy directly, their sale at least partially offsetting the costs of this enormous antipollution machine.

"We must use every possible means of cutting down the burning of organic fuels," said Dr. P. A. Leighton of the Stanford Research Institute. "We must build only nuclear plants from now on and stop burning either gas or oil in steam power plants; we must use only electricity to heat homes, offices and factories; we must make and drive smaller autos and use them less often by riding to work in revived public transport systems, and, above all, we must replace the internal combustion engine with some other power source such as the fuel cell."

The House Committee on Science and Astronautics stated the heart of the matter in its 1966 report on technology for pollution abatement:

> . . . environmental pollution must be considered in a larger context even while dealing with specific problems. That context is the so-called "new conservation" facing our civilization.
>
> We see the necessity for long-range planning and allocation of finite environmental resources, both renewable and consumable. Both conservation and preservation must take account of the rising population in this country and the world.
>
> Economic stability and economic growth are ingredients of the quality of life. The quality of life is not synonymous with, but yet depends to a great extent upon, the quality of the environment. Reflecting this, national attitudes toward the environment have changed from the early exploitation and harvesting, to regulated preservation and wise use and renewal.

The ultimate goal, then, is no different from the earliest days when we began slashing down our forest trees and dipping into the earth for coal, oil, minerals and chemicals. All the wastes of man—automobile exhaust, cardboard cartons or industrial chemicals—are materials which can be reused if proper and economic techniques can be found.

The final answer to pollution is conservation of resources.

The Human City

*If man cannot adapt—he does not
deserve to survive.*

Dr. Edward Tatum, Geneticist, Rockefeller Institute

CITIES GAVE US THE BIRTH OF CULTURE; THEY GAVE US ALSO
waste and pollution.

The city of tomorrow then must in turn generate the ideas,
the work and the power to lead us toward a cleaner, less
frenetic, more human way of life. The new cities must be
human places because within thirty-five years 250 million of
us (in America) will live there.

What may we expect?

In 1966 President Johnson asked Congress to appropriate
$2.3 billion over a six-year period to rebuild entire sections
of sixty to seventy American municipalities. He envisoned a
new physical and social environment in urban areas now suffering blight and decay. Housing, schools, parks and play-
grounds were some of the targets. The President also pro-

posed spending $6.5 million to help metropolitan areas with mass transportation, sewer and water facilities, and recreation areas for smaller communities.

"This can be the year of rebirth for American cities," Johnson said. "This Congress and this people can set in motion forces of change in great urban areas that will make them masterpieces of civilization." The President knew well that the sums he asked were only a beginning. His advisers estimated that it will cost more than two trillion dollars to rebuild the central cities of the nation. "What is now unfolding is a plan for change that will touch nearly every phase of American life," he added. "Government will play an ever-bigger role in people's daily lives and in those of whole communities. This program could mean the rebirth of urban America and eventually a clean room and a patch of sky for every person, a chance to live near an open space and to reach it on a safe street."

Federal money is being used more and more to fight city problems. Subsidies under existing programs have gone up in the past ten years from $4.1 billion to $14.6 billion annually. Part of this money already is channeled into the abatement of pollution as well as into construction of streets and highways. Federal money is being distributed for landscaping, planted areas, malls and plazas, removal of billboards and junk yards along streets and highways. In 1966, $4.4 billion was being aimed toward regional development—new industries, roads, minerals, natural resources. The over-all pattern is a great crossing of small parochial lines to make up large regional improvements.

Local government units in the United States now total ninety thousand. The federal government contributes 15 percent of their total revenue.

Dr. Constantinos A. Doxiadis of Athens, one of the world's most noted architects and municipal planners, said:

> A city is like a heap of garbage—everyone throws in what he likes. It is the function of the planner to try to bring some order to this mixture.

274

It is my experience that in every part of the world areas called ghettos are doomed to be ghettos for the growth around them. The city is a whole organism and we cannot solve problems involving the whole by looking at only one point.

Cities have tended to develop in concentric rings with their business areas in the center. Residential rings have grown about the center, constricting the heart of the city. This may not be important to a small community, say 50,000, but as the city grows to 100,000, to 500,000, to 1 million, it dies progressively from the heart. If the growing heart of a child were encased in steel, that child would die within a short time.

Cities can be saved only through democratic processes. I assure you that a dictator cannot do it. It requires long-term development only possible in democracies. . . .

In our expensive groping for the better way of metropolitan life, we could well take a lesson from the industrious, clear-thinking people of the Netherlands. Twelve million people there are crowded into 12,500 square miles, a population density of 912 per square mile compared with 50 in the United States. At the present time, 4.3 million of the Dutch are concentrated in "Ring City," a horseshoe-shaped megalopolis which extends from Dordrecht and Rotterdam in the southwest to The Hague, Amsterdam and Utrecht in the southeast. The population of this area is expected to reach six million by 1980.

The key to livability, however, lies in the fact that Ring City is strung around a green heart and that planners are determined to keep it from being devoured. They also are insisting on buffer zones of at least a mile between communities to prevent overlapping.

"We don't want miles and miles of brick and mortar," one official said. "We have in mind a chain of major and minor towns, alternated with suburbs and even farming communities separated by buffer zones, metropolitan parks and regional parks." Nine parks of 2500 acres each are planned around the Ring City.

In this tiny nation, which for centuries has been wresting its land from the sea at great cost in both money and labor,

275

the government is attempting to curb the flow of people into cities. A strong campaign is under way to decentralize industry and reorganize farming. To move industry, the government offers land at reduced prices, loans, subsidies along with improved roads and water systems. When old farms fall into the city, farmers are offered new locations on land being reclaimed from the ocean, principally on the Zuider Zee, a two-billion-dollar reclamation effort which began thirty-three years ago. Pumps so far have bared 300,000 acres of new farm land, living space for 500,000 people. The over-all objective is to integrate development of industry, agriculture, housing, transportation, recreation and culture. The tax burden on local communities is eased by way of a "municipal fund" in the national budget, a technique which certainly could be studied in America. This fund ends intercity competition in tax rates and equalizes taxation throughout the nation. Each city or town gets a share of the pot based on population, location and economy. Out of a recent $2.6 billion national budget, $1 billion went to aid municipal development.

The one great threat to Holland's excellent planning is the rapid increase of automobiles. Ownership is expected to grow from one out of nine people now to one in three within fifteen years—an estimated total of five million cars. "We can't keep people from buying cars," a planner said, "but we can make public transportation efficient enough to make them want to use it, instead of autos, when going to and from their jobs." He said industry is cooperating very well with this objective. "If they want workers," he added, "they must keep this city a place people want to live in." Another official commented: "Whether Holland will still be habitable by the year 2000 depends on the order or disorder we create now."

Orderliness has long been the hallmark of Holland, but how do we apply these lessons to a nation where a high degree of municipal hodgepodge already exists?

William Pereira and Victor Gruen, architects and planners, advocate tearing up a third of the structures and streets in Los Angeles and replacing them with huge "superblocks" which would be self-contained residences for thousands of people. A man and his family in such a mammoth structure might live twenty or thirty floors above his shopping center and factory and *ride nothing but the elevator to work*. People living in these superblocks all would view out their window broad expanses of park, farmland and greenery maintained for their use by taxes they would pay. Huge multipurpose buildings were introduced in Rochester, N.Y., and now exist in a number of cities.

"It's the shopping center concept of life," Gruen said; "all you need is around you. This would help break up suburbia, and more important, help get the family back together. Papa will be able to spend two or three hours more a day at home rather than on the freeway. Paternal absence in the past has helped cause breakups in our society. Divorces, juvenile delinquency and the 'no father' influence are high today partially because of poor city planning."

The city dweller—in addition to using the elevator as his primary means of work transportation—might spend the day at the beach and catch an air bus home, ride a golf-cart-type electric vehicle to make a business call, or ride to distant cities (or superblocks) in high-speed underground trains running in tubes bored quickly, easily and cheaply by laser beam.

Our mechanical slaves—our automobiles, pipes, and wires— all will be out of sight by the year 2000 [Gruen predicted]. The air will be cleaner. Life will be quieter. Those who wish can live within walking distance of work. This will revive walking, which is one of the most pleasant things a man can do.

Already our cities are being made more enjoyable with parks, malls and by depressing [below ground level] freeways, blotting out ugly sights with trees and shrubs. They will be more enjoyable still when they offer pleasures for all types and tastes. The daily movement of millions of automobiles back and forth in our cities must be curtailed and discouraged as they are abroad. Traffic engineers no longer can be allowed to think primarily of the car and rarely of the human. Such things as a cultural building costing less than a parking lot must be stopped.

"In a democracy the city to strive for is one in which diverse human beings can live freely together, respect each other's varying tastes and share the immense power of their differences," said Paul Ylvisaker, director of public affairs for the Ford Foundation.

. . . Beauty, order, grace—these are admittedly elusive as civic objectives. At that point the politician takes over from the philosopher to determine how many are willing to fight whom to get what. It's tough to find the enemy, because the enemy is me.

If you want the automobiled, shopping-center city, go on subsidizing highways, parking and single-family homes on large lots. If you want the sort of European city American tourists love to visit and downtown merchants want to keep, subsidize mass transit, zone for apartments, and allow taxpayers to deduct rent as well as mortgage interest on their federal income tax returns.

American cities are now the by-product of other purposes, the residual of countless decisions made with some other intent than an improved environment for the urban population. . . .

The most encouraging of all our urban developments is the fact that the preservation of nature's beauty and man's perfection of his own cities have become presidential themes. Now that the presidency is finally allied to City Hall, the pace of urban progress is bound to quicken.

Once Americans start seeing examples rather than promises, and are given visions rather than alibis, what is to keep them from working and paying for better cities with all the restless energy they have been spending on faster cars and easier kitchens?

The architect and editor Peter Blake finds that American cities are what they are because this "is a nation always on the move, a permanently unfinished country characterized by relentless, unpredictable change.

"It is pretty late in the day now," Blake said, "but I think there is still a chance for American architects to come to terms with the automobile and the highway, to create an entirely new kind of city. When I suggest that we must come to terms with the automibile, I don't mean that the auto need not come to terms with the city. Obviously, it must.

"But the manufacturers and unions in gas, oil, rubber, steel, aluminum and concrete industries, the banks that finance them and the politicians who represent them—all these immensely influential groups see no reason for changing their ways. Why should they bother with the little old ladies in tennis shoes who oppose them?"

By the democratic pendulum swing from one extreme to another, the little old lady in tenins shoes with her dream of blue sky and green trees now is gaining considerable support. The National Academy of Sciences, in its 1966 waste management study, recommended bold federal action including special research centers, pilot projects and the establishment of a "new city" to test out new waste management tools and techniques. The new city, indeed, is an extremely fascinating concept especially when planners try to devise ways for cleaning out the clutter in metropolitan areas which have grown and decayed according to almost no plan at all.

"The great pity of megalopolis," said Dr. Charles N. Kimball, president of the Midwest Research Institute in Kansas City, "is that some of the best minds in the country have to be devoted to stopgapping problems instead of looking into the future for permanent solutions. Americans would be far better served with 100 cities the size of Kansas City or Louisville, Kentucky, or Indianapolis or Denver than by a few more like New York, Chicago and Los Angeles.

"Here we are, talking of spending billions for 300-mile-an-hour commuter trains and more billions to clean up pollution in Lake Erie. Think what you could do with that kind of effort and money if you would build up several smaller cities in some of the wide-open spaces of America. This will become more feasible and necessary as mobility of people and ideas improve."

Many large, completely planned communities are rising in countries across the world even now. Though often located near established metropolitan areas, these are not suburbs because all features are built according to a master plan. Typically they offer open spaces, harmonious surroundings, convenient community facilities and good transportation.

In England the government has been planning and financing

new towns since 1946. The French government recently announced that eight new towns will be built within forty miles of Paris before the end of the century. One of the finest new towns is parklike Tapiola near Helsinki, Finland. No mother must push her pram more than 250 yards to buy groceries, escort children to school or meet friends at a cafe. Heating and hot water is provided by a central power plant.

Pakistan, the Asian nation about the size of Michigan, contains 107 million people but only three cities—one of one million, another of 300,000 and a third of 150,000. In 1966, Pakistan with help from the United Nations embarked upon a program to plan and build an entire series of new cities, deciding their locations, sizes, industries and economics. David Owen, UN expert on municipalities, commented that the "crisis of the world's population results not so much from numbers alone as from the rush into the cities of nations completely unprepared to deal with the problem."

In the United States, the new community of Reston, Virginia, has been cited as an example of excellent planning. It is expected to house 75,000 residents by 1980. Elsewhere, at least one more new city is added to the list almost every month. Many of them are in California with some in Florida, New Jersey, Washington, Maryland, Illinois, Ohio, Colorado, Arizona and Texas. An arc of twelve new towns to ring New York City from Connecticut to New Jersey has been proposed as a partial solution to the transportation and crowding problems caused by population growth in the big city. The big advantage of the new cities is that sewers and water mains all are put in early and properly. Every resident is within a few-minute walk of a bus or train stop, helping to keep automobile traffic to a minimum.

The laws of necessity and economics require that today's new cities incorporate conventional services, such as streets for cars, standard water systems and ordinary sewer networks, but even newer cities are upon the horizon.

Dr. Eugene B. Konecci, of the National Aeronautics and Space Council, foresees self-contained sealed cities enclosed by astrodomes to ward off air pollution. He said that systems which have been developed to sustain men in space or in the ocean depths must be used eventually to prevent continued pollution of land, air and water "if we want to survive on mother Earth."

Konecci advocates "modules" of several thousand persons each, completely self-sufficient and possessing all needed facilities for such things as work, religion and entertainment. The domed and air-conditioned "modules" could be linked to form cities of any size. Within the plastic domes, where the atmosphere would be continuously cleansed and regenerated, automobiles would be banned. Internal transportation would be by electric car. Gasoline-powered vehicles could be kept in garages outside the city, if necessary, for use in cross-country trips in the open air where the fumes would be diluted. Each community would have its own self-contained, recirculating water supply and facilities for converting sewage back into useful products. Much food would be synthetic, but there would be "meat factories" in which animals would be raised in modern, air-conditioned surroundings and fattened on high-nutrient feeds. Glenn T. Seaborg, chairman of the Atomic Energy Commission, follows Konecci's reasoning and told a Texas University audience in 1966 that giant nuclear reactors will be needed in the future of "planet conditioning."

Doxiadis, the Greek planner, in 1966 was given the thirty-thousand-dollar Aspen award presented annually to "that individual anywhere in the world judged to have made the greatest contribution to the advancement of the humanities." While accepting the award amid the beauty of Colorado's Rocky Mountains, Doxiadis described *his* city of tomorrow:

It will be very big, but it will consist of two categories of parts, the cells, and the networks. The cells are going to be the size of cities of the past, no larger than 50,000 inhabitants, no larger than 2000 by 2000 yards, no longer than a 10-minute average walk. They will be built on a human scale on the basis of human experience.

The networks are going to be absolutely mechanical and automatic, interconnecting the cells by transportation and communications, forming enormous organisms with the cells as basic units. Their vehicles will reach speeds of many hundreds of miles, their arteries will be underground, not highways but deepways, as they are in the bodies of all mammals—the higher the speed, the deeper they will go.

Thus man someday will be served in his cities by automatic facilities for supplying water, cleaning his sewage, preventing air pollution, disposing of his solid refuse, and taking him where he wants to go when he wants to go there.

Although Dr. Grebler and others complain that the year 2000 is no magic millennium which will see all our old problems vanish into a new utopia, something still must serve as a goal. Dreams beget plans; plans beget action—there is no other chain to improvement. The new city sparkles in the future with the brilliance of a rare diamond. At the moment, the gem may be inaccessible behind the jewelry store window but someday we will buy it.

In the words of Doxiadis: "Our habitat is the world of man, our goal can only be human happiness and safety leading to the human city."

Select Bibliography

Aerojet General Corporation. *California Waste Management Study*. August 1965.

Baade, Fritz. *The Race to the Year 2000*. London: The Cresset Press, 1963.

Graham, Frank, Jr. *Disaster by Default: Politics and Water Pollution*. Philadelphia: J. B. Lippincott Co., 1966.

Herfindahl, Orris C., and Kneese, Allen V. *Quality of the Environment: An Economic Approach to Some Problems in Using Land, Water and Air*. Baltimore: The John Hopkins Press, 1965.

Lewis, Howard R. *With Every Breath You Take*. New York: Crown Publishers, Inc., 1965.

Lundberg, Ferdinand. *The Coming World Transformation*. New York: Doubleday & Company, Inc., 1963.

McMillen, Wheeler. *Bugs or People*. New York: Appleton-Century, 1965.

Milne, Lorus and Margery. *Water and Life*. New York: Atheneum Publishing, 1964.

Still, Henry. *Will the Human Race Survive?* New York: Hawthorn Books, Inc., 1966.

"The Adequacy of Technology for Pollution Abatement," *Report of the Research Management Advisory Panel*, through the Subcommittee on Science, Research and Development to the Committee on Science and Astronautics, U. S. House of Representatives, 89th Congress, 1966.

"Development, Growth and State of the Atomic Energy Industry," *Hearings before the Joint Committee on Atomic Energy*, 89th Congress, 1965.

"Research Needs for Salt Water Conversion," *Staff Report of the Committee on Science and Astronautics*, U. S. House of Representatives, 87th Congress, March 1961.

"Restoring the Quality of Our Environment," *Report of the Environmental Pollution Panel*, President's Science Advisory Committee, November 1965.

Index

land, 276; junked, 3, 45–46, 49–53

Azusa, Calif., 129

Babylon, L.I., 234
Bad Godesberg, 93
Bagge, Carl E., 181
Baghouse, use of, 172
Baikal, Lake, 72
Bakersfield, Calif., 27
Balchum, Dr. Oscar, 189
Baltimore, Md., 45, 147, 207
Barium 140, 250
Barnum & Bailey Circus, 184
Bateman, Ivan L., 236
Baton Rouge, La., 9
Battery Park City, 51–52
Baudelaire, Charles, 157
Bay Area Rapid Transit District (BARTD), 220–24
Beaches, 62, 64, 73, 99, 105
Beautification campaign, 47–48, 212–13, 260
Bechtel Corp., 127
Beer cans, 37
Belgium, 137
Beltsville, Md., 191
Benjamin, Bernard, 19
Benline, Arthur J., 166, 197
Bergen County, 170
Berkeley, Calif., 221
Bethlehem Steel Co., 147, 263
Beverly Hills, 209
Bibliography, 283–84
Billboards, 48
Biloxi, Miss., 73
Birmingham, England, 176
Bishop Processing Co., 157–58
Black Beetle (train), 232
Black Death. *See* Plague
Blackstone River, 74
Blake, Peter, 183, 204, 277–78
Boeing 747, 266
Bogotá, Colombia, 21
Bolsa Chica State Beach, 127
Boston, 142, 204–5, 207, 228, 233
Bottle caps, 40
Bowerman, Frank, 55, 56

Boyd, Alan S., 230
Bradford, Robert B., 213
Bradley, Walter W., 103–4
Bray, Ulric B., 196, 200, 201, 214
Breakwaters, 51
Breslow, Dr. Lester, 244
Bristol, England, 176
British Ass'n for the Advancement of Science, 258
British Committee on Air Pollution, 143, 176*ff*
Bronchitis, 142, 143, 146
Brooklyn, N.Y., 33, 53, 58
Brown, A. W. A., 243
Brown, Edmund (Pat), 118, 119, 187, 196–97, 198; and highways, 212–13; and systems management study, 267; and transportation study, 217, 219
Brown, Norman, 227
Brush, 40
Bryson, Dr. Reid A., 147
Buckeye, Ariz., 125
Budapest, 204
Budd Co., 231–32
Buffalo, N.Y., 50, 105, 142–43
Buffalo, University of, 96
Bugs or People, 241
Buses, 28, 185, 187, 193, 197, 205, 213, 220, 221, 266; on air cushion, 218; New York, 197, 203, 204, 228; and "tunnel in the sky," 209
Bush, A. F., 130, 214
Byron, George Gordon Byron, Lord, 61

Cadillacs, 184
Calcutta, 11, 23, 24–25
Calgon Corp., 83–84
California, 8, 72, 116*ff*, 127, 212–13, 265; and air pollution, 8, 46, 141, 150–51*ff*, 188, 192–201; and detergents, 83; "new cities," 280; and nuclear power plant, 252; and pesticides, 244; transportation needs, mass transpor-

tation, 217–27; waste management study, 267–70
California, University of, in Riverside, 191
Calumet, Ill., 164
Camden, N.J., 174
Campbell, J. M., 194
Campbell, Ohio, 105
Canada, 39, 62, 64
Canadian Vickers, 227
Cancer, 142, 146, 148, 163
Canton, Ohio, 14
Cape Town, South Africa, 179
Carbon dioxide, 154–55, 188
Carbon-14, 249
Carbon fuels. See Air pollution; specific fuels
Carbon monoxide, 28, 152, 172, 187ff, 214
Cardiff, Wales, 176
Carey, Asher B., 158
Carnegie Inst. of Technology, 230
Casablanca, Morocco, 178
Case, Clifford P., 51
Cassidy, William F., 80–81
Catalytic afterburners, 188
Catskills, 66
Cedar Rapids, Iowa, 21
Ceramics, 40
Cereal boxes, 39
Cesium 137, 250
Cesspools, 4–5, 72
Chamber of Commerce, U.S., 77
Chandrasekhar, Dr. Sripati, 220
Charleston, S.C., 43
Chattanooga, Tenn., 147–48
Chemicals, chemical industry, 47, 63ff, 76, 78, 107; chemical salts, 121–23; and Lake Michigan, 105, 106; pesticides, 239, 240–47
Chicago, 11, 99, 174, 207, 249; and air pollution, 21, 147, 151, 152, 164, 168; and Lake Michigan, 65, 105, 106
Chickens, 131, 157–58
China, 14, 39–40
Chlordane, 242

Chocolate Bayou, Tex., 78
Cholera, 17
Chrysler, 195, 235
Cigarette smoke, 189
Cigarette taxes, 227
Cities, 4–5, 11–32, 273–82. See also specific cities, conditions
Citrus fruits, 59, 151
Ciudad Juárez, Mexico, 118
Clark, Bradford N., 99
Clean Air Act, 158ff, 199
Clean Air Act (British), 177
Cleopatra's Needle, 152
Cleveland, Ohio, 70, 105, 109, 227–28, 232
Clewell, Dayton H., 77
Coal, 4, 28, 93, 94, 135–36ff, 153ff, 159ff, 265
Coil, J. A., 223
Colds, common, 142
Collier, Randolph, 214–15, 227
Colorado, 280
Colorado River, 26, 116ff, 127, 129; chemical salts in, 121–22
Columbia River, 70, 118–19, 120
Columbia University, 165
Commerce, Department of, 232, 251
Commerce and Industry Ass'n of New York, 204
Compost (-ing), 54, 59, 60, 262
Computers, for traffic, 23
Concord, Calif., 221
Conference of State Sanitary Engineers, 263
Congress, 84, 109–10, 119. See also House; Senate; specific Acts
Congressional Record, 187–88
Connecticut, 145
Connecticut River, 70, 74
Conner, W. J., 104
Conquistadores, 178
Conrad, Joseph, 11
Consolidated Edison, 57, 145, 146, 166, 167–68, 171, 173; and transportation strike, 204
Construction industry, 42–43
Contra Costa County, 221

Morgan Guaranty Bank of New York, 260
Moscow, 23, 231
Moskowitz, Karl, 215
Munroe, William, 171
Muratov, Pyotr G., 231
Murphy, Dr. Franklin D., 2

Nanking, 14
Naples, 231
Nassau County, 57
National Academy of Sciences, 47, 68, 114–15, 131, 249–50, 254, 260, 263, 270; and air pollution, 149, 153, 172, 174–75, 190, 191–92, 270; and new cities, 279
National Ass'n of Manufacturers, 78
National Coal Policy Conf., 167
National Conf. on Solid Waste Research, 54
National Interstate Highway System, 185
National Lead, 79
National Research Council, 190
National Water Quality Act, 76
National Wildlife Federation, 132
Natural gas, 28, 153, 155, 159, 165, 179–81, 265
NAWAPA, 120
Neckar River, 82
Neiburger, Dr. Morris, 178–79, 189–90, 235
Nematodes, 242
Netherlands, 275–76
Nevada, 72
Newark, N.J., 170
Newburgh on the Hudson, 68–70
Newcastle (Great Britain), 176
New Brunswick, N.J., 169–70
"New cities," 279–80
New England, 73–74
New Jersey, 71, 79, 106–7, 207, 280; and air, 145, 159, 169, 175
New Orleans, 6, 7, 98, 210
New York City, 11, 24, 27, 30, 33–34, 41, 56–58; and air pollution, 41, 42–43, 56ff, 144–46,

151, 152, 159, 165–69ff, 197, 204; Flatlands Industrial Park, 53; horses in, 19; and mass transportation, 203–5ff, 228, 232, 234; and new towns, 280; proposal to extend Manhattan Island with scrap autos, 51–52; and water, 67, 79–80, 99, 129
New York State, 51–52, 101–2, 196, 260; and air pollution, 151, 169–70; and water, 62, 98, 104, 105
New York Times, 101–2, 204
Niagara Falls (city), 64
Niagara Falls, 64
Niles, Ohio, 105
Nitrates, 63, 72, 123
Nitro, W.Va., 78
Nitrogen oxides, 28, 153, 175, 187ff
Nobel, Joseph, 152
North American Aviation, Inc., 131, 217–19
North American Water and Power Alliance, 120
North Dakota, 117
Northington, C. W., 63–64
Norway, 143
Nuclear power (and radioactivity), 70, 167, 270–71; and desalting, 126–27, 132; and wastes, dangers, 2–3, 43–44, 239, 246–54, 269

Oak Ridge, Tenn., 152
Oakland, Calif., 221ff
Oakland Bay Bridge, 211, 222
Oberhausen, 94
Oceans, 36–37, 111–12, 123, 156, 242; desalting, 57, 124–27, 132
Oceanside, L.I., 57
O'Connell, Mrs. Raymond T., 85–86
O'Donoghue, Ralph H., 144–45
O'Hare Airport, 147
Ohio, 62, 104, 105, 138, 260; gasoline consumption, 196; new cities, 280

Ohio River and Basin, 102–3, 104, 262

Oil, the petroleum industry, 28, 76, 77, 105, 106, 140, 145, 153, 155, 159; auto industry and, 186

Olmstead, George, Jr., 77

Ontario, 62, 64

Ontario, Lake, 64, 103

Orange County, 123, 198, 208, 214

Oranges, 151; peels, 59

Oregon, 119

Osaka, 231

Owen, David, 29–30, 280

Owens River, 116, 129

Owings, Nathaniel, 212

Oxygen, 62ff, 95, 101, 141, 154, 188, 214; for fuel cells, 237; more used to breathe smog, 189

Ozone, 198ff

Pacific Ocean, 26, 27, 120, 129, 140; and insecticides, 242

Packaging, 39, 40

Paige, Hillard W., 48

Pakistan, 280

Palm Beach Shores, Fla., 165–66

Palmdale, Calif., 48, 129

Palomares, Spain, 43, 44

Palos Verdes Peninsula, 56

PAN, 191

Panhandle Freeway, 211

Paper, papermaking, 38–40, 64, 69, 76, 77; Document Disintegration, Inc., 54; Kimberly-Clark, 100–1

Parathion, 244

Paris, 11, 144, 204, 231

Parkhurst, J. D., 129

Parking, 213

Parsons, Ralph M., Co., 120

Particulate matter, 152, 153, 175. *See also* Air pollution

Pasadena, 207, 208

Pasadena Freeway, 207

Passaic County, 170

Paterson, N.J., 234

Paulson, Edgar G., 84

Peabody (George Foster) award, 47

Peach pits, 58

Pectin, 59

PennJerDel, 106–7, 174–75

Pennsylvania, 4, 62, 104ff, 138, 162

Pennsylvana Electric Co., 173

Pennsylvania Railroad, 162, 171, 228, 232

Pennsylvania Station (NYC), 202

Pennsylvania Turnpike, 207

Pepys, Samuel, 18

Pereira, William, 276

Periconi, Joseph F., 144

Peroxyacetylnitrate, 191

Pesticides, 239, 240–47

Petroleum. *See* Oil

Philadelphia, 23, 42, 174, 207, 227

Philippines, 16

Phillips, Arthur C., Jr., 86

Phoenicians, 14

Phoenix, Ariz., 118

Phosphates, 63, 72, 123

Pittsburgh, 102–3, 104, 141, 232–33; and air, 142, 160–63, 265

Pizzarro, Francisco, 22

Plague, 16–17, 25

Plankton, 72

Plants, 113, 154. *See also* Agriculture

Pneumonia, 143, 162

Polar icecaps, 155–56

Pollution Control Act, 98

Pomeroy, Dr. Richard, 122

Pomona, Calif., 129

Pompeii, 15

Population Ref. Bureau, 31

Portland, Ore., 152

Portland, Penna., 172–73

Potomac River, 70

Powell, Lake, 117

President's Science Advisory Commission, 60, 66, 107, 175; and carbon dioxide, 154; on junk cars, 45, 49, 52; on paper, 39; and pesticides, 244; on radioactivity, 250, 251

A HAWTHORN BOOK